How to use this book

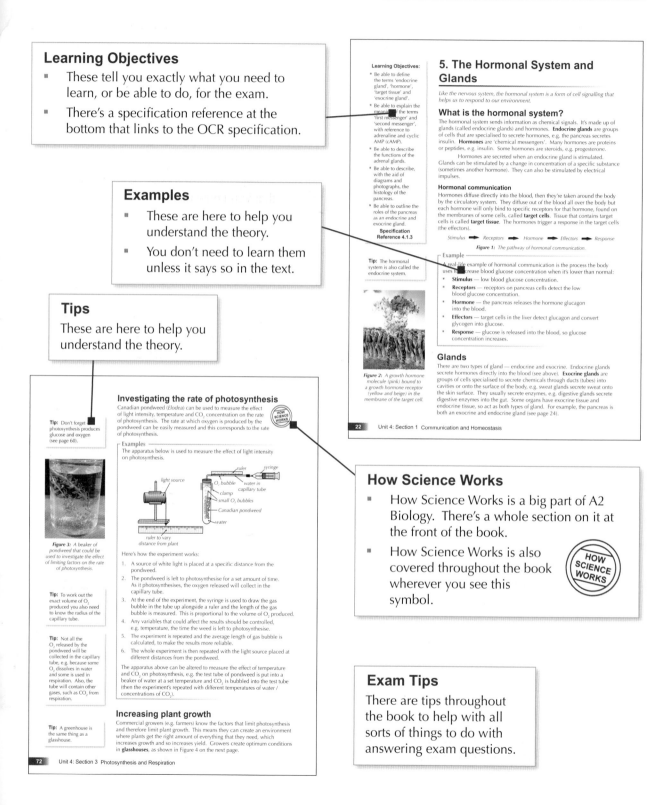

Learning Objectives
- These tell you exactly what you need to learn, or be able to do, for the exam.
- There's a specification reference at the bottom that links to the OCR specification.

Examples
- These are here to help you understand the theory.
- You don't need to learn them unless it says so in the text.

Tips
These are here to help you understand the theory.

Learning Objectives:
- Be able to define the terms 'endocrine gland', 'hormone', 'target tissue' and 'exocrine gland'.
- Be able to explain the meaning of the terms 'first messenger' and 'second messenger', with reference to adrenaline and cyclic AMP (cAMP).
- Be able to describe the functions of the adrenal glands.
- Be able to describe, with the aid of diagrams and photographs, the histology of the pancreas.
- Be able to outline the roles of the pancreas as an endocrine and exocrine gland.

Specification Reference 4.1.3

Tip: The hormonal system is also called the endocrine system.

5. The Hormonal System and Glands
Like the nervous system, the hormonal system is a form of cell signalling that helps us to respond to our environment.

What is the hormonal system?
The hormonal system sends information as chemical signals. It's made up of glands (called endocrine glands) and hormones. **Endocrine glands** are groups of cells that are specialised to secrete hormones, e.g. the pancreas secretes insulin. **Hormones** are 'chemical messengers'. Many hormones are proteins or peptides, e.g. insulin. Some hormones are steroids, e.g. progesterone.

Hormones are secreted when an endocrine gland is stimulated. Glands can be stimulated by a change in concentration of a specific substance (sometimes another hormone). They can also be stimulated by electrical impulses.

Hormonal communication
Hormones diffuse directly into the blood, then they're taken around the body by the circulatory system. They diffuse out of the blood all over the body but each hormone will only bind to specific receptors for that hormone, found on the membranes of some cells, called **target cells**. Tissue that contains target cells is called **target tissue**. The hormones trigger a response in the target cells (the effectors).

Stimulus ➡ Receptors ➡ Hormone ➡ Effectors ➡ Response

***Figure 1:** The pathway of hormonal communication.*

— Example —
A real-life example of hormonal communication is the process the body uses to increase blood glucose concentration when it's lower than normal:
- **Stimulus** — low blood glucose concentration.
- **Receptors** — receptors on pancreas cells detect the low blood glucose concentration.
- **Hormone** — the pancreas releases the hormone glucagon into the blood.
- **Effectors** — target cells in the liver detect glucagon and convert glycogen into glucose.
- **Response** — glucose is released into the blood, so glucose concentration increases.

Glands
There are two types of gland — endocrine and exocrine. Endocrine glands secrete hormones directly into the blood (see above). **Exocrine glands** are groups of cells specialised to secrete chemicals through ducts (tubes) into cavities or onto the surface of the body, e.g. sweat glands secrete sweat onto the skin surface. They usually secrete enzymes, e.g. digestive glands secrete digestive enzymes into the gut. Some organs have exocrine tissue and endocrine tissue, so act as both types of gland. For example, the pancreas is both an exocrine and endocrine gland (see page 24).

***Figure 2:** A growth hormone molecule (pink) bound to a growth hormone receptor (yellow and beige) in the membrane of the target cell.*

Tip: Don't forget photosynthesis produces glucose and oxygen (see page 60).

Investigating the rate of photosynthesis
Canadian pondweed (*Elodea*) can be used to measure the effect of light intensity, temperature and CO_2 concentration on the rate of photosynthesis. The rate at which oxygen is produced by the pondweed can be easily measured and this corresponds to the rate of photosynthesis.

— Examples —
The apparatus below is used to measure the effect of light intensity on photosynthesis.

***Figure 3:** A beaker of pondweed that could be used to investigate the effect of limiting factors on the rate of photosynthesis.*

Tip: To work out the exact volume of O_2 produced you need to know the radius of the capillary tube.

Tip: Not all the O_2 released by the pondweed will be collected in the capillary tube, e.g. because some O_2 dissolves in water and some is used in respiration. Also, the tube will contain other gases, such as CO_2 from respiration.

Here's how the experiment works:
1. A source of white light is placed at a specific distance from the pondweed.
2. The pondweed is left to photosynthesise for a set amount of time. As it photosynthesises, the oxygen released will collect in the capillary tube.
3. At the end of the experiment, the syringe is used to draw the gas bubble in the tube up alongside a ruler and the length of the gas bubble is measured. This is proportional to the volume of O_2 produced.
4. Any variables that could affect the results should be controlled, e.g. temperature, the time the weed is left to photosynthesise.
5. The experiment is repeated and the average length of gas bubble is calculated, to make the results more reliable.
6. The whole experiment is then repeated with the light source placed at different distances from the pondweed.

The apparatus above can be altered to measure the effect of temperature and CO_2 on photosynthesis, e.g. the test tube of pondweed is put into a beaker of water at a set temperature and CO_2 is bubbled into the test tube (then the experiment's repeated with different temperatures of water / concentrations of CO_2).

Increasing plant growth
Tip: A greenhouse is the same thing as a glasshouse.

Commercial growers (e.g. farmers) know the factors that limit photosynthesis and therefore limit plant growth. This means they can create an environment where plants get the right amount of everything that they need, which increases growth and so increases yield. Growers create optimum conditions in **glasshouses**, as shown in Figure 4 on the next page.

How Science Works
- How Science Works is a big part of A2 Biology. There's a whole section on it at the front of the book.
- How Science Works is also covered throughout the book wherever you see this symbol.

Exam Tips
There are tips throughout the book to help with all sorts of things to do with answering exam questions.

A2-Level

Biology

for OCR

The Complete Course for OCR

Contents

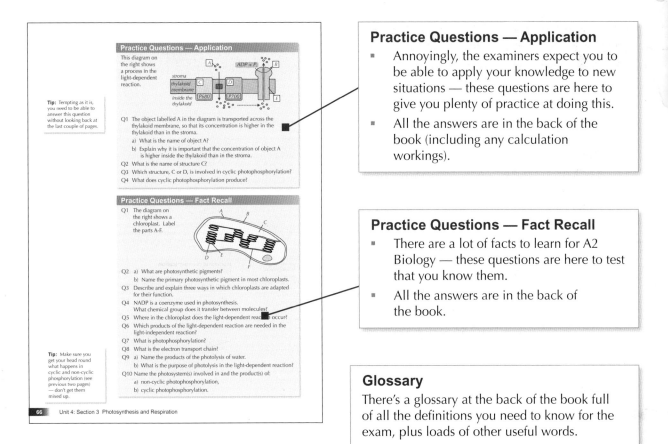

Practice Questions — Application

- Annoyingly, the examiners expect you to be able to apply your knowledge to new situations — these questions are here to give you plenty of practice at doing this.

- All the answers are in the back of the book (including any calculation workings).

Practice Questions — Fact Recall

- There are a lot of facts to learn for A2 Biology — these questions are here to test that you know them.

- All the answers are in the back of the book.

Glossary

There's a glossary at the back of the book full of all the definitions you need to know for the exam, plus loads of other useful words.

Exam-style Questions

- Practising exam-style questions is really important — you'll find some at the end of each section.

- They're the same style as the ones you'll get in the real exams — some will test your knowledge and understanding, some will test that you can apply your knowledge and some will test How Science Works.

- All the answers are in the back of the book, along with a mark scheme to show you how you get the marks.

Exam Help

There's a section at the back of the book stuffed full of things to help with your exams.

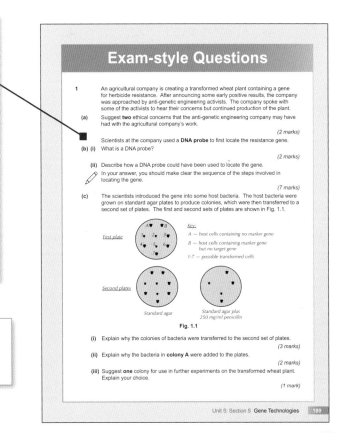

Published by CGP

Editors:
Charlotte Burrows, Emma Elder, Jane Ellingham, Rosie McCurrie, Rachael Rogers,
Camilla Simson, Hayley Thompson and Megan Tyler.

Contributors:
Gloria Barnett, James Foster, Julian Hardwick, Derek Harvey, Stephen Phillips,
Adrian Schmit, Sophie Watkins, Anna Fe Williamson.

ISBN: 978 1 84762 790 2

With thanks to Katherine Craig, Janet Cruse-Sawyer, Rosie McCurrie and Philip Rushworth for the
proofreading. With thanks to Anna Lupton for the copyright research.

Groovy website: www.cgpbooks.co.uk

Printed by Elanders Ltd, Newcastle upon Tyne.
Jolly bits of clipart from CorelDRAW®

1. The Scientific Process

Science tries to explain how and why things happen. It's all about seeking and gaining knowledge about the world around us. Scientists do this by observing things, developing theories and then testing them to see if they're correct — this is the scientific process. There are five main stages...

1. Developing theories

A **theory** is a possible explanation for something. Theories usually come about when scientists observe something and wonder why or how it happens. Scientists also sometimes form a **model** too — a simplified picture of what's physically going on.

Tip: A theory is only scientific if it can be tested.

> ### Examples
>
> - Darwin came up with his theory of evolution by natural selection after observing wildlife (e.g. finches) and fossils during a trip around South America and the Galapagos Islands.
>
> - The theory that smoking causes lung cancer was developed after it was observed that many people who contracted lung cancer also smoked.
>
> - John Snow came up with the theory that cholera is transmitted in water, rather than air, after observing lots of cases of cholera clustered around a water pump.
>
> - Edward Jenner came up with the idea that being infected with cowpox protected you from getting smallpox after observing that milkmaids didn't get smallpox.

Figure 1: *The doctor, John Snow.*

Tip: Sometimes data from one experiment can be the starting point for developing a new theory.

2. Testing the theories

The next step is to make a **prediction** or **hypothesis** — a specific testable statement, based on the theory, about what will happen in a test situation. Then an experiment or study is carried out to provide evidence that will support the prediction (or help to disprove it). If it's disproved it's back to the drawing board — the theory is modified or a completely new one is developed.

Tip: The results of one experiment can't prove that a theory is true — they can only suggest that it's true. They can however disprove a theory — show that it's wrong.

> ### Examples
>
> - Louis Pasteur designed an experiment to test his idea that 'germs' in the air caused disease and decomposition. He boiled two flasks of broth, both of which were left open to the air. One of the flasks had a curved neck (see Figure 2) to trap any airborne bacteria so they couldn't get into the broth. The broth in the flask with the curved neck stayed fresh, whereas the other broth went off. This provided evidence to support his theory. (After more evidence like this modern microbiology was born.)
>
> - Edward Jenner tested his idea that getting cowpox protected people from getting smallpox by infecting a boy with cowpox, then exposing him to smallpox. The boy didn't get smallpox, which provided evidence to support his theory. (Eventually this lead to the development of a smallpox vaccine.)

Figure 2: *Pasteur's experiment — the flask with the curved neck stayed fresh.*

3. Communicating the results

The results are then published — scientists need to let others know about their work. Scientists publish their results in **scientific journals**. These are just like normal magazines, only they contain scientific reports (called papers) instead of the latest celebrity gossip.

Scientific reports are similar to the lab write-ups you do in school. And just as a lab write-up is reviewed (marked) by your teacher, reports in scientific journals undergo **peer review** before they're published. The report is sent out to peers — other scientists who are experts in the same area. They examine the data and results, and if they think that the conclusion is reasonable it's published. This makes sure that work published in scientific journals is of a good standard.

But peer review can't guarantee the science is correct — other scientists still need to reproduce it. Sometimes mistakes are made and flawed work is published. Peer review isn't perfect but it's probably the best way for scientists to self-regulate their work and to publish quality reports.

Tip: Some well known biological journals are Nature, The Lancet and the British Medical Journal.

Tip: Scientific findings are also communicated at conferences around the world.

Tip: Other scientists need to reproduce results to make sure they're reliable — see the next page for more.

Tip: Even negative results are communicated — knowing that something is wrong improves scientific knowledge.

Tip: Once an experimental method is found that gives good evidence it becomes a protocol — an accepted method to test that particular thing that all scientists can use.

Tip: 'Good evidence' means reliable evidence — see the next page.

4. Validating the theory by more testing

Other scientists read the published theories and results, and try to test the theory themselves in order to validate it (back it up). This involves:

- Repeating the exact same experiments.
- Using the theory to make new predictions and then testing them with new experiments.

Examples

- In 1998 a study was published that linked the MMR vaccine to autism (a developmental disorder). Other scientists then conducted different studies to try to find the same link, but their results didn't back up (validate) the theory.
- In the 1940s a study was published linking smoking and lung cancer. After this many more studies were conducted all over the world that validated the conclusion of the first study.

5. The theory is rejected, or accepted

If multiple experiments show a theory to be incorrect then scientists either have to modify the theory or develop a new one, and start the testing again. If all the experiments in all the world provide good evidence to back a theory up, the theory is thought of as scientific 'fact' (for now) — see Figure 3. But it will never become totally indisputable fact. Scientific breakthroughs or advances could provide new ways to question and test the theory, which could lead to new evidence that conflicts with the current evidence. Then the testing starts all over again... And this, my friend, is the tentative nature of scientific knowledge — it's always changing and evolving.

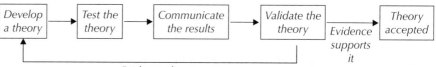

Figure 3: Flow diagram summarising the scientific process.

2. Scientific Evidence

So scientists need good evidence to back up their theories. A lot of scientific evidence comes from laboratory experiments, but there are things you can't investigate in a lab (e.g. whether stress causes heart attacks) — so you have to do a study instead. Good evidence basically means reliable evidence...

Reliable evidence

Scientific evidence needs to be **reliable**. This means that it can be consistently reproduced in independent experiments.

┌─ **Example** ───

Experiment 1 result = 15 ⎫ Reliable
Experiment 2 result = 16 ⎬ evidence
Experiment 3 result = 15 ⎭

Experiment 1 result = 15 ⎫ Unreliable
Experiment 2 result = 200 ⎬ evidence
Experiment 3 result = 79 ⎭

If the results are reproducible they're more likely to be true. If the data isn't reliable for whatever reason you can't draw a valid conclusion.

The results of an experiment also need to be as **accurate** and **precise** as possible. Accurate results are those that are really close to the true answer. Precise results are those taken using sensitive instruments that measure in small increments, e.g. using a ruler with a millimetre scale gives more precise data than using a ruler with a scale in centimetres.

Getting reliable evidence

To get reliable evidence you need to do the following things:

1. Control the variables

A **variable** is a quantity that has the potential to change, e.g. weight, temperature, concentration. In an experiment you usually change one variable and measure its effect on another variable:

- The variable you change is called the **independent variable**.
- The variable that you measure is called the **dependent variable**.

Every other variable that could affect the results has to be kept the same (controlled) throughout the experiment. These variables are called **control variables**. If all the variables that could possibly affect the result are controlled then the investigation is said to be a **fair test**.

┌─ **Example** ───

For an investigation into how light intensity affects the rate of photosynthesis in plants:

- The independent variable is light intensity (as it's the one you change).
- The dependent variable is the rate of photosynthesis (the thing you measure).
- The control variables are the type of plants you use, the temperature, the carbon dioxide concentration, etc. (as these could all affect the result if they aren't kept the same throughout).

It's usually straightforward to control all the variables in a lab experiment, but it can be quite tricky when doing studies. You often can't control all the variables, but the more you do control the more reliable the results will be.

2. Use control experiments and control groups

Even if you do manage to keep all the control variables the same, it's still possible that something else you're doing could affect the results. Scientists use control experiments and control groups to eliminate this possibility.

Figure 1: *Well-designed lab experiments where all the variables are controlled give reliable results.*

In lab experiments, controls or **control experiments** are used.

Example

You investigate antibiotic resistance in bacteria by growing cultures of bacteria on agar plates, then adding paper discs soaked in antibiotic.

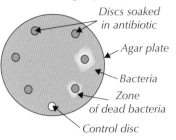

Discs soaked in antibiotic

Agar plate

Bacteria

Zone of dead bacteria

Control disc

If the bacteria are resistant to the antibiotic they will continue to grow. If they aren't resistant a clear patch will appear around the disc where they have died.

A disc that isn't soaked in antibiotic is included to act as a **negative control**. This makes sure any result is down to the antibiotic, not the presence of a paper disc.

Tip: A negative control is not expected to have any effect on the experiment.

In studies, **control groups** are used. The subjects in the study are split into two groups — the experimental group and the control group. The control group is treated in exactly the same way as the experimental group, except for the factor you're investigating.

Example

Say you're investigating the effect of eating a low sodium (salt) diet on blood pressure. You'd have two groups. One group would be the experimental group and be given a diet low in sodium. The other group would be a control group, who would be given a diet in which sodium wasn't reduced. This is done so that you can tell that any decrease in blood pressure is due to the low sodium diet and nothing else.

Exam Tip
If you get an exam question asking why a control group is important in a particular experiment make sure your answer is specific to that experiment (not just generally about why control groups are good).

When testing new drugs to see if they work, control groups should always be used. The control group is treated in exactly the same way as the experimental group, except they're given a thing called a **placebo** instead of the drug. A placebo is a dummy pill or injection that looks exactly like the real drug, but doesn't contain the drug. It's used to make sure that people don't improve just because they think they're being treated.

Drug trials also should be **double-blind trials**. This means that the doctor involved doesn't know whether the patient is getting the drug or the placebo, and neither does the patient. This is done to remove **bias**, e.g. doctors who expect the patients on the drugs to get better might report a greater improvement than there was.

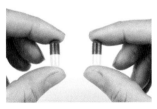

Figure 2: *The placebo (left) should look identical to the real drug (right).*

3. Use a large sample size

Sample size is the number of samples in the investigation, e.g. the number of people in a drug trial. The general rule is the larger the sample size, the more reliable the data is. This is because it reduces the chance of getting a freak result (e.g. if you get the same result twice it might be because of chance, but if you get it 100 times it's much more likely that it's not due to chance).

Annoyingly, there are no rules about how big the sample size has to be to be for the investigation to be considered as 'reliable' — all you need to know is that bigger is always better.

Tip: A large data set is the same thing as a large sample size.

4. Collect data carefully

The method used to collect the data can affect how reliable it is. For example, people aren't always truthful when answering questionnaires, which reduces the reliability of the data. Also, if you're using control groups, it's important that subjects are split into the two groups at **random**. This helps to avoid bias, and so makes the data more reliable.

Tip: Bias is when someone intentionally, or unintentionally, favours a particular result.

5. Repeat the measurements

The reliability of a single experiment can be improved by repeating the measurements and calculating the mean. Also, the larger the number of repeats the easier it is to spot **anomalous data** (measurements that fall outside the range of values you'd expect or any pattern you already have).

Drawing conclusions from data

Conclusions need to be **valid**. A conclusion can only be considered as valid if it answers the original question and uses reliable data. It's quite tricky to draw conclusions from data — so scientists need to look out for a couple of things:

Correlations and causal relationships

The results of investigations often show a relationship between two variables, e.g. between smoking and lung cancer. A relationship between two variables is called a **correlation**. There are two types of correlation — **positive correlations** and **negative correlations**.

Positive	_Negative_	_No correlation_
As one variable increases the other increases.	_As one variable increases the other decreases._	_There is no relationship between the variables._

Scientists have to be very careful when drawing conclusions from data like this because a correlation between two variables doesn't always mean that a change in one variable causes a change in the other.

> **Example**
>
> There's a correlation in the UK between a decrease in temperature and the number of adults who are treated in hospital for serious injuries — the lower the temperature, the greater the number of people who are treated. But low temperatures don't cause serious injuries — the reason for the correlation is that there's more likely to be ice and snow around during a period of cold weather. This increases the likelihood that people will slip, fall badly and injure themselves.

If there's a relationship between two variables and a change in one variable does cause a change in the other (e.g. more ice and snow around does cause an increase in serious injuries) it's called a **causal relationship**. It can be concluded that a correlation is a causal relationship if every other variable that could possibly affect the result is controlled. In reality this is very hard to do — correlations are generally accepted to be causal relationships if lots of studies have found the same thing, and scientists have figured out exactly how one factor causes the other.

Drawing specific conclusions

Scientists can't make broad generalisations from data — they have to be very specific. They can only conclude what the results show and no more.

> **Example**
>
> The graph shows the results from a study into the effect of antibiotic X on protein synthesis in _E. coli_. The only conclusion you can draw is that as the concentration of antibiotic X increases, the rate of protein synthesis in _E. coli_ decreases. You can't conclude this is true for any other antibiotic or any other species of bacteria.
>
>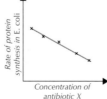

Tip: Repeating measurements in an experiment improves reliability in the same way as a large sample size — it reduces the likelihood that the results are due to chance.

Tip: All data will vary a bit, but anomalous results vary a lot from what you'd expect.

Tip: A causal relationship is sometimes called a causal link.

Tip: What conclusion is drawn might be affected by bias, e.g. if someone works for a chemical company they might be more likely to ignore data that showed their product causing environmental problems.

3. Science and Decision Making

Lots of scientific work eventually leads to important discoveries or breakthroughs that could benefit humankind. These results are used by society to make decisions.

How society uses science to make decisions

Scientific knowledge is used by society (that's you, me and everyone else) to make decisions — about the way we live, what we eat, what we drive, etc. All sections of society use scientific evidence to make decisions, e.g. politicians use it to devise policies and individuals use science to make decisions about their own lives.

Examples

- The maximum amount of salt people are advised to eat per day was reduced in government guidelines in 2004, due to the results of a study which showed that reducing salt intake could significantly reduce heart disease.

- Leaded petrol in cars was phased out in many countries after it was found to cause air pollution that damaged the brain.

Factors affecting decision making

Other factors can influence decisions about science or the way science is used:

Economic factors

Society has to consider the cost of implementing changes based on scientific conclusions. Sometimes it decides the cost doesn't outweigh the benefits.

Example

The NHS can't afford the most expensive drugs without sacrificing something else. Sometimes they decide to use a less effective, but less expensive drug, despite evidence showing there's a more effective one.

Social factors

Decisions affect people's lives — sometimes people don't want to follow advice, or are strongly against some recommendations.

Examples

- Scientists may suggest banning smoking and alcohol to prevent health problems, but shouldn't we be able to choose whether we want to smoke and drink or not?

- Scientists may be able to cure many diseases using stem cells, but some people are strongly against the idea of embryonic stem cell research.

Environmental factors

Some scientific research and breakthroughs might affect the environment. Not everyone thinks the benefits are worth the possible environmental damage.

Examples

- Scientists believe unexplored regions like remote parts of rainforests might contain untapped drug resources. But some people think we shouldn't exploit these regions because any interesting finds may lead to deforestation and reduced biodiversity in these areas.

- Scientists have developed genetically modified (GM) crops (e.g. with frost resistance, or high nutrient content), but some people think the possible environmental harm they could do outweighs their benefits.

1. Communication Basics

Learning Objectives:

- Be able to outline the need for communication systems within multicellular organisms, with reference to the need to respond to changes in the internal and external environment and to coordinate the activities of different organs.

- Know that cells need to communicate with each other by a process called cell signalling.

- Know that the nervous system and the hormonal system are examples of cell signalling.

  Specification Reference 4.1.1

In order to survive, organisms need to respond to what's going on around them. Communication systems make sure information gets passed on from one part of the organism to another.

Responding to the environment

Animals increase their chances of survival by responding to changes in their external environment, e.g. by avoiding harmful environments such as places that are too hot or too cold. They also respond to changes in their internal environment to make sure that the conditions are always optimal for their metabolism (all the chemical reactions that go on inside them). Any change in the internal or external environment, e.g. a change in temperature, light intensity or pressure, is called a **stimulus**.

Receptors and effectors

Receptors detect stimuli. They are specific — they only detect one particular stimulus, e.g. pressure, light or glucose concentration. There are many different types of receptor that each detect a different type of stimulus, e.g. pressure receptors only detect pressure. Some receptors are cells, e.g. photoreceptors are receptor cells that connect to the nervous system. Some receptors are proteins on cell surface membranes, e.g. glucose receptors are proteins found in the cell membranes of some pancreatic cells.

Effectors are cells that bring about a response to a stimulus, to produce an effect. Effectors include muscle cells and cells found in glands, e.g. the pancreas.

Receptors and effectors play an important role in communicating information from one part of the organism to another. This makes sure that the activities of different organs are coordinated to keep the organism working effectively. For example, when receptor cells in the pancreas detect a low concentration of glucose in the blood, they communicate with effector cells in the liver to release more glucose into the blood (see pages 33-34).

Tip: There's much more about how receptors work on pages 9-10.

Cell signalling

Receptors communicate with effectors via the nervous system (see next page) or the hormonal system (see p. 22), or sometimes using both. Nervous and hormonal communication are both examples of **cell signalling** (ways cells communicate with each other).

Practice Questions — Fact Recall

Q1 Define the term 'stimulus'.

Q2 Why is it important that organisms respond to stimuli?

Q3 What is the role of a receptor?

Q4 Give two types of cell that act as effectors.

Q5 What is cell signalling?

Tip: Make sure that you're confident with the basics of cellular communication and that you can answer all of these questions, before moving onto the rest of the section.

- Be able to describe, with the aid of diagrams, the structure and functions of sensory and motor neurones.
- Be able to outline the roles of sensory receptors in mammals in converting different forms of energy into nerve impulses.

Specification Reference 4.1.2

Tip: Relay neurones are also called intermediate neurones, interneurones or association neurones.

Tip: <u>D</u>endrites and <u>d</u>endrons carry information towar<u>d</u>s the cell body, <u>a</u>xons carry it <u>a</u>way from the cell body.

Figure 1: *A light micrograph of a motor neurone — many dendrites can be seen extending from the cell body.*

Tip: This is a non-myelinated motor neurone — see page 14 for the structure of a myelinated one.

Tip: Nerve impulses are electrical impulses. They're also called action potentials.

2. The Nervous System

The nervous system passes on information from one part of an organism to another using nerve impulses. It's a very fast form of communication.

Neurones

The nervous system is made up of a complex network of cells called neurones. There are three main types of neurone:

1. **Sensory neurones** transmit nerve impulses from receptors to the central nervous system (CNS) — the brain and spinal cord.
2. **Motor neurones** transmit nerve impulses from the CNS to effectors.
3. **Relay neurones** transmit nerve impulses between sensory neurones and motor neurones.

Structure of neurones

All neurones have a cell body with a nucleus (plus cytoplasm and all the other organelles you usually get in a cell). The cell body has extensions that connect to other neurones — dendrites and dendrons carry nerve impulses towards the cell body (dendrites are smaller branches of a dendron), and axons carry nerve impulses away from the cell body. You need to learn the structure of sensory and motor neurones:

- Sensory neurones have short dendrites and one long dendron to carry nerve impulses from receptor cells to the cell body, and one short axon that carries nerve impulses from the cell body to the CNS.

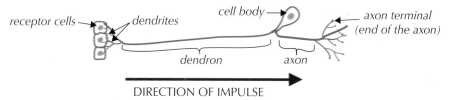

DIRECTION OF IMPULSE

- Motor neurones have many short dendrites that carry nerve impulses from the CNS to the cell body, and one long axon that carries nerve impulses from the cell body to effector cells.

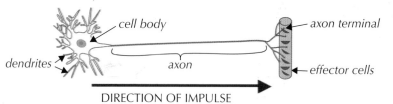

DIRECTION OF IMPULSE

Nervous communication

A stimulus is detected by receptor cells and a nerve impulse is sent along a sensory neurone. When a nerve impulse reaches the end of a neurone chemicals called neurotransmitters take the information across the gap (called a synapse) to the next neurone, which then continues to send the nerve impulse (see p. 16). The CNS processes the information, decides what to do about it and sends impulses along motor neurones to an effector (see Figure 2).

sensory neurone   motor neurone

Stimulus ➡ Receptors ➡ CNS ➡ Effectors ➡ Response

Figure 2: *The pathway of nervous communication.*

A real-life example of nervous communication is when you see a friend waving to you and you wave back in response:

- **Stimulus** — you see a friend waving.
- **Receptors** — light receptors (photoreceptors) in your eyes detect the wave. The electrical impulse is carried by a sensory neurone to the CNS.
- **CNS** — processes information and decides what to do about it. An electrical impulse is sent along a motor neurone.
- **Effectors** — muscle cells are stimulated by the motor neurone.
- **Response** — muscles contract to make your arm wave.

Sensory receptors

Different stimuli have different forms of energy, e.g. light energy or chemical energy. But your nervous system only sends information in the form of nerve impulses (electrical impulses). Sensory receptors convert the energy of a stimulus into electrical energy. They act as **transducers** — something that converts one form of energy into another.

Here's a bit more about how receptor cells that communicate information via the nervous system work...

Tip: Sensory receptors are cells. There are other types of receptors, such as proteins on cell surface membranes, but they work in a different way.

The resting potential

When a nervous system receptor is in its resting state (not being stimulated), there's a difference in charge between the inside and the outside of the cell — the inside is negatively charged relative to the outside (see Figure 3). This means there's a **voltage** across the membrane. Voltage is also known as the **potential difference**. The potential difference when a cell is at rest is called its **resting potential**. The resting potential is generated by ion pumps and ion channels (see p. 11).

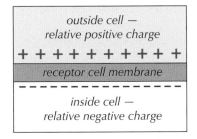

*outside cell —
relative positive charge*

+ + + + + + + + +

receptor cell membrane

– – – – – – – – –

*inside cell —
relative negative charge*

Figure 3: *Relative charges either side of a receptor cell membrane at rest.*

The generator potential

When a stimulus is detected, the cell membrane is excited and becomes more permeable, allowing more ions to move in and out of the cell — altering the potential difference. The change in potential difference due to a stimulus is called the **generator potential**. A bigger stimulus excites the membrane more, causing a bigger movement of ions and a bigger change in potential difference — so a bigger generator potential is produced (see Figure 4).

Tip: An ion is a particle with a positive or negative electrical charge, e.g. sodium ions (Na^+).

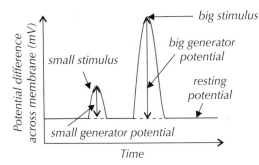

big stimulus

big generator potential

resting potential

small stimulus

small generator potential

Time

Figure 4: *The bigger stimulus produces the bigger generator potential.*

Tip: Potential difference across a cell membrane is usually measured in millivolts (mV).

The action potential

Tip: There's much more on action potentials on pages 12-13.

If the generator potential is big enough it'll trigger an action potential (nerve impulse) along a neurone. An action potential is only triggered if the generator potential reaches a certain level called the **threshold level**. If the stimulus is too weak the generator potential won't reach the threshold, so there's no action potential (see Figure 5).

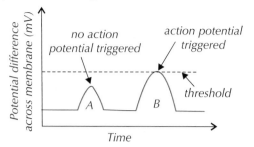

Figure 5: *Generator potential not reaching the threshold (A) and reaching the threshold (B).*

Practice Questions — Application

For a particular receptor cell, an action potential is triggered when the generator potential reaches −60 mV.

Q1 What name is given to the value at which an action potential will be triggered?

Q2 The graph below shows generator potentials in the receptor cell.

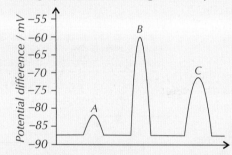

a) Which curve shows a generator potential that would trigger an action potential? Give a reason for your answer.

b) What is the resting potential of this receptor cell?

Practice Questions — Fact Recall

Q1 What is the function of:

a) a sensory neurone?   b) a motor neurone?

Q2 The diagram on the right shows a non-myelinated motor neurone. Name the structures labelled A-D.

Q3 Give two structural differences between a sensory neurone and a motor neurone.

Q4 Describe the pathway of nervous communication from stimulus to response.

Q5 Why are sensory receptors described as 'transducers'?

Q6 Explain how a generator potential is produced.

Q7 Explain how a bigger stimulus causes a bigger generator potential than a smaller stimulus.

Exam Tip
Questions on the structure of neurones come up a lot in the exam, so make sure you learn the structures really well to pick up some easy marks.

3. The Nervous Impulse

Nervous impulses are the electrical charges transmitted along a neurone.
They're created by the movement of sodium and potassium ions across a
neurone cell membrane.

The resting membrane potential

In a neurone's resting state (when it's not being stimulated), the outside of
the membrane is positively charged compared to the inside. This is because
there are more positive ions outside the cell than inside. So the membrane is
polarised — there's a difference in charge. The voltage across the membrane
when it's at rest is called the resting potential — it's about –70 mV.

Movement of sodium and potassium ions

The resting potential is created and maintained by **sodium-potassium pumps**
and **potassium ion channels** in a neurone's membrane (see Figure 1).

- Sodium-potassium pumps use **active transport** to move three sodium ions
  (Na^+) out of the neurone for every two potassium ions (K^+) moved in.
  ATP is needed to do this.

- Potassium ion channels allow **facilitated diffusion** of potassium ions (K^+)
  out of the neurone, down their concentration gradient.

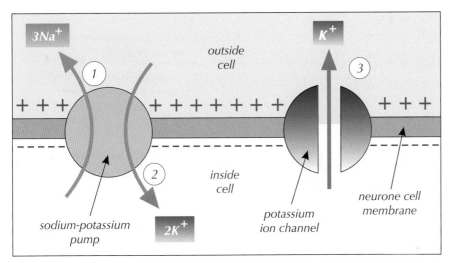

Figure 1: *Movement of sodium and potassium ions across a resting cell membrane.*

1. The sodium-potassium pumps move sodium ions out of the neurone,
   but the membrane isn't permeable to sodium ions, so they can't
   diffuse back in. This creates a sodium ion **electrochemical gradient**
   (a concentration gradient of ions) because there are more positive
   sodium ions outside the cell than inside.

2. The sodium-potassium pumps also move potassium ions in to the neurone.

3. When the cell's at rest, most potassium ion channels are open.
   This means that the membrane is permeable to potassium ions,
   so some diffuse back out through potassium ion channels.

Even though positive ions are moving in and out of the cell, in total more
positive ions move out of the cell than enter. This makes the outside of the
cell positively charged compared to the inside.

Learning Objectives:

- Be able to describe
  and explain how
  the resting potential
  is established and
  maintained.

- Be able to describe
  and explain how an
  action potential is
  generated.

- Be able to interpret
  graphs of the voltage
  changes taking place
  during the generation
  and transmission of an
  action potential.

- Be able to describe
  and explain how
  an action potential
  is transmitted in a
  myelinated neurone,
  with reference to
  the roles of voltage-
  gated sodium ion
  and potassium ion
  channels.

- Be able to outline the
  significance of the
  frequency of impulse
  transmission.

- Be able to compare
  and contrast the
  structure and function
  of myelinated and
  non-myelinated
  neurones.

**Specification
Reference 4.1.2**

Tip: The neurone cell
membrane also has
sodium ion channels
(see next page), but
these are closed when
the cell's at rest.

Tip: Remember,
sodium-potassium pumps
are SOPI — Sodium Out,
Potassium In.

Action potentials

When a neurone is stimulated, other ion channels in the cell membrane, called sodium ion channels, open. If the stimulus is big enough, it'll trigger a rapid change in potential difference. This causes the cell membrane to become **depolarised** (it's no longer polarised). The sequence of events that happens is known as an action potential — see Figure 2.

Exam Tip
You don't have to learn the mV values given here — they're only approximate and vary from neurone to neurone. Don't be thrown in the exam if you're given a graph with different values.

Exam Tip
You might be asked to explain the shape of this graph in your exam, so make sure you know what's happening at each point.

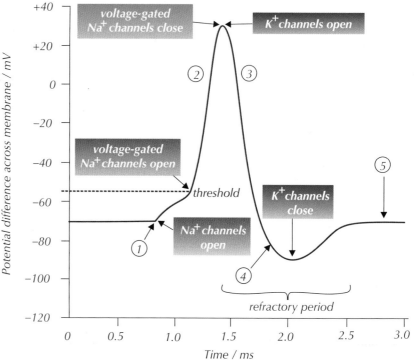

Figure 2: *A graph to show the changes in potential difference across a neurone cell membrane during an action potential.*

Tip: The graph below shows when the <u>sodium ion channels</u> (orange) are open during an action potential (dotted line):

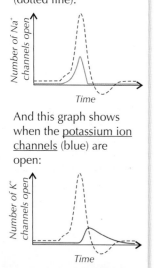

And this graph shows when the <u>potassium ion channels</u> (blue) are open:

1. **Stimulus** — this excites the neurone cell membrane, causing sodium ion channels to open. The membrane becomes more permeable to sodium, so sodium ions diffuse into the neurone down the sodium ion electrochemical gradient. This makes the inside of the neurone less negative.

2. **Depolarisation** — if the potential difference reaches the threshold (around -55 mV), voltage-gated sodium ion channels open and more sodium ions diffuse into the neurone. Voltage-gated ion channels are channels that only open at a certain voltage.

3. **Repolarisation** — at a potential difference of around $+30$ mV the sodium ion channels close and potassium ion channels open. The membrane is more permeable to potassium so potassium ions diffuse out of the neurone down the potassium ion concentration gradient. This starts to get the membrane back to its resting potential.

4. **Hyperpolarisation** — potassium ion channels are slow to close so there's a slight 'overshoot' where too many potassium ions diffuse out of the neurone. The potential difference becomes more negative than the resting potential (i.e. less than -70 mV).

5. **Resting potential** — the ion channels are reset. The sodium-potassium pump returns the membrane to its resting potential by pumping sodium ions out and potassium ions in, and maintains the resting potential until the membrane's excited by another stimulus.

The refractory period

After an action potential, the neurone cell membrane can't be excited again straight away. This is because the ion channels are recovering and they can't be made to open — sodium ion channels are closed during repolarisation and potassium ion channels are closed during hyperpolarisation. This period of recovery is called the refractory period (see Figure 3).

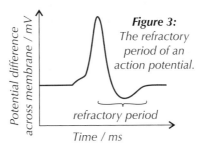

Figure 3: The refractory period of an action potential.

The refractory period acts as a time delay between one action potential and the next. This makes sure that action potentials don't overlap but pass along as discrete (separate) impulses. The refractory period also makes sure action potentials are unidirectional (they only travel in one direction).

Waves of depolarisation

When an action potential happens, some of the sodium ions that enter the neurone diffuse sideways. This causes sodium ion channels in the next region of the neurone to open and sodium ions diffuse into that part. This causes a wave of depolarisation to travel along the neurone. The wave moves away from the parts of the membrane in the refractory period because these parts can't fire an action potential.

Tip: A wave of depolarisation is like a Mexican wave travelling through a crowd — sodium ions rushing inwards causes a wave of activity along the membrane.

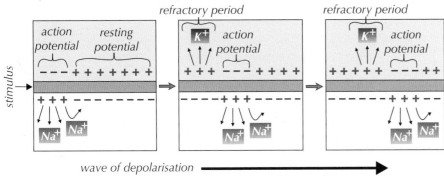

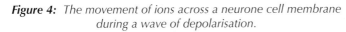

Figure 4: The movement of ions across a neurone cell membrane during a wave of depolarisation.

Tip: The electrical impulse can be said to 'propagate' along the neurone. This just describes the wave-like movement of the action potential.

Frequency of impulses

Once the threshold is reached, an action potential will always fire with the same change in voltage, no matter how big the stimulus is. If the threshold isn't reached, an action potential won't fire (see Figure 5). This is the **all-or-nothing** nature of action potentials.

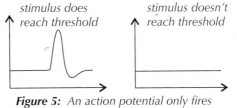

Figure 5: An action potential only fires if the stimulus reaches the threshold.

A bigger stimulus won't cause a bigger action potential but it will cause them to fire more frequently (see Figure 6). So if the brain receives a high frequency of action potentials, it interprets this as a big stimulus and responds accordingly.

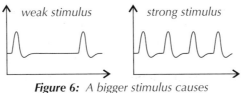

Figure 6: A bigger stimulus causes more frequent action potentials.

Tip: The all-or-nothing principle stops the brain from getting over-stimulated by not responding to very small stimuli.

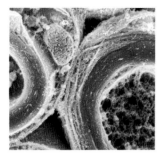

Figure 7: A cross-section through a myelinated neurone. The myelin sheath (orange/brown) surrounds the axon (dark brown).

Exam Tip
You need to know the structure and function of neurones — both the myelinated ones (like those in Figure 8) and the non-myelinated ones (see page 8).

Tip: Long neurones, like a motor neurone from your spinal cord to your foot, are myelinated to speed up the conduction of action potentials. Short neurones, like those in the CNS, don't need to be myelinated (as it's quicker to transmit signals over short distances anyway).

Tip: If you imagine a Mexican wave travelling through a crowd, then saltatory conduction is like every tenth person doing the wave instead of everyone doing the wave — so it travels much faster.

Tip: The pumps and channels that move ions across the membrane are proteins, so these will denature at high temperatures.

Speed of conduction

Three factors affect the speed of conduction of action potentials:

1. Myelination

Some neurones are myelinated — they have a **myelin sheath** (see Figure 8). The myelin sheath is an electrical insulator. It's made of a type of cell called a **Schwann cell**, which is wrapped around the axon (and/or dendron). Between the Schwann cells are tiny patches of bare membrane called the **nodes of Ranvier**. Sodium ion channels are concentrated at the nodes of Ranvier.

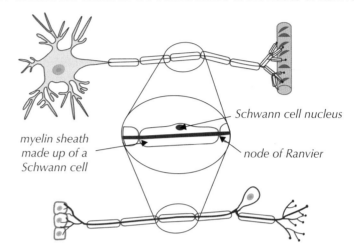

Figure 8: Structure of a myelinated motor neurone (top) and a myelinated sensory neurone (bottom), with the myelin sheath enlarged.

Saltatory conduction

In a myelinated neurone, depolarisation only happens at the nodes of Ranvier (where sodium ions can get through the membrane). The neurone's cytoplasm conducts enough electrical charge to depolarise the next node, so the impulse 'jumps' from node to node. This is called saltatory conduction and it's really fast — see Figure 9.

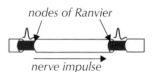

Figure 9: Saltatory conduction along a myelinated neurone.

In a non-myelinated neurone, the impulse travels as a wave along the whole length of the axon membrane (see Figure 10). This is slower than saltatory conduction (although it's still pretty quick).

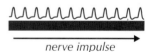

Figure 10: Conduction along a non-myelinated neurone.

2. Axon diameter

Action potentials are conducted quicker along axons with bigger diameters because there's less resistance to the flow of ions than in the cytoplasm of a smaller axon. With less resistance, depolarisation reaches other parts of the neurone cell membrane quicker.

3. Temperature

The speed of conduction increases as the temperature increases too, because ions diffuse faster. The speed only increases up to around 40 °C though — after that the proteins begin to denature and the speed decreases.

Practice Questions — Application

Tip: Remember, the potential difference is the voltage across the membrane.

The graph below shows the changes in potential difference across a neurone cell membrane during an action potential.

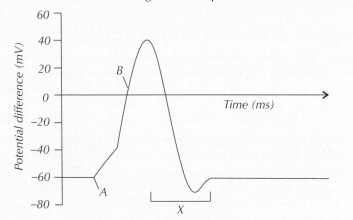

Q1 Describe the different events occurring at points A and B.

Q2 What is the threshold level for this action potential?

Q3 What is the resting potential of this neurone cell membrane?

Q4 a) Explain the shape of the curve during the period marked X.

    b) What name is given to the period marked X?

Q5 How would the graph look if a bigger stimulus triggered the action potential? Explain your answer.

Exam Tip
Always be clear in your exam answers as to whether you're talking about <u>sodium ions</u> (Na^+) or <u>potassium ions</u> (K^+) — don't just write 'sodium', 'potassium' or 'ions'.

Practice Questions — Fact Recall

Q1 Which two proteins in a neurone's cell membrane are responsible for creating and maintaining the resting membrane potential?

Q2 Following a stimulus, explain how the opening of sodium ion channels affects the potential difference across a neurone cell membrane.

Q3 Describe and explain the movement of sodium ions if the potential difference across a neurone cell membrane reaches the threshold level.

Q4 a) After an action potential, why can't the neurone cell membrane be excited again straight away?

    b) What two effects does this have on the conduction of action potentials along a neurone?

Q5 Explain how waves of depolarisation are produced.

Q6 Describe the structure of a myelinated neurone.

Q7 How does conduction along a myelinated neurone differ compared to conduction along a non-myelinated neurone?

Q8 Give two factors, other than myelination, that affect the conduction of action potentials.

Exam Tip
In your exam, be careful not to use phrases like 'ions move across the membrane' — you need to make it clear whether they're moving <u>into</u> or <u>out of</u> the cell.

4. Synapses

If you've ever wondered how information passes from one neurone to the next, now's your chance to find out...

Synapses and neurotransmitters

A synapse is the junction between a neurone and another neurone, or between a neurone and an effector cell, e.g. a muscle or gland cell. The tiny gap between the cells at a synapse is called the synaptic cleft. The presynaptic neurone (the one before the synapse) has a swelling called a synaptic knob. This contains synaptic vesicles filled with chemicals called neurotransmitters.

When an action potential reaches the end of a neurone it causes neurotransmitters to be released into the synaptic cleft. They diffuse across to the postsynaptic membrane (the one after the synapse) and bind to specific receptors. When neurotransmitters bind to receptors they might trigger an action potential (in a neurone), cause muscle contraction (in a muscle cell), or cause a hormone to be secreted (from a gland cell).

Neurotransmitters are removed from the cleft so the response doesn't keep happening, e.g. they're taken back into the presynaptic neurone or they're broken down by enzymes (and the products are taken into the neurone).

Cholinergic synapses

There are different types of synapses, each with a slightly different structure that relates to their function. You need to learn the structure of a **cholinergic synapse** — see Figure 2. A cholinergic synapse uses the neurotransmitter **acetylcholine** (**ACh**) which binds to receptors called cholinergic receptors.

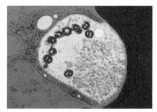

Figure 1: *A synaptic knob (yellow) containing vesicles (large red circles).*

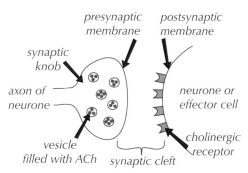

Figure 2: *The structure of a cholinergic synapse.*

Synaptic transmission

This is how a nerve impulse is transmitted across a cholinergic synapse:

1. Arrival of an action potential

An action potential arrives at the synaptic knob of the presynaptic neurone. The action potential stimulates voltage-gated calcium ion channels in the presynaptic neurone to open. Calcium ions (Ca^{2+}) diffuse into the synaptic knob. (They're pumped out afterwards by active transport.)

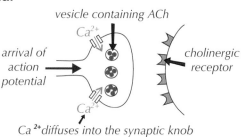

Ca^{2+} diffuses into the synaptic knob

2. Fusion of the vesicles

The influx of calcium ions into the synaptic knob causes the synaptic vesicles to move to the presynaptic membrane. They then fuse with the presynaptic membrane. The vesicles release ACh into the synaptic cleft by **exocytosis**.

vesicles fuse with the membrane and release ACh

3. Diffusion of ACh

ACh diffuses across the synaptic cleft and binds to specific cholinergic receptors on the postsynaptic membrane. This causes sodium ion channels in the postsynaptic neurone to open. The influx of sodium ions into the postsynaptic neurone causes depolarisation. An action potential on the postsynaptic membrane is generated if the threshold is reached. ACh is removed from the synaptic cleft so the response doesn't keep happening. It's broken down by an enzyme called acetylcholinesterase (AChE) and the products are re-absorbed by the presynaptic neurone and used to make more ACh.

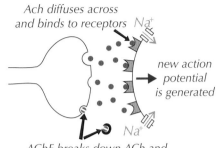

Ach diffuses across and binds to receptors Na^+

new action potential is generated

Na^+

AChE breaks down ACh and the products are re-absorbed

Tip: Look back at page 12 if you need a reminder of how action potentials are generated.

Disruption of synaptic transmission

Because synapses use chemical communication, they can be affected by chemicals like drugs, toxins or poisons. For example, some chemicals are the same shape as neurotransmitters so they mimic their action at receptors (these drugs are called agonists). This means more receptors are activated.

Exam Tip
Don't worry, you don't have to learn the action of any specific drug or toxin for your exam. But examiners like to test your knowledge of synapses, e.g. by asking about how drugs or toxins would affect their activity, so make sure you understand these examples.

Example

Nicotine mimics acetylcholine. It binds to certain types of cholinergic receptors in the brain.

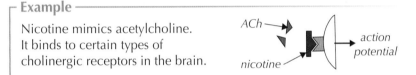

ACh → *action potential*

nicotine

Some chemicals block receptors so they can't be activated by neurotransmitters. This means fewer receptors (if any) can be activated.

Example

Curare blocks the effects of acetylcholine by blocking certain cholinergic receptors at neuromuscular junctions, so muscle cells can't be stimulated. This results in the muscle being paralysed.

ACh → *no action potential*

curare

Some chemicals inhibit the enzyme that breaks down neurotransmitters (they stop it from working). This means there are more neurotransmitters in the synaptic cleft to bind to receptors and they're there for longer.

Tip: The nervous system uses lots of different neurotransmitters, not just acetylcholine. You'll come across ones called dopamine and noradrenaline too.

Example

Nerve gases stop acetylcholine from being broken down in the synaptic cleft. This can lead to loss of muscle control.

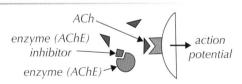

ACh → *action potential*

enzyme (AChE) inhibitor

enzyme (AChE)

Some chemicals inhibit the release of neurotransmitters from the presynaptic neurone so fewer receptors are activated.

Example

Opioids block calcium ion channels in the presynaptic neurone. This means fewer vesicles fuse with the presynaptic membrane so less neurotransmitter is released.

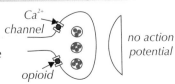

Ca^{2+} *channel*

no action potential

opioid

Q1 Acetylcholine (ACh) is involved in many functions in the body, including saliva production. Carbachol is a drug that binds and activates cholinergic receptors. Predict the effect of carbachol on saliva production and explain your answer.

Q2 Endorphins are endogenous opioid peptides that function as inhibitory neurotransmitters. This means that when they bind to receptors on the postsynaptic neurone they hyperpolarise the membrane, preventing it from firing an action potential. Endorphins bind to opioid receptors on neurones that transmit pain signals.

a) Suggest what effect endorphins have on the sensation of pain. Explain your answer.

b) Morphine is an opioid drug that's very similar in structure to an endorphin molecule. Suggest what effect taking morphine will have on a person's sensation of pain. Explain your answer.

Exam Tip
Don't worry if you've never heard of particular drug names — all the information you need to answer the question will be in the question itself.

Roles of synapses

Synapses play vital roles in the nervous system. The way they work affects how information is passed on throughout the body.

Divergence and convergence

When one neurone connects to many neurones information can be dispersed to different parts of the body. This is called **synaptic divergence** (see Figure 3). When many neurones connect to one neurone information can be amplified (made stronger). This is called **synaptic convergence** (see Figure 4).

Tip: Synaptic divergence is when information from one neurone divides, and synaptic convergence is when information from many neurones comes together.

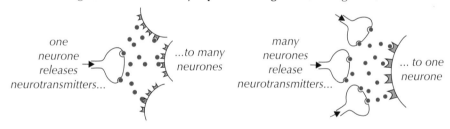

one neurone releases neurotransmitters...   *...to many neurones*

many neurones release neurotransmitters...   *... to one neurone*

Figure 3: Synaptic divergence.   **Figure 4:** Synaptic convergence.

Summation

If a stimulus is weak, only a small amount of neurotransmitter will be released from a neurone into the synaptic cleft. This might not be enough to excite the postsynaptic membrane to the threshold level and stimulate an action potential. Summation is where the effect of neurotransmitters released from many neurones (or one neurone that's stimulated a lot in a short period of time) is added together. It means synapses accurately process information, finely tuning the response. There are two types of summation:

Tip: Summation is where the sum total of lots of smaller impulses triggers an action potential.

1. **Spatial summation** is where two or more presynaptic neurones release their neurotransmitters at the same time onto the same postsynaptic neurone. The small amount of neurotransmitter released from each of these neurones can be enough altogether to reach the threshold in the postsynaptic neurone and trigger an action potential — see Figure 5 on the next page.

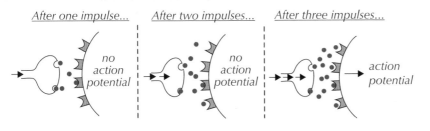

Figure 5: One presynaptic neurone only releases a few neurotransmitters (left) but three presynaptic neurones release enough to trigger an action potential (right).

2. **Temporal summation** is where two or more nerve impulses arrive in quick succession from the same presynaptic neurone. This makes an action potential more likely because more neurotransmitter is released into the synaptic cleft — see Figure 6.

Figure 6: The effects of temporal summation at a synapse.

Tip: Impulses have to follow each other very quickly, otherwise the neurotransmitter will be removed from the cleft before it's reached a level high enough to trigger an action potential.

Unidirectional transmission

Synapses make sure impulses are unidirectional — the nervous impulse can only travel in one direction. This is because neurotransmitters are only released from presynaptic neurones and receptors for neurotransmitters are only on the postsynaptic membranes.

Practice Questions — Fact Recall

Q1 Give three types of cell that have receptors for neurotransmitters.

Q2 The diagram on the right shows a cholinergic synapse. Name the structures labelled A to G on the diagram.

Q3 At a cholinergic synapse:

a) Describe and explain the movement of calcium ions following the arrival of an action potential at a presynaptic neurone.

b) Explain how acetylcholine (ACh) leaves the presynaptic neurone and causes an action potential in the postsynaptic neurone.

Q4 Explain the purpose of:
   a) synaptic divergence,   b) synaptic convergence.

Q5 Explain how an action potential may be more likely as a result of:

   a) spatial summation,   b) temporal summation.

Q6 Explain why impulses at a synapse are unidirectional.

Tip: Don't get the presynaptic and postsynaptic neurones mixed up — remember 'pre' means before and 'post' means after.

Exam-style Questions

1 The nervous system uses electrical and chemical communication to carry information from receptors to effectors. Action potentials along a neurone are triggered when the neurone cell membrane is stimulated. During an action potential, the potential difference across the neurone cell membrane changes.

(a) A small stimulus may be enough to trigger an action potential. Describe the effect a **bigger stimulus** would have on the potential difference across the neurone cell membrane during an action potential.

(1 mark)

(b) Action potentials pass along the neurone as discrete impulses — they don't overlap. Explain why action potentials don't overlap.

(3 marks)

(c) Fig. 1.1 shows a neurone cell membrane at two different times during one action potential.

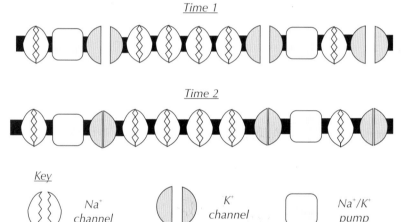

Time 1

Time 2

Key

 Na^+ channel K^+ channel Na^+/K^+ pump

Fig. 1.1

(i) Describe the stages of the action potential that are occurring at Times 1 and 2. Use evidence from Fig. 1.1 to support your answer.

(6 marks)

The neurone cell membrane shows **sodium-potassium (Na^+/K^+) pumps**.

(ii) Describe the movement of sodium and potassium ions across a sodium-potassium pump.

(3 marks)

(iii) Explain why a sodium-potassium pump is needed by the neurone cell membrane after Time 2.

(3 marks)

(d) Saxitoxin is a chemical that blocks **voltage-gated sodium ion channels**.

Use your knowledge of action potentials to explain the effect that saxitoxin is likely to have upon the nervous system.

(3 marks)

2   Fig. 2.1 shows the structure of a myelinated motor neurone.

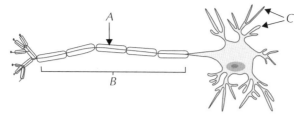

Fig. 2.1

(a) (i) Name the type of cell that forms structure **A**.

(1 mark)

(ii) Complete the table to give the names of the structures labelled **B** and **C** and their functions.

	Structure	Function
B		
C		

(4 marks)

(b) Sensory neurones differ in structure and function to motor neurones.
Give the **function** of a sensory neurone.

(1 mark)

(c) Guillain-Barré syndrome is an auto-immune disease whereby the myelin sheath around certain neurones is damaged.
Use your knowledge of myelination to explain how Guillain-Barré syndrome can result in muscle weakness and paralysis.

more resistance to ion,
fall weak, no more st conhoi posent
- nosd tory conduction

(2 marks)

3   A neuromuscular junction is a specialised synapse between a motor neurone and a muscle cell. It uses **acetylcholine** as a neurotransmitter.

(a) Explain how an action potential along a motor neurone results in acetylcholine being released at the neuromuscular junction.

(4 marks)

(b) An action potential is more likely if two or more nerve impulses arrive in quick succession from the same presynaptic neurone.

(i) What is the name given to this effect?

temperal

(1 mark)

(ii) Explain why this effect makes an action potential in the muscle cell more likely.

(5 marks)

(c) The drug tubocurarine blocks receptors at neuromuscular junctions.

Doctors use this drug as an anaesthetic as it temporarily paralyses muscles.
Suggest how tubocurarine works.

(4 marks)

- Be able to define the terms 'endocrine gland', 'hormone', 'target tissue' and 'exocrine gland'.

- Be able to explain the meaning of the terms 'first messenger' and 'second messenger', with reference to adrenaline and cyclic AMP (cAMP).

- Be able to describe the functions of the adrenal glands.

- Be able to describe, with the aid of diagrams and photographs, the histology of the pancreas.

- Be able to outline the roles of the pancreas as an endocrine and exocrine gland.

Specification Reference 4.1.3

Tip: The hormonal system is also called the endocrine system.

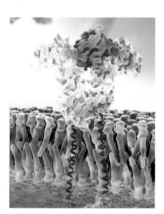

Figure 2: *A growth hormone molecule (pink) bound to a growth hormone receptor (yellow and beige) in the membrane of the target cell.*

5. The Hormonal System and Glands

Like the nervous system, the hormonal system is a form of cell signalling that helps us to respond to our environment.

What is the hormonal system?

The hormonal system sends information as chemical signals. It's made up of glands (called endocrine glands) and hormones. **Endocrine glands** are groups of cells that are specialised to secrete hormones, e.g. the pancreas secretes insulin. **Hormones** are 'chemical messengers'. Many hormones are proteins or peptides, e.g. insulin. Some hormones are steroids, e.g. progesterone.

Hormones are secreted when an endocrine gland is stimulated. Glands can be stimulated by a change in concentration of a specific substance (sometimes another hormone). They can also be stimulated by electrical impulses.

Hormonal communication

Hormones diffuse directly into the blood, then they're taken around the body by the circulatory system. They diffuse out of the blood all over the body but each hormone will only bind to specific receptors for that hormone, found on the membranes of some cells, called **target cells**. Tissue that contains target cells is called **target tissue**. The hormones trigger a response in the target cells (the effectors).

Stimulus ➡ *Receptors* ➡ *Hormone* ➡ *Effectors* ➡ *Response*

Figure 1: *The pathway of hormonal communication.*

┌─ **Example** ──────────────────────────

A real-life example of hormonal communication is the process the body uses to increase blood glucose concentration when it's lower than normal:

- **Stimulus** — low blood glucose concentration.

- **Receptors** — receptors on pancreas cells detect the low blood glucose concentration.

- **Hormone** — the pancreas releases the hormone glucagon into the blood.

- **Effectors** — target cells in the liver detect glucagon and convert glycogen into glucose.

- **Response** — glucose is released into the blood, so glucose concentration increases.

Glands

There are two types of gland — endocrine and exocrine. Endocrine glands secrete hormones directly into the blood (see above). **Exocrine glands** are groups of cells specialised to secrete chemicals through ducts (tubes) into cavities or onto the surface of the body, e.g. sweat glands secrete sweat onto the skin surface. They usually secrete enzymes, e.g. digestive glands secrete digestive enzymes into the gut. Some organs have exocrine tissue and endocrine tissue, so act as both types of gland. For example, the pancreas is both an exocrine and endocrine gland (see page 24).

Action of hormones

A hormone is called a **first messenger** because it carries the chemical message the first part of the way, from the endocrine gland to the receptor on the target cells. When a hormone binds to its receptor it activates an enzyme in the cell membrane. The enzyme catalyses the production of a molecule inside the cell called a signalling molecule — this molecule signals to other parts of the cell to change how the cell works.

The signalling molecule is called a **second messenger** because it carries the chemical message the second part of the way, from the receptor to other parts of the cell. Second messengers activate a cascade (a chain of reactions) inside the cell.

Adrenaline

Adrenaline is a hormone that's secreted from your adrenal glands (see below). It's secreted when there's a low concentration of glucose in your blood, when you're stressed and when you're exercising. Adrenaline gets the body ready for action by making more glucose available for muscles to respire, e.g. by activating glycogenolysis (the breakdown of glycogen to glucose).

Adrenaline is a first messenger. It binds to specific receptors in the cell membranes of many cells, e.g. liver cells. When adrenaline binds it activates an enzyme in the membrane called adenylate cyclase. Activated adenylate cyclase catalyses the production of a second messenger called cyclic AMP (cAMP). cAMP activates a cascade, e.g. a cascade of enzyme reactions make more glucose available to the cell — see Figure 3.

> **Tip:** The release of adrenaline also has an effect on heart rate — there's more about this on page 39.

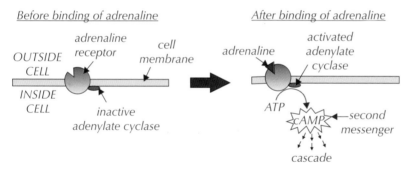

Before binding of adrenaline

After binding of adrenaline

Figure 3: *Diagram showing the action of adrenaline as a first messenger and cAMP as a second messenger.*

> **Tip:** Lots of cells in the body have receptors for adrenaline. The cascade that's activated is not the same in every type of cell and the second messenger isn't always cAMP, so adrenaline affects different tissues in different ways.

Adrenal glands

The adrenal glands are endocrine glands that are found just above your kidneys. Each adrenal gland has an outer part called the cortex and an inner part called the medulla (see Figure 4). The cortex and the medulla have different functions:

- The cortex secretes steroid hormones, e.g. it secretes glucocorticoids such as cortisol when you're stressed.
- The medulla secretes catecholamine hormones (modified amino acids), e.g. it secretes adrenaline when you're stressed.

> **Tip:** The medulla is the name given to the middle of an organ. The cortex is the outer layer.

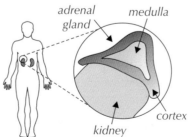

Figure 4: *The location and structure of an adrenal gland.*

> **Tip:** Cortisol and adrenaline work together to control your response to stress.

Tip: One of the learning objectives is to be able to describe the histology of the pancreas — this just means its structure as seen under a microscope.

Tip: See page 35 for more detail on the structure of beta cells.

The pancreas

The pancreas is an endocrine and an exocrine gland that's found below the stomach. You need to know about its endocrine function and its exocrine function.

Endocrine function

The areas of endocrine tissue are called the **islets of Langerhans.** They're found in clusters around blood capillaries and they secrete hormones directly into the blood. They're made up of two types of cell, alpha (α) cells and beta (β) cells (see Figure 6). α cells secrete a hormone called glucagon and β cells secrete a hormone called insulin. Glucagon and insulin help to control blood glucose concentration (see p. 33).

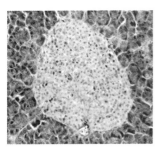

Figure 5: *Islet of Langerhans (white) in the pancreas containing α cells and β cells.*

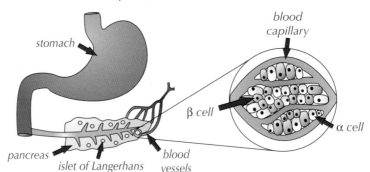

Figure 6: *The location of α and β cells in the islets of Langerhans.*

Exocrine function

Most of the pancreas is exocrine tissue. The exocrine cells are called **acinar cells**. They're found in clusters around the pancreatic duct — a duct that goes to the duodenum (part of the small intestine) — see Figure 8. The acinar cells secrete digestive enzymes into the pancreatic duct. The enzymes digest food in the duodenum, e.g. amylase breaks down starch to glucose.

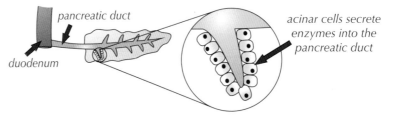

Figure 8: *The location of acinar cells in the pancreas.*

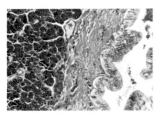

Figure 7: *Acinar cells (dark purple and pink, left) surrounding a pancreatic duct (light purple and white). A layer of connective tissue runs between them (blue).*

Practice Questions — Application

Read the passage below and then answer the questions that follow on the next page.

> When a baby sucks on its mother's nipple, electrical impulses are sent from the nipple via the central nervous system to the mother's posterior pituitary gland, which is stimulated to secrete oxytocin into the blood. Oxytocin binds to specific receptors on myoepithelial cells, found in the epithelial tissue of mammary glands in the mother's breast. This causes contraction of the myoepithelial cells, which in turn causes milk to be secreted via milk ducts, out of the mother's nipple.

Q1 Copy and complete the table below by naming the molecules and structures involved in the pathway of communication described on the previous page.

Molecule / Structure	Name
Hormone	
Target cells	
Target tissue	
Endocrine gland	
Exocrine gland	

Exam Tip
Apart from 'target cells', you need to know the definitions of all the terms in the table on the left for your exam. Q1 checks you know what they all mean, so make sure you can answer this question.

Q2 It can take several minutes from when the baby starts sucking its mother's nipple to when milk is released. Suggest why this is.

Practice Questions — Fact Recall

Q1 What is an endocrine gland?

Q2 Give two types of stimuli that trigger hormone secretion.

Q3 Once a hormone is in the bloodstream, why doesn't it affect every cell in the body?

Q4 Give one way in which exocrine glands differ from endocrine glands.

Q5 Give two examples of substances secreted by exocrine glands.

Q6 When adrenaline binds to receptors in the cell membrane of liver cells, it activates the enzyme adenylate cyclase. This then catalyses the production of a second messenger inside the cell.

a) What is the name of the second messenger produced?

b) What effect does the second messenger have inside the cell?

c) What is the first messenger in this example?

Q7 a) Are the adrenal glands endocrine or exocrine glands? Explain your answer.

b) The adrenal glands have an inner part and an outer part. Name both parts and state the role of each part when the body is stressed.

Exam Tip
Make sure you read questions in the exam carefully — e.g. if you're asked to give two examples of something make sure you give two. You'll miss out on marks if you only give one and waste time if you give more than two (and if you give extra answers that are wrong, you could even lose marks).

Q8 The image on the right shows a light micrograph of a section through the pancreas. The yellow tissue contains α and β cells.

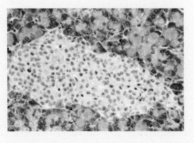

a) What is the name of the yellow tissue shown in the micrograph?

b) Name the hormone secreted by:

i) α cells,

ii) β cells.

c) Acinar cells are found in the pink tissue. Describe the function of acinar cells.

Learning Objectives:

- Be able to define the terms 'homeostasis' and 'negative feedback'.

- Be able to explain the principles of homeostasis in terms of receptors, effectors and negative feedback.

- Be able to define the term 'positive feedback'.

Specification Reference 4.1.1

6. Homeostasis Basics

The body has some pretty clever systems to control its internal environment...

What is homeostasis?

Changes in your external environment can affect your internal environment — the blood and tissue fluid that surrounds your cells. Homeostasis is the maintenance of a constant internal environment. It involves control systems that keep your internal environment roughly constant (within certain limits). Keeping your internal environment constant is vital for cells to function normally and to stop them being damaged.

It's particularly important to maintain the right core body temperature. This is because temperature affects enzyme activity, and enzymes control the rate of metabolic reactions (chemical reactions in living cells).

Tip: It's also important to maintain the right concentration of glucose in the blood (see page 33), so there's always enough available for respiration.

Temperature

The rate of metabolic reactions increases when the temperature's increased. More heat means more kinetic energy, so molecules move faster. This makes the substrate molecules more likely to collide with the enzymes' active sites. The energy of these collisions also increases, which means each collision is more likely to result in a reaction.

But, if the temperature gets too high (e.g. over 40 °C), the reaction essentially stops. The rise in temperature makes the enzyme's molecules vibrate more. If the temperature goes above a certain level, this vibration breaks some of the hydrogen bonds that hold the enzyme in its 3D shape. The active site changes shape and the enzyme and substrate no longer fit together. At this point, the enzyme is denatured — it no longer functions as a catalyst (see Figure 1).

Tip: When an enzyme is denatured the reaction may still happen but it'll be too slow for the body's needs.

If body temperature is too low enzyme activity is reduced, slowing the rate of metabolic reactions. The highest rate of enzyme activity happens at their optimum temperature — about 37 °C in humans (see Figure 1).

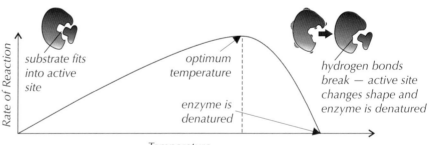

Figure 1: *Effect of temperature on the rate of a metabolic reaction.*

Negative feedback

Homeostatic systems involve receptors, a communication system and effectors. Receptors detect when a level is too high or too low, and the information's communicated via the nervous system or the hormonal system to effectors. The effectors respond to counteract the change — bringing the level back to normal. The mechanism that restores the level to normal is called a **negative feedback mechanism** — see Figure 2 (on the next page).

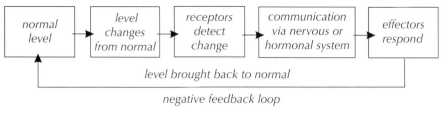

level brought back to normal

negative feedback loop

Figure 2: *A negative feedback mechanism.*

Tip: The 'level' in Figure 2 refers to something inside the body that needs to be controlled, e.g. temperature level, blood glucose level.

Negative feedback keeps things around the normal level.

Example

Body temperature is usually kept within 0.5 °C above or below 37 °C.

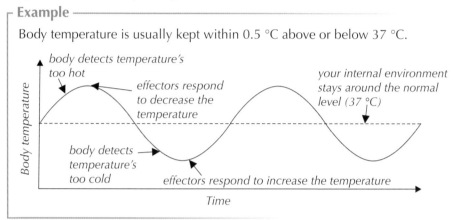

Tip: There are various ways in which effectors respond to change body temperature in mammals — see pages 30-32 for more.

Negative feedback only works within certain limits though — if the change is too big then the effectors may not be able to counteract it, e.g. a huge drop in body temperature caused by prolonged exposure to cold weather may be too large to counteract.

Positive feedback

Some changes trigger a positive feedback mechanism, which amplifies the change. The effectors respond to further increase the level away from the normal level. The mechanism that amplifies a change away from the normal level is called a **positive feedback mechanism** — see Figure 3.

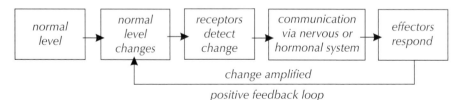

change amplified

positive feedback loop

Figure 3: *A positive feedback mechanism.*

Positive feedback isn't involved in homeostasis because it doesn't keep your internal environment constant. Positive feedback is useful to rapidly activate processes in the body.

Example

During the formation of a blood clot after an injury, platelets become activated and release a chemical — this triggers more platelets to be activated, and so on. This means platelets very quickly form a blood clot at the injury site. (The process ends with negative feedback, when the body detects the blood clot has been formed.)

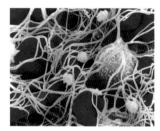

Figure 4: *At a site of injury, more and more platelets (shown above as small, green balls) are produced to form a clot as part of a positive feedback mechanism.*

Q1 Read the following two passages about control systems in the body:

<u>Passage A</u>

A high blood concentration of carbon dioxide lowers the pH of the blood. Chemoreceptors in the blood vessels detect this change and send signals to the brain to increase the respiration rate.

<u>Passage B</u>

When oestrogen concentration is high it stimulates the anterior pituitary gland to release LH. LH stimulates the ovaries to release more oestrogen.

For each passage, state whether it's an example of negative or positive feedback and explain your answer.

Q2 When low blood calcium concentration is detected, the secretion of parathyroid hormone (PTH) from the parathyroid gland is stimulated. When high blood calcium concentration is detected, the secretion of the hormone calcitonin, from the thyroid gland, is stimulated. These two hormones work via negative feedback mechanisms to control the blood calcium concentration. Their effects are shown on the graph.

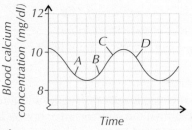

a) Suggest an explanation for the shape of the graph between:

   i) A and B.   ii) C and D.

b) Suggest what could happen to the blood calcium concentration of someone who has had a parathyroid gland removed. Explain your answer.

Practice Questions — Fact Recall

Q1 What is homeostasis?

Q2 Explain why it is important for the body to maintain its internal temperature within normal limits.

Q3 The diagram below shows a negative feedback loop. Describe what happens in the missing labels, A-C.

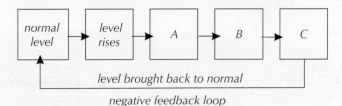

negative feedback loop

Q4 Describe how positive feedback mechanisms differ from negative feedback mechanisms.

7. Control of Body Temperature

Some organisms can control their body temperature internally. Many different mechanisms allow them to do this and they're controlled by the brain.

Temperature control in ectotherms and endotherms

Animals are classed as either ectotherms (e.g. reptiles, fish) or endotherms (e.g. mammals, birds), depending on how they control their body temperature.

Ectotherms

Ectotherms can't control their body temperature internally — they control their temperature by changing their behaviour.

> **Example**
> A lizard is an ectotherm. When its internal temperature drops a lizard will move to find a warmer area, such as a place in the sunshine. When its internal temperature gets too high it will move to somewhere cooler such as a burrow beneath the sand.

This means the internal temperature of ectotherms depends on the external temperature (their surroundings).

Ectotherms have a variable metabolic rate because they can't keep their internal temperature constant. They generate very little heat themselves. This means the activity level of ectotherms depends on the external temperature too — they're more active at higher temperatures and less active at lower temperatures.

Endotherms

Endotherms control their body temperature internally by homeostasis, as well as by altering their behaviour.

> **Example**
> An elephant is an endotherm. Its temperature is mainly controlled internally by homeostasis, but it may also change its behaviour to control its temperature. For example, it may wallow in mud or flap its ears to help it cool down.

This means that, compared to ectotherms, the internal temperature of endotherms is less affected by the external temperature (within certain limits).

Endotherms have a constantly high metabolic rate because they can keep their internal temperature constant. They generate a lot of heat from metabolic reactions. This means the activity level of endotherms is largely independent of the external temperature — they can be active at any temperature (within certain limits).

Learning Objective:

- Be able to describe the physiological and behavioural responses that maintain a constant core body temperature in ectotherms and endotherms, with reference to peripheral temperature receptors, the hypothalamus and effectors in skin and muscles.

Specification Reference 4.1.1

Figure 1: *A lizard basking in the sun to warm up.*

Tip: In ectotherms, respiration and other metabolic reactions happen faster in warmer weather. This means in warmer weather more energy is available for faster movement, etc., so ectotherms are more active in warmer weather.

Practice Questions — Application

Q1 On a thermal image, areas of heat radiation appear brightly coloured. On the right is a thermal image of a mouse and a snake.

a) What can you conclude about the temperature of the external environment when the image was taken? Explain your answer.

b) Would you expect the mouse or the snake to be more active at the time the image was taken? Explain your answer.

Q2 In an experiment, the internal temperatures of a chuckwalla and a hoatzin were recorded over a range of external temperatures controlled by a heat source. The organisms were kept in enclosed environments with a heat source. The results are shown in the table below.

	Temperature (°C)				
External	20	24	28	32	38
Chuckwalla	26.7	30.4	37.7	40.1	43.2
Hoatzin	38.5	38.7	38.8	39.0	38.9

a) Use information from the table to explain which organism is an ectotherm and which is an endotherm.

b) Will the metabolic reactions of the chuckwalla or the hoatzin be most affected during this investigation? Explain your answer.

Exam Tip
Don't be thrown in the exam by names of unfamiliar organisms — just concentrate on what the question's asking you.

Mechanisms to change body temperature

Mammals use different mechanisms to reduce or increase their body temperature.

Tip: Remember, mammals are endotherms.

Mechanisms to reduce body temperature

1. **Sweating** — more sweat is secreted from sweat glands when the body's too hot. The water in sweat evaporates from the surface of the skin and takes heat from the body. The skin is cooled.

2. **Hairs lie flat** — mammals have a layer of hair that provides insulation by trapping air (air is a poor conductor of heat). When it's hot, erector pili muscles relax so the hairs lie flat. Less air is trapped, so the skin is less insulated and heat can be lost more easily.

3. **Vasodilation** — when it's hot, arterioles near the surface of the skin dilate (this is called vasodilation). More blood flows through the capillaries in the surface layers of the dermis. This means more heat is lost from the skin by radiation and the temperature is lowered.

Tip: Heat radiation is the transfer of heat energy to surroundings by infrared radiation.

Tip: Thermoreceptors detect changes in temperature — see next page.

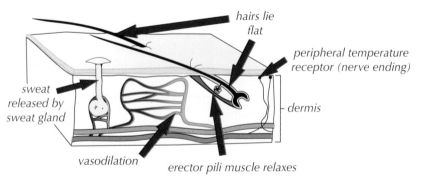

Figure 2: Mechanisms to reduce body temperature in a mammal.

Mechanisms to increase body temperature

1. **Shivering** — when it's cold, muscles contract in spasms. This makes the body shiver and more heat is produced from increased respiration.

2. **Hormones** — the body releases adrenaline and thyroxine. These increase metabolism and so more heat is produced.

Tip: The products of respiration are CO_2, water and energy (heat) — see page 60 for more.

3. **Much less sweat** — less sweat is secreted from sweat glands when it's cold, reducing the amount of heat loss.

4. **Hairs stand up** — erector pili muscles contract when it's cold, which makes the hairs stand up. This traps more air and so prevents heat loss.

5. **Vasoconstriction** — when it's cold, arterioles near the surface of the skin constrict (this is called vasoconstriction) so less blood flows through the capillaries in the surface layers of the dermis. This reduces heat loss.

Tip: These three mechanisms are all ways to conserve heat, whereas the previous two mechanisms (shivering and hormones) actually produce heat.

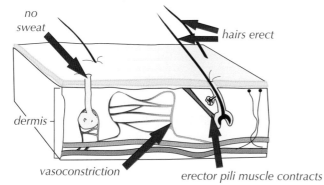

Figure 3: *Mechanisms to increase body temperature in a mammal.*

Control of body temperature by the hypothalamus

Body temperature in mammals is maintained at a constant level by a part of the brain called the **hypothalamus**. The hypothalamus receives information about both internal and external temperature from **thermoreceptors** (temperature receptors):

Tip: Control of body temperature is called thermoregulation.

- Thermoreceptors in the hypothalamus detect internal temperature (the temperature of the blood).
- Thermoreceptors in the skin (called peripheral temperature receptors) detect external temperature (the temperature of the skin).

Thermoreceptors send impulses along sensory neurones to the hypothalamus, which sends impulses along motor neurones to effectors (e.g. skeletal muscles, or sweat glands and erector pili muscles in the skin). The effectors respond to restore the body temperature back to normal.

Tip: The levels of some things in our body are controlled by the nervous system (like body temperature here) and others are controlled by the hormonal system.

Rise in body temperature

When thermoreceptors detect body temperature is too high, they send impulses to the hypothalamus, which sends impulses to effectors. Effectors respond to increase heat loss from the body (e.g. sweat glands produce sweat) and to reduce the amount of heat that's produced by the body. Body temperature then returns to normal — see Figure 4.

Tip: When you feel hot (e.g. when you exercise) you might find yourself sweaty and red-faced — this is just your body's (unattractive) response to the rise in internal body temperature.

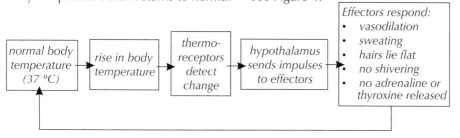

body temperature falls

Figure 4: *Negative feedback mechanism activated by a rise in body temperature.*

Fall in body temperature

When thermoreceptors detect body temperature is too low, they send impulses to the hypothalamus, which sends impulses to effectors. Effectors respond to produce more heat (e.g. adrenaline and thyroxine are released to increase metabolism) and to conserve it. Body temperature then returns to normal — see Figure 5 below.

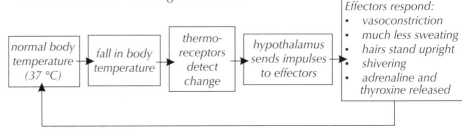

body temperature rises

Figure 5: *Negative feedback mechanism activated by a fall in body temperature.*

Practice Questions — Application

Q1 If a person spends a long time in a hot bath, their skin might appear pink when they get out. Explain the role of the nervous system in this response.

Q2 When blood glucose concentration gets low, the brain receives signals which stimulate feelings of hunger. Assuming activity levels are the same, is a person likely to feel hungry more quickly in a hot or cold external environment? Explain your answer.

Q3 The effects of some sympathomimetic drugs, such as cocaine, include vasoconstriction and an increase in muscular activity. In hot weather people who have taken cocaine are at risk of hyperthermia (their internal body temperature becomes dangerously high). Suggest why this occurs.

Practice Questions — Fact Recall

Q1 How is body temperature controlled in:
   a) an ectotherm?
   b) an endotherm?

Q2 How do the metabolic rates of an ectotherm and an endotherm differ?

Q3 Explain how sweat glands are important for controlling body temperature.

Q4 Describe two mechanisms that the body uses to increase heat production and explain how they work.

Q5 Describe how arterioles near the skin surface respond when low temperatures are detected by thermoreceptors.

Q6 What part of a mammal's brain controls body temperature?

Q7 Describe how the brain receives information about the external temperature of the body.

Q8 Briefly describe how the nervous system returns internal body temperature to normal following a fall in body temperature.

8. Control of Blood Glucose Concentration

Blood glucose concentration is under tight control by a hormonal system. If this control system doesn't work properly it may result in diabetes.

Glucose concentration in the blood

All cells need a constant energy supply to work — so blood glucose concentration must be carefully controlled. The concentration of glucose in the blood is normally around 90 mg per 100 cm³ of blood. It's monitored by cells in the **pancreas**. Blood glucose concentration rises after eating food containing carbohydrate. It falls after exercise, as more glucose is used in respiration to release energy.

Hormonal control of blood glucose concentration

The hormonal system (see p. 22) controls blood glucose concentration using two hormones called insulin and glucagon. They're both secreted by clusters of cells in the pancreas called the **islets of Langerhans** (see page 24). The islets of Langerhans contain **beta (β) cells** and **alpha (α) cells**. β cells secrete insulin into the blood. α cells secrete glucagon into the blood. Insulin and glucagon act on effectors, which respond to restore the blood glucose concentration to the normal level.

Insulin

Insulin lowers blood glucose concentration when it's too high. It binds to specific receptors on the cell membranes of liver cells and muscle cells and increases the permeability of cell membranes to glucose, so the cells take up more glucose.

Insulin also activates enzymes that convert glucose into glycogen. Liver and muscle cells are able to store glycogen in their cytoplasm, as an energy source. The process of forming glycogen from glucose is called **glycogenesis** (see Figure 1). Insulin also increases the rate of respiration of glucose, especially in muscle cells.

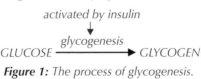

Figure 1: The process of glycogenesis.

Glucagon

Glucagon raises blood glucose concentration when it's too low. It binds to specific receptors on the cell membranes of liver cells and activates enzymes that break down glycogen into glucose. The process of breaking down glycogen is called **glycogenolysis**.

Glucagon also promotes the formation of glucose from glycerol and amino acids. The process of forming glucose from non-carbohydrates is called **gluconeogenesis** (see Figure 2). Glucagon also decreases the rate of respiration of glucose in cells.

Figure 2: The processes of glycogenolysis and gluconeogenesis.

Learning Objectives:

- Be able to explain how blood glucose concentration is regulated, with reference to insulin, glucagon and the liver.
- Be able to outline how insulin secretion is controlled, with reference to potassium channels and calcium channels in beta cells.
- Be able to compare and contrast the causes of Type I (insulin-dependent), and Type II (non-insulin dependent), diabetes mellitus.
- Be able to discuss the use of insulin produced by genetically modified bacteria to treat diabetes mellitus.
- Be able to discuss the potential use of stem cells to treat diabetes mellitus.

Specification Reference 4.1.3

Tip: Liver cells are also called hepatocytes.

Tip: You learnt about glycogen at AS level — it's a polysaccharide made up of branched chains of α–glucose.

Exam Tip
Take care not to write 'a cells' and 'b cells' instead of 'α cells' and 'β cells'. Read through your answers before the end of the exam to catch easy mistakes like this, so that you don't end up throwing away marks.

Negative feedback mechanisms and glucose concentration

Negative feedback mechanisms keep blood glucose concentration normal.

Rise in blood glucose concentration

Tip: 'Genesis' means 'making' — so glycogenesis means making glycogen.

When the pancreas detects blood glucose concentration is too high, the β cells secrete insulin and the α cells stop secreting glucagon. Insulin then binds to receptors on liver and muscle cells (the effectors). The liver and muscle cells respond to decrease the blood glucose concentration, e.g. glycogenesis is activated (see previous page). Blood glucose concentration then returns to normal.

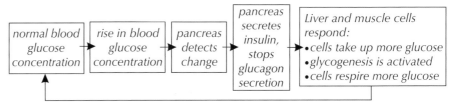

blood glucose concentration falls

Figure 3: *Negative feedback mechanism activated by a rise in blood glucose.*

Fall in blood glucose concentration

Tip: 'Lysis' means 'splitting' — so glycogenolysis means splitting glycogen.

When the pancreas detects blood glucose is too low, the α cells secrete glucagon and the β cells stop secreting insulin. Glucagon then binds to receptors on liver cells (the effectors). The liver cells respond to increase the blood glucose concentration, e.g. glycogenolysis is activated (see previous page). Blood glucose concentration then returns to normal.

Tip: 'Neo' means 'new' — so gluconeogenesis means making new glucose.

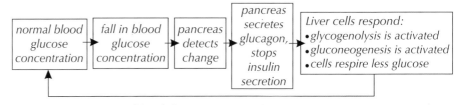

blood glucose concentration rises

Figure 4: *Negative feedback mechanism activated by a fall in blood glucose.*

Practice Questions — Application

Q1 Adrenaline activates glycogenolysis. What effect will adrenaline have on blood glucose concentration?

Q2 After eating a big bowl of pasta describe how a person's blood glucose concentration will change and explain how their body returns it back to normal.

Q3 Von Gierke's disease is a glycogen storage disease. It's caused by an enzyme deficiency, which means the processes of glycogenolysis and gluconeogenesis can't work properly. Explain why someone with von Gierke's disease might suffer from hypoglycaemia if they don't eat regularly.

Tip: Hypoglycaemia is a condition where blood glucose concentration is abnormally low. (And hyperglycaemia is a condition where blood glucose concentration is abnormally high.)

Control of insulin secretion by beta cells

β cells contain insulin stored in vesicles. They have potassium ion (K^+) channels and calcium ion (Ca^{2+}) channels in their membrane (see Figure 5). When the blood glucose concentration is around the normal level (or lower), the K^+ channels are open and the Ca^{2+} channels are closed. Potassium ions diffuse out of the cell through the open K^+ channels, which makes the inside of the cell membrane more negatively charged compared to the outside. This is because there are more positive ions outside the cell than inside — the membrane is polarised.

Tip: The β cell is similar to a sensory receptor cell. When it's at rest (not being stimulated) its membrane is polarised — see page 9.

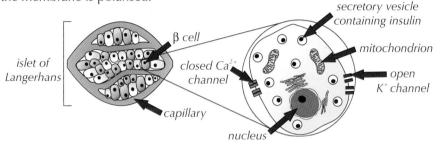

Tip: You should be familiar with the functions of the organelles inside an animal cell from AS.

Figure 5: *Diagram showing location of β cells in the islets of Langerhans, with the structure of a β cell enlarged.*

When the β cell detects a high blood glucose concentration, changes within the cell result in the secretion of insulin. Here's how it happens:

1. High blood glucose concentration detected

When blood glucose concentration is high, more glucose enters the β cells by facilitated diffusion. More glucose in a β cell causes the rate of respiration to increase, making more ATP.

Tip: Facilitated diffusion means particles (e.g. glucose molecules) diffuse across a membrane with the help of carrier proteins or channel proteins in the plasma membrane.

2. Potassium ion channels close

The rise in ATP triggers the potassium ion channels in the β cell plasma membrane to close. This means potassium ions (K^+) can't get through the membrane — so they build up inside the cell. This makes the inside of the β cell less negative because there are more positively-charged potassium ions inside the cell — so the plasma membrane of the β cell is depolarised.

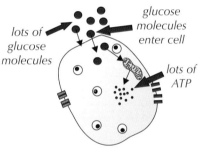

Tip: The calcium ion channels are voltage-gated — they open at a certain voltage.

3. Calcium ion channels open

Depolarisation triggers calcium ion channels in the membrane to open, so calcium ions diffuse into the β cell. This causes the vesicles to move to and fuse with the β cell plasma membrane, releasing insulin by exocytosis.

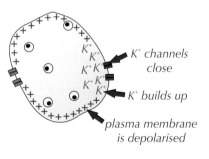

Diabetes

Diabetes mellitus is a condition where blood glucose concentration can't be controlled properly. There are two types:

Type I diabetes (insulin-dependent diabetes)

Tip: An auto-immune disease is where a person's immune system mistakes their own cells for pathogens, so it starts to attack them.

Type I diabetes is an auto-immune disease, in which the body attacks and destroys the β cells in the islets of Langerhans. This means people with Type I diabetes don't produce any insulin. After eating, the blood glucose level rises and stays high, which can result in death if left untreated. The kidneys can't reabsorb all this glucose, so some of it's excreted in the urine.

Type 1 diabetes usually develops in children or young adults. A person's risk of developing Type I diabetes is slightly increased if there's a close family history of the disease.

Type II diabetes (non-insulin-dependent diabetes)

Type II diabetes occurs when the β cells don't produce enough insulin or when the body's cells don't respond properly to insulin. Cells don't respond properly because the insulin receptors on their membranes don't work properly, so the cells don't take up enough glucose. This means the blood glucose concentration is higher than normal.

Type II diabetes is usually acquired later in life than Type I, and it's often linked with obesity. The risk of developing Type II diabetes is also increased in people from certain ethnic groups, e.g African or Asian, and in people with a close family history of the disease.

Treating diabetes

Tip: Simple carbohydrates are more easily broken down to glucose, which is then absorbed by the digestive system, than complex carbohydrates.

Type I diabetes can be treated by regular injections of insulin. But this has to be carefully controlled because too much can produce a dangerous drop in blood glucose levels. Eating regularly and controlling simple carbohydrate intake (sugars) helps to avoid a sudden rise in glucose. Type II diabetes can be treated by controlling simple carbohydrate intake and losing weight. Glucose-lowering tablets can be taken if diet and weight loss can't control it.

Insulin from GM bacteria

Tip: GM bacteria have had a gene from another organism inserted into them, so that they'll produce the protein coded for by that gene.

Insulin used to be extracted from animal pancreases (e.g. pigs and cattle), to treat people with Type I diabetes. But nowadays, human insulin can be made by genetically modified (GM) bacteria (see p. 178). Using GM bacteria to produce insulin is much better for many reasons, for example:

- Producing insulin using GM bacteria is cheaper than extracting it from animal pancreases.
- Larger quantities of insulin can be produced using GM bacteria.
- GM bacteria make human insulin. This is more effective than using pig or cattle insulin (which is slightly different to human insulin) and it's less likely to trigger an allergic response or be rejected by the immune system.
- Some people prefer insulin from GM bacteria for ethical or religious reasons. E.g. some vegetarians may object to the use of animals, and some religious people object to using insulin from pigs.

Curing diabetes

Tip: Look back at your AS notes if you need to remind yourself about stem cells.

Your body is made up of many different types of cells that are specialised for their function, e.g. liver cells, β cells. All specialised cells originally came from stem cells. Stem cells are unspecialised cells — they have the ability to develop into any type of cell.

Using stem cells could potentially cure diabetes. Stem cells could be grown into β cells, which would then be implanted into the pancreas of a person with Type I diabetes. This means the person would be able to make insulin as normal. This treatment is still being developed but, if it's effective, it'll cure people with Type I diabetes — they won't have to have regular injections of insulin.

Tip: Scientists need to make sure that they have enough reliable evidence and that their theory can be validated before a treatment can be recommended to patients (see pages 2-4 for more).

Practice Questions — Application

In an experiment, the blood glucose concentrations of a Type II diabetic and a non-diabetic were recorded at regular intervals in a 150 minute time period. 15 minutes into the experiment a glucose drink was given. The normal range for blood glucose concentration in a healthy individual is between 82 and 110 mg/100 cm³. The results of the experiment are shown on the graph below.

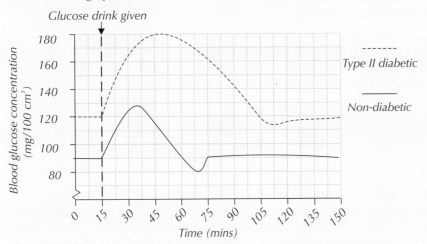

Glucose drink given

Type II diabetic

Non-diabetic

Blood glucose concentration (mg/100 cm³)

Time (mins)

Q1 Explain why the Type II diabetic's blood glucose concentration takes longer to decrease after they take the glucose drink than the non-diabetic's.

Q2 Suggest how the blood glucose concentration of a Type I diabetic would differ from the Type II diabetic after having the glucose drink.

Tip: Think about the causes of the two different types of diabetes for Q2.

Q3 Suggest what time insulin is released in the non-diabetic. Explain your answer.

Q4 Blood glucose concentration continues to rise after the release of insulin. Why is this?

Q5 Explain how negative feedback works to increase the blood glucose concentration in the non-diabetic between 65 and 75 minutes.

Practice Questions — Fact Recall

Q1 Give three ways in which insulin reduces blood glucose concentration.

Q2 Name the process that converts glucose to glycogen.

Q3 Name and describe two processes activated by glucagon.

Q4 What is Type I diabetes?

Q5 Give three advantages of using genetically modified bacteria to produce insulin rather than using animal pancreases.

Q6 Describe how stem cells may be able to cure Type I diabetes.

Exam Tip
There are lots of similar sounding words in this section so you need to make sure you get your spelling spot on in the exam, e.g. if you write 'glycogon' the examiner won't know whether you mean glucagon or glycogen so you won't get the marks.

Learning Objective:
- Be able to outline the nervous and hormonal mechanisms involved in the control of heart rate in humans.

Specification Reference 4.1.3

9. Control of Heart Rate

You can't consciously control your heart rate — it's controlled by a part of the nervous system (the autonomic nervous system) and the hormonal system.

Structure of the nervous system

The nervous system is split into two different systems — the central nervous system (CNS) and the peripheral nervous system. The CNS is made up of the brain and spinal cord, whereas the peripheral nervous system is made up of the neurones that connect the CNS to the rest of the body.

The peripheral nervous system also has two different systems — the somatic and autonomic nervous systems. The somatic nervous system controls conscious activities, e.g. running and playing video games. The autonomic nervous system controls unconscious activities, e.g. it's involved in the control of heart rate (see below).

The autonomic nervous system is split into the sympathetic and parasympathetic nervous systems, which have opposite effects on the body. The sympathetic nervous system is the 'fight or flight' system that gets the body ready for action. Sympathetic neurones release a neurotransmitter called noradrenaline. The parasympathetic system is the 'rest and digest' system that calms the body down. Parasympathetic neurones release a neurotransmitter called acetylcholine.

Tip: To help you remember the difference between the sympathetic and parasympathetic nervous systems, remember: <u>s</u>ympathetic for <u>s</u>tress, <u>p</u>arasympathetic for <u>p</u>eacefulness.

The structure of the nervous system is summarised below:

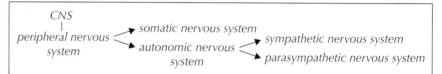

CNS
|
peripheral nervous system → somatic nervous system
→ autonomic nervous system → sympathetic nervous system
→ parasympathetic nervous system

Control of heart rate — the nervous system

There's a small mass of tissue in the wall of the right atrium of the heart called the sinoatrial node (SAN). The SAN generates electrical impulses that cause the cardiac muscles to contract. The rate at which the SAN fires (i.e. heart rate) is unconsciously controlled by the cardiovascular centre in a part of the brain called the medulla oblongata.

Animals need to alter their heart rate to respond to internal stimuli, e.g. to prevent fainting due to low blood pressure or to make sure the heart rate is high enough to supply the body with enough oxygen. Internal stimuli are detected by pressure receptors and chemical receptors:

- There are pressure receptors called baroreceptors in the aorta, the vena cava and carotid arteries. They're stimulated by high and low blood pressure.

Tip: The carotid arteries are major arteries in the neck.

- There are chemical receptors called chemoreceptors in the aorta, the carotid arteries and in the medulla oblongata. They monitor the oxygen level in the blood and also carbon dioxide and pH (which are indicators of O_2 level).

Electrical impulses from receptors are sent to the cardiovascular centre along sensory neurones. The cardiovascular centre processes the information and sends impulses to the SAN along motor neurones.

Control of heart rate in response to different stimuli

1. High blood pressure

Baroreceptors detect high blood pressure and send impulses along sensory neurones to the cardiovascular centre, which sends impulses along parasympathetic neurones. These secrete acetylcholine, which binds to receptors on the SAN. This causes the heart rate to slow down in order to reduce blood pressure back to normal.

2. Low blood pressure

Baroreceptors detect low blood pressure and send impulses along sensory neurones to the cardiovascular centre, which sends impulses along sympathetic neurones. These secrete noradrenaline, which binds to receptors on the SAN. This causes the heart rate to speed up in order to increase blood pressure back to normal.

3. High blood O_2, low CO_2 or high blood pH levels

Chemoreceptors detect chemical changes in the blood and send impulses along sensory neurones to the cardiovascular centre, which sends impulses along parasympathetic neurones. These secrete acetylcholine, which binds to receptors on the SAN. This causes the heart rate to decrease in order to return oxygen, carbon dioxide and pH levels back to normal.

Tip: The effectors in all of these situations are the cardiac muscles of the heart.

4. Low blood O_2, high CO_2 or low blood pH levels

Chemoreceptors detect chemical changes in the blood and send impulses along sensory neurones to the cardiovascular centre, which sends impulses along sympathetic neurones. These secrete noradrenaline, which binds to receptors on the SAN. This causes the heart rate to increase in order to return oxygen, carbon dioxide and pH levels back to normal.

Tip: Low blood O_2, high CO_2 or low blood pH levels are a result of increased respiration.

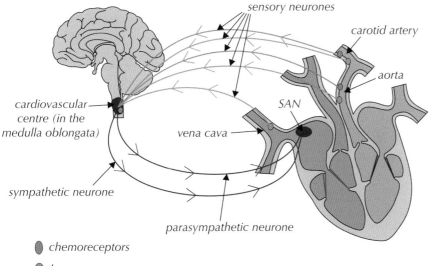

Figure 1: *Summary of the control of heart rate by the nervous system.*

Control of heart rate — the hormonal system

When an organism is threatened (e.g. by a predator) the adrenal glands release adrenaline. Adrenaline binds to specific receptors in the heart. This causes the cardiac muscle to contract more frequently and with more force, so heart rate increases and the heart pumps more blood.

Tip: Adrenaline and the adrenal glands are covered on page 23.

Q1 Anaemia is a condition in which the oxygen carrying capacity of the blood is reduced. Use your knowledge of the nervous control of heart rate to explain why a person with anaemia is likely to have a more rapid heart rate than someone without anaemia.

Q1 a) What type of receptor detects a fall in blood pressure?

b) Where are these receptors located in the body?

Q2 Name the neurotransmitter secreted by sympathetic neurones.

Q3 What effect do impulses from parasympathetic neurones have on heart rate?

Section Summary

Make sure you know...

- That multicellular organisms need to respond to changes in their internal and external environment to increase their chances of survival.

- That organisms communicate information from receptors to effectors by cell signalling (via the nervous and/or hormonal system) to coordinate the activities of different organs.

- That sensory neurones have long dendrons, short axons and transmit nerve impulses from receptors to the central nervous system (CNS), whereas motor neurones have short dendrites, long axons and transmit nerve impulses from the CNS to effectors.

- That receptor cells act as transducers, as they convert the energy of a stimulus into electrical energy.

- That when a receptor cell is stimulated it causes a change in the potential difference across the membrane and that this is called a generator potential.

- How a resting membrane potential is established and maintained by sodium-potassium pumps and potassium ion channels in a neurone's cell membrane.

- That when sodium ion channels in the membrane open, the membrane becomes more permeable to sodium ions and that this causes depolarisation (the potential difference of the membrane becomes more positive), resulting in an action potential if the threshold level is reached.

- How to interpret a graph showing the changes in potential difference across a neurone cell membrane at different stages of an action potential, including the detection of a stimulus, depolarisation, repolarisation, hyperpolarisation, the refractory period and the return to resting potential.

- That an action potential is transmitted along a neurone in a wave of depolarisation.

- That if the threshold is reached, an action potential will always fire with the same change in voltage and if the threshold isn't reached there'll be no action potential.

- The structure of a myelinated neurone.

- That action potentials are passed more quickly along myelinated than unmyelinated neurones because impulses are only conducted at the nodes of Ranvier (where sodium channels are concentrated).

- The structure of a cholinergic synapse including the synaptic knob, vesicles filled with acetylcholine (ACh), the synaptic cleft and specific cholinergic receptors on the postsynaptic membrane.

- That the arrival of an action potential at the presynaptic neurone triggers voltage-gated calcium channels to open, so calcium ions diffuse into the synaptic knob causing vesicles to fuse with the presynaptic membrane. Neurotransmitters diffuse across the synaptic cleft to bind to receptors on the postsynaptic membrane. This causes sodium ion channels to open and the influx of sodium ions triggers an action potential if the threshold is reached.

- The roles of synapses in the nervous system, including synaptic divergence (one neurone connecting to many neurones), synaptic convergence (many neurones connecting to one neurone), summation (the effect of neurotransmitters from many neurones or one that's stimulated a lot in a short space of time added together) and unidirectional transmission (impulses only travelling in one direction).

- How to define an endocrine gland (a group of cells specialised to secrete hormones), a hormone (a chemical messenger), a target tissue (a tissue that contains target cells with receptors for certain chemicals such as hormones or neurotransmitters) and an exocrine gland (a group of cells specialised to secrete chemicals through ducts).

- That a first messenger (e.g. adrenaline) activates an enzyme in a cell membrane and this catalyses the production of a second messenger inside a cell (e.g. cAMP), which activates a cascade inside the cell.

- That the cortex of an adrenal gland secretes steroid hormones, e.g. cortisol, and the medulla secretes catecholamine hormones, e.g. adrenaline.

- That the pancreas has endocrine tissue (islets of Langerhans with α and β cells), which helps to control blood glucose concentration, and exocrine tissue (acinar cells), which secretes digestive enzymes.

- How to define homeostasis (the maintenance of a constant internal environment) and negative feedback (a mechanism that restores a level back to normal).

- That homeostatic systems involve receptors, a communication system (hormonal or nervous system) and effectors.

- How to define positive feedback (a mechanism that amplifies a change away from the normal level).

- That an ectotherm is an animal that can't control its body temperature internally and an endotherm is an animal that can control its body temperature internally (by homeostasis).

- The mechanisms involved in reducing body temperature (sweating, flat hairs, vasodilation) and increasing body temperature (shivering, adrenaline and thyroxine release, less sweat, hairs stand up, vasoconstriction) in mammals.

- That a mammal controls its body temperature internally with communication via peripheral temperature receptors, the hypothalamus and effectors in skin and muscles.

- That glycogenesis is the conversion of glucose to glycogen, glycogenolysis is the conversion of glycogen to glucose, and gluconeogenesis is the conversion of glycerol or amino acids to glucose.

- That insulin lowers blood glucose level when it's too high by binding to receptors on liver and muscle cells causing cells to take up and respire more glucose, and activating glycogenesis.

- That glucagon raises blood glucose level when it's too low by binding to receptors on liver cells and activating glycogenolysis and gluconeogenesis, and causing the cells to respire less glucose.

- That insulin secretion from β cells happens when blood glucose concentration is high and more glucose molecules enter the β cell, which increases the rate of respiration and increases ATP production. This causes potassium ion channels to close, depolarising the β cell membrane. This causes calcium ion channels to open and allows calcium ions to enter the cell, which cause vesicles to move to and fuse with the cell membrane so that insulin is released by exocytosis.

- The similarities and differences between Type I and Type II diabetes.

- That insulin can nowadays be produced by genetically modified bacteria and this has many advantages over using insulin from animals (e.g. it's cheaper, larger quantities can be produced, it's more effective as it makes human insulin, people prefer it for religious or ethical reasons).

- That it may be possible to grow stem cells into β cells and insert these into the pancreas of someone with Type I diabetes, as a potential way of curing the disease.

- That baroreceptors and chemoreceptors detect changes in blood pressure or chemistry and send impulses via the autonomic nervous system to the cardiovascular centre in the medulla oblongata.

- That the cardiovascular centre in the medulla oblongata sends signals via sympathetic neurones or parasympathetic neurones to the SAN, which controls heart rate.

- That the hormonal system is also involved in the control of heart rate, and that adrenaline increases heart rate and causes the heart to pump more blood.

Exam-style Questions

1   β cells respond to changes in blood glucose concentration as part of a negative feedback mechanism.

   (a)   What is a negative feedback mechanism?

(1 mark)

   (b)   Fig 1.1 shows a diagram of a cell in the body of someone who has recently eaten a meal high in carbohydrates.

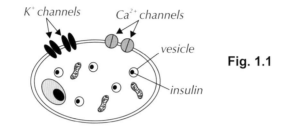

Fig. 1.1

   (i)   Name the type of cell shown in Fig 1.1.

(1 mark)

   (ii)   The potassium ion channels are **closed** in Fig 1.1. Describe and explain the events that have caused these channels to close.

(5 marks)

   (iii)   When the potassium ion channels are closed, potassium ions can't diffuse through the membrane, which causes them to build up inside the cell. Explain how this leads to the release of insulin from the vesicle.

(5 marks)

   (c)   Diabetes mellitus is a disease in which the negative feedback mechanism which controls blood glucose concentration doesn't work properly.

   Complete the following passage by using the most appropriate terms from the list to fill the gaps. Each term **should not** be used more than once.

   endocrine   β   glycogenolysis   acinar   exocrine   digestive enzymes

   increasing   glucagon   α   glycogenesis   gluconeogenesis   decreasing   insulin

   Type I diabetes is caused when the .... cells are destroyed.

   This affects the .... function of the pancreas and means the body

   doesn't produce any .... Without this hormone, the process

   of .... can't be activated. This may result in the blood glucose

   concentration .... to a dangerous level unless the condition is

   controlled.

(5 marks)

2 The activity levels of a squirrel and a tortoise living in the same area were recorded over a 20 hour period. The temperature of the external environment in the test period was also recorded. The results are shown in Fig 2.1.

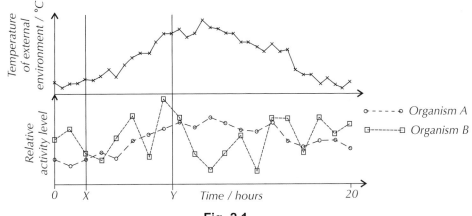

Fig. 2.1

(a) Describe the activity levels of the organisms in relation to temperature.

(2 marks)

(b) Tortoises are ectotherms, squirrels are endotherms.

(i) Which organism, **A** or **B**, is the tortoise? Explain your answer.

(1 mark)

(ii) Squirrels have a much wider geographical range than tortoises.
Suggest why this is.

(2 marks)

(c) (i) It was observed that the hairs on the squirrel were standing up at point **X**.
Explain how and why this response came about.

(4 marks)

(ii) The squirrel has mechanisms that work to reduce its body temperature.
Describe and explain **two** of these mechanisms that may occur at point **Y** in Fig 2.1.
In your answer, you should use appropriate technical terms, spelled correctly.

(5 marks)

3 Effective control of a person's heart rate is important for their survival.
Heart rate is controlled by the hormonal system and the nervous system.

(a) (i) During times of danger, more adrenaline will be secreted into a person's bloodstream. Where is adrenaline released from?

(1 mark)

(ii) Describe how adrenaline triggers a cascade inside a cell.

(3 marks)

(iii) Give **two** ways in which adrenaline affects the heart.

(2 marks)

(b) Outline how heart rate is controlled by the nervous system in response to **low blood pressure**.

(5 marks)

Learning Objectives:

- Be able to define the term 'excretion'.
- Be able to explain the importance of removing metabolic wastes, including carbon dioxide and nitrogenous waste, from the body.
- Be able to describe, with the aid of diagrams and photographs, the histology and gross structure of the liver.
- Be able to describe the formation of urea in the liver, including an outline of the ornithine cycle.
- Be able to describe the roles of the liver in detoxification.

Specification Reference 4.2.1

1. The Liver and Excretion

Excretion is all about removing waste. Without it, the waste products our cells produce would build up inside us — not good. The main organs involved in excretion are the liver and the kidneys. Let's kick off with the liver...

What is excretion?

All the chemical reactions that happen in your cells make up your metabolism. Metabolism produces waste products — substances that aren't needed by the cells, such as carbon dioxide and nitrogenous (nitrogen-containing) waste. Many of these products are toxic, so if they were allowed to build up in the body they would cause damage. This is where excretion comes in. Excretion is the removal of the waste products of metabolism from the body.

> **Example**
>
> Carbon dioxide is a waste product of respiration. Too much in the blood is toxic, so it's removed from the body by the lungs (e.g. in mammals) or gills (e.g. in fish). The lungs and gills act as excretory organs.

The liver

One of the functions of the liver is to break down metabolic waste products and other substances that can be harmful, like drugs and alcohol. They're broken down into less harmful products that can then be excreted.

You need to learn all the different veins, arteries and ducts connected to the liver. These are listed below and shown in Figure 1.

- The hepatic artery supplies the liver with oxygenated blood from the heart, so the liver has a good supply of oxygen for respiration, providing plenty of energy.

- The hepatic vein takes deoxygenated blood away from the liver.

- The hepatic portal vein brings blood from the duodenum and ileum (parts of the small intestine), so it's rich in the products of digestion. This means any ingested harmful substances are filtered out and broken down straight away.

- The bile duct takes bile (a substance produced by the liver to emulsify fats) to the gall bladder to be stored.

Tip: 'Hepatic' means anything to do with the liver. For example, the hepatic artery is the artery supplying the liver with blood, and the hepatocytes are the liver cells (see next page).

Tip: Don't get the hepatic vein and hepatic portal vein mixed up — remember, the hepatic portal vein brings the products of digestion to the liver.

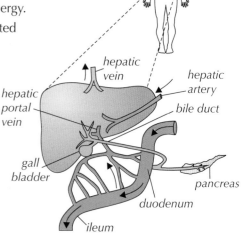

Figure 1: *The location of the liver in the body and its associated blood vessels.*

Liver histology

The liver is made up of liver lobules — cylindrical structures made of cells called hepatocytes that are arranged in rows radiating out from the centre (see Figure 2). Each lobule has a central vein in the middle that connects to the hepatic vein. Many branches of the hepatic artery, hepatic portal vein and bile duct are also found connected to each lobule (only one of each is shown in Figure 2).

Tip: The histology of the liver just means its structure as seen under a microscope.

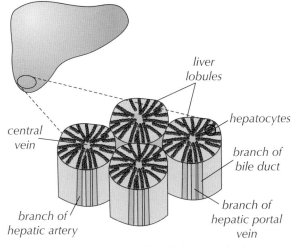

Figure 2: *Structure of liver lobules in the liver.*

The hepatic artery and the hepatic portal vein are connected to the central vein by capillaries called sinusoids (see Figure 4). Blood runs through the sinusoids, past the hepatocytes that remove harmful substances and oxygen from the blood. The harmful substances are broken down by the hepatocytes into less harmful substances that then re-enter the blood. The blood runs to the central vein, and the central veins from all the lobules connect up to form the hepatic vein. Cells called Kupffer cells are also attached to the walls of the sinusoids. They remove bacteria and break down old red blood cells. The bile duct is connected to the central vein by tubes called canaliculi.

Tip: Remember, the liver receives two blood supplies — oxygenated blood from the heart and blood from the digestive system.

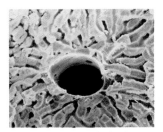

Figure 3: *An electron micrograph of a liver lobule, showing the sinusoids (grey tracks) between the hepatocytes (pink), radiating out from the cental vein (the black hole).*

Tip: Kupffer cells are liver macrophages — a type of white blood cell that carries out phagocytosis (engulfing and digesting pathogens such as bacteria).

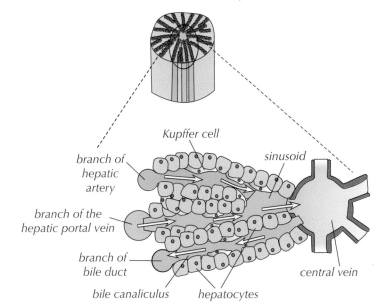

Figure 4: *Enlarged diagram of a liver lobule, showing the sinusoid and hepatocytes radiating out from the central vein.*

Figure 5: *An electron micrograph of a Kupffer cell attached to the wall of a sinusoid.*

Deamination and the ornithine cycle

Tip: All amino acids share the same basic structure, shown below:

Tip: All amino acids share the same basic structure, shown below:

$$H_2N - \overset{\overset{\displaystyle R}{|}}{\underset{\underset{\displaystyle H}{|}}{C}} - COOH$$

Each amino acid has an amino group (-NH$_2$), containing nitrogen.

One of the liver's most important roles is getting rid of excess amino acids produced by eating and digesting protein. Amino acids contain nitrogen in their amino groups. Nitrogenous substances can't usually be stored by the body. This means excess amino acids can be damaging to the body, so they must be used by the body (e.g. to make proteins) or be broken down and excreted. Here's how excess amino acids are broken down in the liver:

1. First, the nitrogen-containing amino groups are removed from any excess amino acids, forming ammonia and organic acids — this process is called **deamination**.

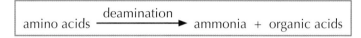

2. The organic acids can be respired to give ATP or converted to carbohydrate and stored as glycogen.

3. Ammonia is too toxic for mammals to excrete directly, so it's combined with CO$_2$ in the **ornithine cycle** to create urea and water.

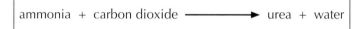

4. The urea is released from the liver into the blood. The kidneys then filter the blood and remove the urea as urine (see pages 48-50), which is excreted from the body. Figure 6 below summarises the processes of deamination and the ornithine cycle.

Tip: Glycogen stored in the liver is important in the control of blood glucose level (see page 33 for more).

Tip: Don't worry too much about citrulline, arginine and ornithine — they are just substances produced in the process of converting ammonia to urea. The important thing to remember in the ornithine cycle is that ammonia from deamination is combined with carbon dioxide to produce water and urea.

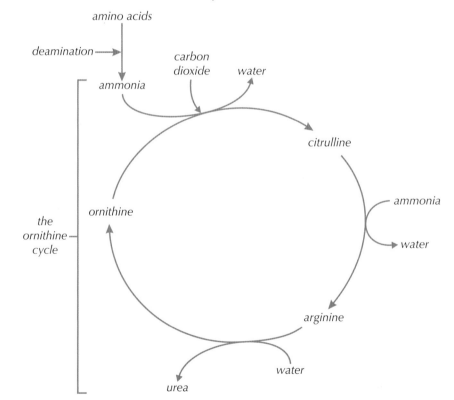

Figure 6: *Deamination and the ornithine cycle.*

Detoxification

The liver also breaks down other harmful substances, like alcohol, drugs and unwanted hormones. They're broken down into less harmful compounds that can then be excreted from the body — this process is called detoxification. Some of the harmful products broken down by the liver include:

Alcohol (ethanol)

Alcohol is a toxic substance that can damage cells. It's broken down by the liver into ethanal, which is then broken down into a less harmful substance called acetic acid. Excess alcohol over a long period can lead to cirrhosis of the liver — this is when the cells of the liver die and scar tissue blocks blood flow.

Paracetamol

Paracetamol is a common painkiller that's broken down by the liver. Excess paracetamol in the blood can lead to liver and kidney failure.

Insulin

Insulin is a hormone that controls blood glucose concentration. Insulin is also broken down by the liver as excess insulin can cause problems with blood sugar levels.

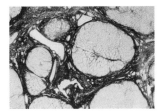

Figure 7: *Light micrograph of a liver tissue with cirrhosis. The lobules (pale yellow circles) are surrounded by fibrous scar tissue (red).*

Tip: For more on insulin's role in the control of blood glucose concentration, see page 33.

Practice Questions — Application

Argininosuccinate synthetase (AS) is an enzyme which catalyses the conversion of citrulline to argininosuccinate in the ornithine cycle, as shown in the diagram below. If there's an AS deficiency then ammonia builds up in the blood, which can be fatal.

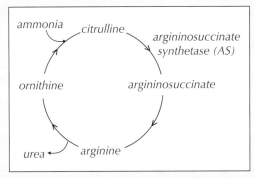

Q1 a) Predict whether there would be a high or a low level of argininosuccinate in the blood of a person with AS deficiency. Explain why.

b) Predict whether there would be a high or a low level of citrulline in the blood of a person with AS deficiency. Explain why.

Q2 AS deficiency can be treated by eating a low protein diet. Explain how this treatment works.

Exam Tip
Don't panic in the exam if you're given the name of something like an enzyme or a disease that you don't recognise. Just apply your knowledge of how the ornithine cycle works normally and you'll be able to work out the answer.

Tip: To answer Q2 think about where the ammonia entering the ornithine cycle is coming from.

Practice Questions — Fact Recall

Q1 Define the term 'excretion'.

Q2 Where does blood from the hepatic portal vein come from?

Q3 Which blood vessel do the central veins in liver lobules connect to?

Q4 What are sinusoids?

- Be able to describe, with the aid of diagrams and photographs, the histology and gross structure of the kidney.

- Be able to describe, with the aid of diagrams and photographs, the detailed structure of a nephron and its associated blood vessels.

- Be able to describe and explain the production of urine, with reference to the processes of ultrafiltration and selective reabsorption.

Specification Reference 4.2.1

2. The Kidneys and Excretion

One of the main functions of the kidneys is to excrete waste products, e.g. urea produced by the liver.

Excretion of waste products

Blood enters the kidney through the renal artery and then passes through capillaries in the cortex of the kidneys. As the blood passes through the capillaries, substances are filtered out of the blood and into long tubules that surround the capillaries. This process is called **ultrafiltration** (see below). Useful substances (e.g. glucose) are reabsorbed back into the blood from the tubules in the medulla and cortex — this is called **selective reabsorption** (see next page). The remaining unwanted substances (e.g. urea) pass along the tubules, then along the ureter to the bladder, where they're expelled as urine. The filtered blood passes out of the kidneys through the renal vein.

You need to learn the structure of the kidneys (see Figure 1).

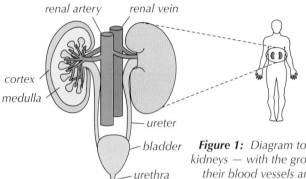

Figure 1: *Diagram to show the location of the kidneys — with the gross structure of the kidneys, their blood vessels and the bladder enlarged.*

The nephrons

The long tubules along with the bundle of capillaries where the blood is filtered are called nephrons — there are thousands of nephrons in each kidney.

Ultrafiltration

Blood from the renal artery enters smaller arterioles in the cortex. Each arteriole splits into a structure called a glomerulus — a bundle of capillaries looped inside a hollow ball called a renal capsule (see Figure 3). This is where ultrafiltration takes place.

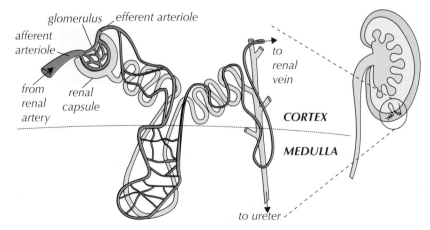

Figure 3: *The location and structure of one nephron. Ultrafiltration takes place in the glomerulus and renal capsule (highlighted in blue).*

Tip: The kidneys also regulate the body's water content — there's more about this on pages 51-53.

Tip: 'Renal' means anything to do with the kidney.

Tip: The renal capsule is also known as the Bowman's capsule.

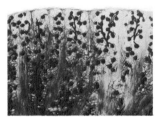

Figure 2: *Light micrograph of a section through the cortex, showing the glomeruli (tiny balls) and the vessels that supply them.*

The arteriole that takes blood into each glomerulus is called the afferent arteriole, and the arteriole that takes the filtered blood away from the glomerulus is called the efferent arteriole (see Figure 3 on the previous page). The efferent arteriole is smaller in diameter than the afferent arteriole, so the blood in the glomerulus is under high pressure. The high pressure forces liquid and small molecules in the blood out of the capillary and into the renal capsule.

The liquid and small molecules pass through three layers to get into the renal capsule and enter the nephron tubules — the capillary endothelium, a membrane (called the basement membrane) and the epithelium of the renal capsule (see Figure 4).

Figure 4: *Diagram to show the three layers separating the glomerular capillary and the renal capsule.*

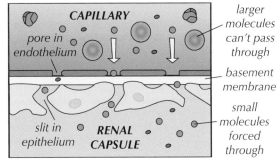

Tip: The cells that make up the epithelium of the renal capsule are called podocytes.

Larger molecules like proteins and blood cells can't pass through and stay in the blood. The liquid and small molecules, now called **filtrate**, pass along the rest of the nephron and useful substances are reabsorbed along the way — see below. Finally, the filtrate flows through the collecting duct and passes out of the kidney along the ureter.

Tip: The filtrate can also be called the tubular fluid.

Selective reabsorption

Selective reabsorption of the useful substances takes place as the filtrate flows along the proximal convoluted tubule (PCT), through the loop of Henle, and along the distal convoluted tubule (DCT) — see Figure 5. Useful substances leave the tubules of the nephrons and enter the capillary network that's wrapped around them.

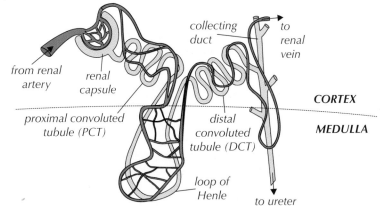

Figure 5: *Diagram to show the structure of one nephron. Selective reabsorption takes place in the areas highlighted in yellow.*

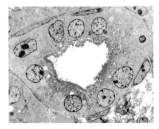

Figure 6: *Electron micrograph of a cross section through the proximal convoluted tubule (PCT). Microvilli (shown in reddish-brown) line the inside of the tubule, increasing the surface area for reabsorption.*

The epithelium of the wall of the PCT has microvilli to provide a large surface area for the reabsorption of useful materials from the filtrate (in the tubules) into the blood (in the capillaries). Useful solutes like glucose, amino acids, vitamins and some salts are reabsorbed along the PCT by **active transport** and **facilitated diffusion**. Some urea is also reabsorbed by diffusion.

Water enters the blood by **osmosis** because the water potential of the blood is lower than that of the filtrate. Water is reabsorbed from the loop of Henle, DCT and the collecting duct (see next page). The filtrate that remains is urine, which passes along the ureter to the bladder.

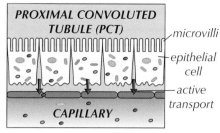

Figure 7: *Epithelial wall of the proximal convoluted tubule (PCT).*

Urine

Urine is usually made up of water and dissolved salts, urea and other substances such as hormones and excess vitamins. Urine doesn't usually contain proteins or blood cells as they're too big to be filtered out of the blood. Glucose, amino acids and vitamins are actively reabsorbed back into the blood (see previous page), so they're not usually found in the urine either.

Practice Questions — Application

Q1 The kidneys filter the blood in order to produce urine. The flow diagram below shows the sequence of urine production. Name the missing structures, A to D.

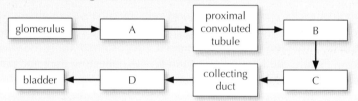

Q2 The diagram below shows an electron micrograph of a cross section of the barrier between the renal capsule and the blood supply.

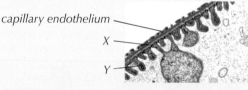

a) Name the structures labelled X and Y.

b) Hereditary nephrotic syndrome is an inherited disease which affects the structure of the barrier shown above, resulting in the presence of large amounts of protein in the urine (proteinuria). Suggest why hereditary nephrotic syndrome causes proteinuria.

Practice Questions — Fact Recall

Q1 The diagram below shows a glomerulus and surrounding structures.

a) Name blood vessel A.

b) Name the structure labelled C.

c) Vessel A has a larger diameter than vessel B. Explain why this is important in the process of ultrafiltration.

Q2 Name three substances that are reabsorbed in the proximal convoluted tubule.

3. The Kidneys and Water Content

Learning Objective:

- Be able to explain, using water potential terminology, the control of the water content of the blood, with reference to the roles of the kidney, osmoreceptors in the hypothalamus and the posterior pituitary gland.
  Specification Reference 4.2.1

In topic 2 you saw that one of the kidneys' roles is to excrete waste products. But that's not all folks... no, no. The kidneys also play a major role in regulating the body's water content — they're pretty busy organs...

Regulation of water content

Water is essential to keep the body functioning, so the amount of water in the blood needs to be kept constant. Mammals excrete urea (and other waste products) in solution, which means water is lost during excretion. Water is also lost in sweat. The kidneys regulate the water content of the blood (and urine), so the body has just the right amount:

- If the water content of the blood is too low (the body is dehydrated), more water is reabsorbed by osmosis into the blood from the tubules of the nephrons. This means the urine is more concentrated, so less water is lost during excretion.

- If the water content of the blood is too high (the body is too hydrated), less water is reabsorbed by osmosis into the blood from the tubules of the nephrons. This means the urine is more dilute, so more water is lost during excretion (see next page).

Regulation of the water content of the blood takes place in the middle and last parts of the nephron — the loop of Henle, the distal convoluted tubule (DCT) and the collecting duct (see below). The volume of water reabsorbed is controlled by hormones (see next page).

Tip: For more on reabsorption in the nephrons, see pages 49-50.

The loop of Henle

The loop of Henle is made up of two 'limbs' — the descending limb and the ascending limb. They help set up a mechanism called the **countercurrent multiplier mechanism** — see Figure 1. It's this mechanism that helps to reabsorb water back into the blood.

Tip: Figure 1 is explained in detail on the next page.

Tip: Na^+ is a sodium ion and Cl^- is a chloride ion. These ions help establish the water potential that drives the reabsorption of water from the filtrate back into the blood.

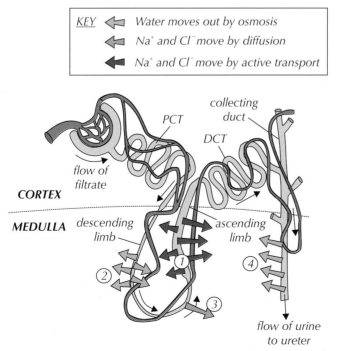

KEY
- Water moves out by osmosis
- Na^+ and Cl^- move by diffusion
- Na^+ and Cl^- move by active transport

Figure 1: *The countercurrent multiplier mechanism.*

Here's how the countercurrent multiplier mechanism works:

1. Near the top of the ascending limb, Na$^+$ and Cl$^-$ ions are actively pumped out into the medulla. The ascending limb is impermeable to water, so the water stays inside the tubule. This creates a low water potential in the medulla, because there's a high concentration of ions.

2. Because there's a lower water potential in the medulla than in the descending limb, water moves out of the descending limb into the medulla by osmosis. This makes the filtrate more concentrated (the ions can't diffuse out — the descending limb isn't permeable to them). The water in the medulla is reabsorbed into the blood through the capillary network.

3. Near the bottom of the ascending limb Na$^+$ and Cl$^-$ ions diffuse out into the medulla, further lowering the water potential in the medulla. (The ascending limb is impermeable to water, so it stays in the tubule.)

4. The first three stages massively increase the ion concentration in the medulla, which lowers the water potential. This causes water to move out of the collecting duct by osmosis. As before, the water in the medulla is reabsorbed into the blood through the capillary network.

The volume of water reabsorbed from the collecting duct into the capillaries is controlled by changing the permeability of the collecting duct (see below).

Loop of Henle length in different animals

Different animals have different length loops of Henle. The longer an animal's loop of Henle, the more water they can reabsorb from the filtrate. When there's a longer ascending limb, more ions are actively pumped out into the medulla, which creates a really low water potential in the medulla. This means more water moves out of the nephron and collecting duct into the capillaries, giving very concentrated urine. Animals that live in areas where there's little water usually have long loops to save as much water as possible.

Figure 2: The fennec fox (top), desert kangaroo rat (middle) and camel (bottom) all have long loops of Henle.

— Examples —————————————
- The fennec fox, desert kangaroo rat and camel (see Figure 1) live in hot, dry environments such as deserts. As a result they have evolved long loops of Henle, which enable them to produce small volumes of concentrated urine in order for them to conserve water.

- In contrast, frogs and toads don't have a loop of Henle at all, so they can't produce concentrated urine. This is because they live in a wet environment, so they don't have to conserve water.

Antidiuretic hormone (ADH)

The water content, and so water potential, of the blood is monitored by cells called osmoreceptors in a part of the brain called the hypothalamus. When the osmoreceptors are stimulated by low water content in the blood, the hypothalamus sends nerve impulses to the posterior pituitary gland to release a hormone called antidiuretic hormone (ADH) into the blood.

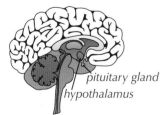

pituitary gland
hypothalamus

Figure 3: Location of the hypothalamus and the pituitary gland in the brain.

ADH molecules bind to receptors on the plasma membranes of cells in the DCT and the collecting duct. When this happens, protein channels called aquaporins are inserted into the plasma membrane. These channels allow water to pass through via osmosis, making the walls of the DCT and collecting duct more permeable to water. This means more water is reabsorbed from these tubules into the medulla and into the blood by osmosis. A small amount of concentrated urine is produced, which means less water is lost from the body.

ADH changes the water content of the blood when it's too low or too high:

Dehydration — blood water content is too low

Dehydration is what happens when you lose water, e.g. by sweating during exercise, so the water content of the blood needs to be increased:

- The water content of the blood drops, so its water potential drops.
- This is detected by osmoreceptors in the hypothalamus.
- The posterior pituitary gland is stimulated to release more ADH into the blood.
- More ADH means that the DCT and collecting duct are more permeable, so more water is reabsorbed into the blood by osmosis.
- A small amount of highly concentrated urine is produced and less water is lost.

Hydration — blood water content is too high

If you're hydrated, you've taken in lots of water, so the water content of the blood needs to be reduced:

- The water content of the blood rises, so its water potential rises.
- This is detected by the osmoreceptors in the hypothalamus.
- The posterior pituitary gland releases less ADH into the blood.
- Less ADH means that the DCT and collecting duct are less permeable, so less water is reabsorbed into the blood by osmosis.
- A large amount of dilute urine is produced and more water is lost.

Tip: Diuresis is when lots of dilute urine is produced. Antidiuretic hormone is so called because it causes a small amount of concentrated urine to be produced (the opposite of diuresis).

Tip: Like many hormones, ADH is a protein. Once it's had its effect, it travels in the bloodstream to the liver where it's broken down (see page 46).

Practice Questions — Application

Q1 A runner is dehydrated whilst running on a hot, sunny day. He left his drink at home and is producing a lot of sweat during his run.
- a) Why is the runner dehydrated?
- b) How does the runner's body detect that he is dehydrated?
- c) The runner's posterior pituitary gland releases antidiuretic hormone (ADH). Explain what effect ADH has on the distal convoluted tubule and the collecting duct of the runner's kidneys.
- d) When he returns home, he rehydrates by drinking a sports drink containing sodium and chloride ions. Explain how the presence of these ions helps the runner's kidneys to conserve water.

Q2 Exercise-associated hyponatremia (EAH) is condition experienced by some athletes who drink excessive amounts of fluid when competing in endurance events like marathons. The condition affects the balance of fluid in cells and is potentially fatal if it affects the brain cells.
- a) Explain what normally happens when a person consumes too much fluid.
- b) Athletes who experience EAH are often unable to suppress their ADH production. Explain why this can cause problems if they have consumed too much fluid.

Practice Questions — Fact Recall

Q1 Which limb of the loop of Henle is impermeable to water?
Q2 Explain why a longer loop of Henle allows more concentrated urine to be produced.

Learning Objective:

- Be able to outline the problems that arise from kidney failure, and discuss the use of renal dialysis and transplants for the treatment of kidney failure.

Specification Reference 4.2.1

4. Kidney Failure

If things start going wrong with the kidneys, it can cause big problems...

What is kidney failure?

Kidney failure is when the kidneys can't carry out their normal functions because they can't work properly. Kidney failure can be caused by many things, including kidney infection and high blood pressure.

Kidney infections

Kidney infections can cause inflammation (swelling) of the kidneys, which can damage the cells. This interferes with filtering in the renal capsules, or with reabsorption in the other parts of the nephrons.

High blood pressure

High blood pressure can damage the glomeruli. The blood in the glomeruli is already under high pressure but the capillaries can be damaged if the blood pressure gets too high. This means larger molecules like proteins can get through the capillary walls and into the urine.

Problems arising from kidney failure

Kidney failure causes lots of problems, for example:

- Waste products that the kidneys would normally remove (e.g. urea) begin to build up in the blood. Too much urea in the blood causes weight loss and vomiting.

- Fluid starts to accumulate in the tissues because the kidneys can't remove excess water from the blood. This causes parts of the body to swell, e.g. the person's legs, face and abdomen can swell up.

- The balance of ions in the body becomes, well, unbalanced. The blood may become too acidic, and an imbalance of calcium and phosphate can lead to brittle bones. Salt build-up may cause more water retention.

- Long-term kidney failure causes anaemia — a lack of haemoglobin in the blood.

If the problems caused by kidney failure can't be controlled, it can eventually lead to death.

Tip: Kidney failure is also called renal failure.

Exam Tip:
Kidney failure can cause all kinds of health problems — make sure you learn these examples for the exam.

Treating kidney failure

When the kidneys can no longer function (i.e. they've totally failed), a person is unable to survive without treatment. There are two main treatment options — renal dialysis or a kidney transplant.

Renal dialysis

Renal dialysis is where a machine is used to filter a patient's blood. The patient's blood is passed through a dialysis machine — the blood flows on one side of a partially permeable membrane and dialysis fluid flows on the other side (see Figure 2 on the next page). The blood and dialysis fluid flow in opposite directions in order to maintain a steep concentration gradient between the two fluids, to increase the rate of diffusion. During dialysis, waste products and excess water and ions diffuse across the membrane into the dialysis fluid, removing them from the blood. Blood cells and larger molecules like proteins are prevented from leaving the blood.

One of the problems with renal dialysis is that patients can feel increasingly unwell between dialysis sessions because waste products and fluid starts to build up in their blood.

Figure 1: *A renal dialysis machine, which acts as an artificial kidney.*

Also, each dialysis session takes three to five hours, and patients need two or three sessions a week, usually in hospital. This is quite expensive and is pretty inconvenient for the patient. But dialysis can keep a person alive until a transplant is available (see below), and it's a lot less risky than having the major surgery involved in a transplant.

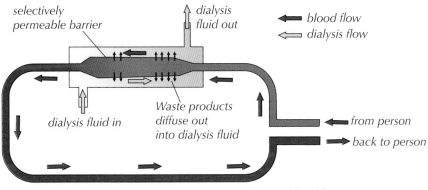

selectively permeable barrier

↑ *dialysis fluid out*

◀── *blood flow*
◁── *dialysis flow*

dialysis fluid in

Waste products diffuse out into dialysis fluid

◀── *from person*
──▶ *back to person*

Figure 2: *A simplified diagram showing blood flow and dialysis flow in a renal dialysis machine.*

Tip: During a dialysis session, an anticoagulant is added to the blood to prevent it from clotting in the machine. Towards the end of the session no more anticoagulant is added, to allow the blood to clot as normal once the session has finished.

Kidney transplant

A kidney transplant is where a new kidney is implanted into a patient's body to replace a damaged kidney. The new kidney has to be from a person with the same blood and tissue type. They're often donated from a living relative, as people can survive with only one kidney. They can also come from other people who've recently died — organ donors.

Transplants have a lot of advantages over dialysis. For example, it's cheaper to give a person a transplant than keep them on dialysis for a long time. Having a kidney transplant is more convenient for a person than having regular dialysis sessions, and patients don't have the problem of feeling unwell between dialysis sessions.

However, there are also disadvantages to having a kidney transplant. These include the fact that the patient will have to undergo a major operation, which is risky. There's also the risk that the immune system may reject the transplant. This means that the patient has to take drugs to suppress it.

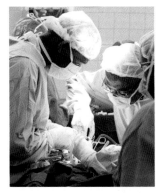

Figure 3: *A kidney transplant is a risky but potentially life saving operation for a patient with kidney failure.*

Practice Questions — Application

A patient has kidney failure and is having dialysis while he waits for a transplant. The diagram below shows a renal dialysis machine.

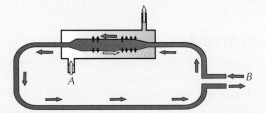

A

◀── *B*

Q1 At which point, A or B, does the patient's blood enter the machine?

Q2 In renal dialysis, why must the blood and the dialysis fluid flow in opposite directions?

Q3 The patient is old and weak. Suggest one reason why his doctor may be concerned about him having a kidney transplant.

Exam Tip:
In the exam you might be asked to weigh up the positive and negative aspects of a treatment such as renal dialysis or a kidney transplant — so make sure you know both sides of the story.

- Be able to describe how urine samples can be used to test for pregnancy and detect misuse of anabolic steroids.

Specification Reference 4.2.1

Tip: Even though hCG is a protein hormone, it's small enough to pass from the blood into the filtrate at the renal capsule (see page 49 for more).

Tip: Antibodies are proteins that bind to antigens (molecules found on the surface of cells) to form an antigen-antibody complex. In a pregnancy test, the hCG antibodies in the test strip will bind to the antigens on the hCG in the urine.

5. Detecting Hormones

You can have a look at what's in a person's blood by testing their urine. Nice.

Human chorionic gonadotrophin (hCG)

Human chorionic gonadotrophin (hCG) is a hormone that is only found in the urine of pregnant women. This means you can test if a woman is pregnant by looking for hCG.

Testing for pregnancy

- A stick is used with an application area that contains antibodies for hCG bound to a coloured bead (blue).
- When urine is applied to the application area any hCG will bind to the antibody on the beads.
- The urine moves up to the test strip, carrying the beads with it.
- The test strip has antibodies to hCG stuck in place (immobilised).
- If there is hCG present the test strip turns blue because the immobilised antibody binds to any hCG attached to the blue beads, concentrating the blue beads in that area. If no hCG is present, the beads will pass through the test area without binding to anything, and so it won't go blue.

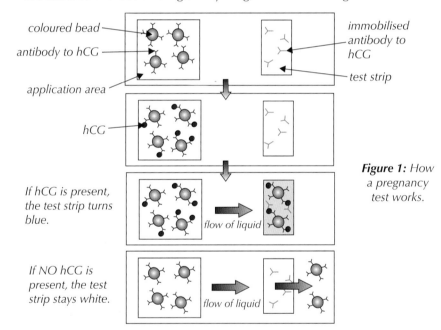

Figure 1: How a pregnancy test works.

Figure 2: A lab technician testing a urine sample for hCG.

Anabolic steroids

Anabolic steroids are drugs that build up muscle tissue. Testosterone is an anabolic steroid, and there are other common ones such as Nandrolone. Some athletes are banned from taking anabolic steroids. This is to try to stop the misuse of steroids that can have dangerous side-effects, such as liver damage. Also, it's considered unfair for some athletes to use steroids.

However, there are some athletes who continue to take steroids, as there is an increasing pressure on elite athletes to perform well (e.g. for sponsorship deals, etc.). Taking steroids can have positive effects on performance, such as increased strength and power owing to the build up of athletes' muscle tissue.

Testing for steroids

Steroids are removed from the blood in the urine, so athletes regularly have their urine tested for steroids (or the products made when they're broken down), by a technique called gas chromatography. The urine sample is vaporised (turned into a gas) and passed through a column containing a liquid — different substances move through the column at different speeds. The length of time taken for substances in the sample to pass through the column is compared to the time taken for a steroid to pass through the column. If the time taken is the same then the sample contains the steroid.

Figure 3: Drug testing in sport uses gas chromatography to test for the presence of steroids in an athlete's urine.

Practice Questions — Fact Recall

Q1 Which hormone is detected in a pregnancy test?

Q2 A pregnancy test uses antibodies bound to a blue bead.
    What colour will the test strip turn in a negative pregnancy test?

Q3 What effect do anabolic steroids have on muscle?

Q4 a) What technique is used to test a urine sample for the presence of anabolic steroids?

    b) Briefly explain how this technique works.

Section Summary

Make sure you know...

- That excretion is the removal of waste products of metabolism (e.g. carbon dioxide and nitrogenous waste) from the body. This prevents them building up, which could cause damage.

- The gross structure of the liver, including the hepatic artery, hepatic vein, hepatic portal vein and bile duct.

- The histology of the liver, including the liver lobules, hepatocytes, sinusoids, central vein, Kupffer cells and canaliculi.

- That the liver plays an essential role in the excretion of nitrogenous substances from the body. This process involves the deamination of excess amino acids, and the conversion of ammonia and carbon dioxide into urea and water via the ornithine cycle.

- That the liver breaks down substances such as alcohol, paracetamol and insulin into less harmful substances in a process known as detoxification.

- The gross structure of the kidney, including the kidney cortex and medulla, renal artery, renal vein, ureter, bladder and urethra.

- The detailed structure of the nephron and its associated blood vessels, including the afferent artery, glomerulus, renal capsule, efferent artery, proximal convoluted tubule (PCT), loop of Henle, distal convoluted tubule (DCT) and collecting duct.

- How urine is formed through the processes of ultrafiltration and selective reabsorption.

- How the kidney reabsorbs water as it travels through the loop of Henle, the distal convoluted tubule and the collecting duct.

- That the water content of the blood is monitored by osmoreceptors in the hypothalamus, and how the release of antidiuretic hormone (ADH) from the posterior pituitary gland is used to control the reabsorption of water in the kidney.

- The problems that arise from kidney failure, and the positive and negatives aspects of the treatment options available to patients with kidney failure (renal dialysis and kidney transplants).

- How urine samples can be used to test for the presence of human chorionic gonadotrophin (hCG) and therefore pregnancy in women, and for the presence of anabolic steroids in athletes.

Exam-style Questions

1 (a) Fig. 1.1 is an electron micrograph showing a section through the proximal convoluted tubule of the kidney.

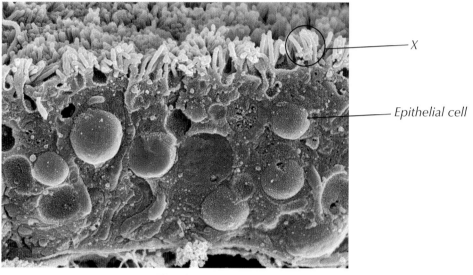

Fig. 1.1

(i) Outline what happens to the filtrate in the proximal convoluted tubule.

(1 mark)

(ii) Name the structure labelled **X** on Fig. 1.1 and explain how this structure helps the epithelial cells of the proximal convoluted tubule to carry out their function.

(3 marks)

(b) Fig. 1.2 shows a nephron.

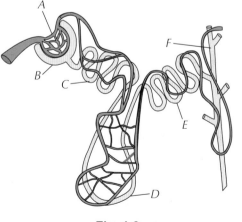

Fig. 1.2

(i) What name is given to structure **A**?

(1 mark)

(ii) Which **two** letters (**A** to **F**) indicate the locations where antidiuretic hormone (ADH) acts?

(2 marks)

(iii) Structure **D** is longer in some desert dwelling animals, such as the camel.

Name structure **D** and explain how a longer length allows the camel to survive in hot, dry conditions.

(6 marks)

2 (a) The tubular fluid to blood plasma concentration ratio (TF/P ratio) is an index used to measure how well the kidney is working. If substances are able to pass freely from the glomerulus into the renal capsule they will have a TF/P ratio of 1.0, as their concentration in the plasma is the same as in the initial tubular fluid.

(i) Complete the table to show which of the following substances will have a TF/P ratio of 1.0 in a healthy kidney. The first two have been done for you.

(3 marks)

Substance	TF/P ratio of 1.0
glucose	✓
serum albumin (protein)	X
sodium ions (Na^+)	
urea	
red blood cells	

(ii) The TF/P ratio of the protein serum albumin is normally less than 1.0 in a healthy kidney, meaning that the concentration of serum albumin is higher in the plasma than the tubular fluid. Explain why this is the case.

(1 mark)

(iii) Kidney failure can be caused by high blood pressure. Suggest why high blood pressure may result in a TF/P ratio of 1.0 for the protein serum albumin.

(3 marks)

(b) A patient has kidney failure as a result of high blood pressure. Her doctor prescribes diuretics to reduce her blood pressure. Diuretics can reduce the amount of Na^+ that is reabsorbed by the nephron.

Suggest how diuretics can be used to decrease blood pressure.

(5 marks)

(c) The patient needs to have renal dialysis as waste products, such as urea, start to build up in her body. Urea is a result of the breakdown of amino acids by the liver.

(i) Name the **two** processes involved in the conversion of amino acids to urea.

(2 marks)

(ii) Give **one** possible health problem the patient may experience as a result of the accumulation of urea in her blood.

(1 mark)

(iii) Give **two** disadvantages to the patient of having renal dialysis.

(2 marks)

3 Complete the following passage using the most suitable term in each case.

Human chorionic .... (hCG) is a hormone that can be used to test if a woman is .... When urine is applied to a test strip, any hCG present will bind to ....: for hCG which are attached to blue beads. The urine moves up to the test strip, carrying the beads with it. If hCG is present the test strip turns .... because the immobilised antibody binds to any hCG attached to the beads.

(4 marks)

Learning Objectives:

- Be able to outline why plants, animals and microorganisms need to respire, with reference to active transport and metabolic reactions.

- Be able to define the terms 'autotroph' and 'heterotroph'.

- Know that light energy is used during photosynthesis to produce complex organic molecules.

- Be able to explain how respiration in plants and animals depends upon the products of photosynthesis.

- Be able to describe, with the aid of diagrams, the structure of ATP.

- Know that ATP provides the immediate source of energy for biological processes.

Specification Reference 4.3.1, 4.4.1

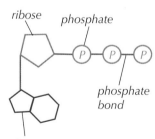

Figure 1: *The structure of adenosine triphosphate (ATP). It consists of adenine, ribose and three phosphate groups.*

1. Storing and Releasing Energy

Energy is required for all life processes. This means that being able to store and release energy is really important for plants and animals.

Why is energy important?

Plant and animal cells need energy for biological processes to occur.

┌─ **Examples** ───

- Plants need energy for things like photosynthesis, active transport (e.g. to take in minerals via their roots), DNA replication and cell division.

- Animals need energy for things like muscle contraction, maintenance of body temperature, active transport, DNA replication and cell division.

Photosynthesis and energy

Plants are **autotrophs** — they can make their own food (glucose). They do this using photosynthesis. Photosynthesis is the process where energy from light is used to make glucose from water (H_2O) and carbon dioxide (CO_2). (The light energy is converted to chemical energy in the form of glucose — $C_6H_{12}O_6$.) The overall equation is:

$$6CO_2 + 6H_2O + \text{Energy} \rightarrow C_6H_{12}O_6 + 6O_2$$

Energy is stored in the glucose until the plants release it by respiration. Animals are **heterotrophs** — they can't make their own food. So, they obtain glucose by eating plants (or other animals), then respire the glucose to release energy.

Photosynthesis is an example of a **metabolic pathway** — the process occurs in a series of small reactions controlled by enzymes.

Respiration and energy

Plant and animal cells release energy from glucose — this process is called respiration. This energy is used to power all the biological processes in a cell. There are two types of respiration:

- **Aerobic respiration** — respiration using oxygen.

- **Anaerobic respiration** — respiration without oxygen.

Aerobic respiration produces carbon dioxide and water, and releases energy. The overall equation is:

$$C_6H_{12}O_6 + 6O_2 \rightarrow 6CO_2 + 6H_2O + \text{Energy}$$

Respiration is another example of a metabolic pathway.

ATP

ATP (adenosine triphosphate) is the immediate source of energy in a cell. A cell can't get its energy directly from glucose. So, in respiration, the energy released from glucose is used to make ATP. ATP is made from the nucleotide base adenine, combined with a ribose sugar and three phosphate groups, (see Figure 1). It carries energy around the cell to where it's needed.

ATP is synthesised from ADP (adenosine diphosphate) and inorganic phosphate (P_i) using energy from an energy-releasing reaction, e.g. the breakdown of glucose in respiration. The energy is stored as chemical energy in the phosphate bond (see Figure 2). The enzyme **ATP synthase** catalyses this reaction.

Tip: Inorganic phosphate (P_i) is just the fancy name for a single phosphate.

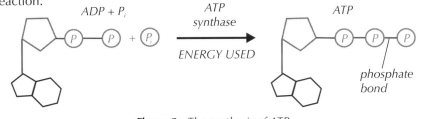

Figure 2: The synthesis of ATP.

Tip: Adenosine <u>di</u>phosphate has <u>two</u> phosphates. Adenosine <u>tri</u>phosphate has <u>three</u> phosphates.

This process is known as **phosphorylation** — adding phosphate to a molecule. ADP is phosphorylated to ATP.

ATP then diffuses to the part of the cell that needs energy. Here, it's broken down back into ADP and inorganic phosphate (P_i). Chemical energy is released from the phosphate bond and used by the cell. **ATPase** catalyses this reaction.

Tip: In a cell there's a constant cycle between ADP and P_i, and ATP. This allows energy to be stored and released as it's needed.

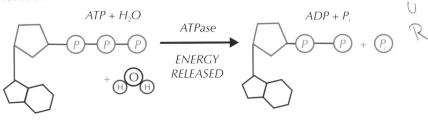

Figure 3: The breakdown of ATP.

This process is known as **hydrolysis**. It's the splitting (lysis) of a molecule using water (hydro).

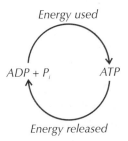

ATP's properties

ATP has specific properties that make it a good energy source.

- ATP stores or releases only a small, manageable amount of energy at a time, so no energy is wasted.
- It's a small, soluble molecule so it can be easily transported around the cell.
- It's easily broken down, so energy can be easily released.
- It can transfer energy to another molecule by transferring one of its phosphate groups.
- ATP can't pass out of the cell, so the cell always has an immediate supply of energy.

Tip: It's important to remember that ATP doesn't make energy — it's a store of energy. Energy is used to make ATP, then it's released when ATP is hydrolysed to ADP and P_i.

→ make (phosphorylated substance) more reactive.
lower Ec.

Practice Questions — Fact Recall

Q1 Name three biological processes in plants that need energy.

Q2 Define the terms autotroph and heterotroph.

Q3 What is the function of ATP?

Q4 Describe the structure of a molecule of ATP.

Q5 a) What is ATP broken down into by ATPase?

b) By what process is ATP broken down?

- Be able to
  explain, with the
  aid of diagrams
  and electron
  micrographs, how
  the structure of
  chloroplasts enables
  them to carry out
  their functions.

- Be able to define the
  term photosynthetic
  pigment.

- Be able to explain
  the importance
  of photosynthetic
  pigments in
  photosynthesis.

- Know that in plants,
  photosynthesis is a
  two-stage process
  taking place in
  chloroplasts.

- Know that the
  light-dependent
  stage takes place
  in thylakoid
  membranes and
  that the light-
  independent stage
  takes place in the
  stroma.

- Be able to outline
  how light energy
  is converted to
  chemical energy
  (ATP and reduced
  NADP) in the light-
  dependent stage.

- Be able to explain
  the role of water in
  the light-dependent
  stage.

  **Specification
  Reference 4.3.1**

2. Photosynthesis and the Light-dependent Reaction

In photosynthesis, light energy is used to make glucose. It involves a series of reactions, but before we get stuck into it you need to know a bit of background information...

Chloroplasts

Photosynthesis takes place in the chloroplasts of plant cells. Chloroplasts are small, flattened organelles found in plant cells (see Figure 1). They have a double membrane called the chloroplast envelope. Thylakoids (fluid-filled sacs) are stacked up in the chloroplast into structures called grana (singular = granum). The grana are linked together by bits of thylakoid membrane called lamellae (singular = lamella).

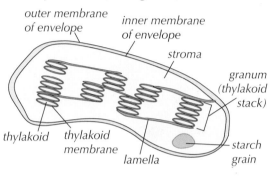

Figure 1: *The structure of a chloroplast.*

Chloroplasts contain **photosynthetic pigments** (e.g. chlorophyll a, chlorophyll b and carotene). These are coloured substances that absorb the light energy needed for photosynthesis. The pigments are found in the thylakoid membranes — they're attached to proteins. The protein and pigment is called a **photosystem**.

A photosystem contains two types of photosynthetic pigments — primary pigments and accessory pigments. Primary pigments are **reaction centres** where electrons are excited during the light-dependent reaction (see page 64) — in most chloroplasts the primary pigment is chlorophyll a. Accessory pigments surround the primary pigments and transfer light energy to them. There are two photosystems used by plants to capture light energy. Photosystem I (or PSI) absorbs light best at a wavelength of 700 nm and photosystem II (PSII) absorbs light best at 680 nm.

Contained within the inner membrane of the chloroplast and surrounding the thylakoids is a gel-like substance called the stroma — see Figure 1. It contains enzymes, sugars and organic acids. Carbohydrates produced by photosynthesis and not used straight away are stored as starch grains in the stroma.

Adaptations for photosynthesis

The structure of a chloroplast is adapted for photosynthesis in many ways:

- The chloroplast envelope keeps the reactants for photosynthesis close to their reaction sites.

- The thylakoids have a large surface area to allow as much light energy to be absorbed as possible.

- Lots of ATP synthase molecules (see previous page) are present in the thylakoid membranes to produce ATP in the light-dependent reaction.

- The stroma contains all the enzymes, sugars and organic acids for the light-independent reaction to take place.

Tip: The light-independent reaction is explained in more detail on the next page.

Redox reactions

Redox reactions are reactions that involve **oxidation** and **reduction**.
They occur in photosynthesis (and in respiration) so it's really important that you get your head round them:

- If something is reduced it has gained electrons (e⁻), and may have gained hydrogen or lost oxygen.
- If something is oxidised it has lost electrons, and may have lost hydrogen or gained oxygen.
- Oxidation of one molecule always involves reduction of another molecule.

Tip: One way to remember electron and hydrogen movement is OILRIG. **O**xidation **I**s **L**oss, **R**eduction **I**s **G**ain.

Coenzymes

A coenzyme is a molecule that aids the function of an enzyme. They work by transferring a chemical group from one molecule to another. A coenzyme used in photosynthesis is **NADP**. NADP transfers hydrogen from one molecule to another — this means it can reduce (give hydrogen to) or oxidise (take hydrogen from) a molecule.

Tip: When hydrogen is transferred between molecules, electrons are transferred too.

The stages of photosynthesis

There are actually two stages that make up photosynthesis — the light-dependent reaction and the light-independent reaction. The next few pages are all about the light-dependent reaction, but before we get into all that you need to know how the two stages link together.

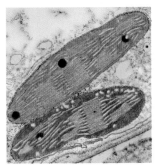

Figure 2: A cross-sectional image of two chloroplasts.

1. The light-dependent reaction

As the name suggests, this reaction needs light energy — see Figure 3. It takes place in the thylakoid membranes of the chloroplasts. Here, light energy is absorbed by photosynthetic pigments in the photosystems and converted to chemical energy. The light energy is used to add a phosphate group to ADP to form ATP, and to reduce NADP to form reduced NADP. ATP transfers energy and reduced NADP transfers hydrogen to the light-independent reaction. During the process water (H_2O) is oxidised to oxygen (O_2).

Tip: Reduced NADP is also written as NADPH — it's NADP that's gained a hydrogen. Remember OILRIG — reduction is gain.

2. The light-independent reaction (the Calvin cycle)

As the name suggests, this reaction doesn't use light energy directly. (But it does rely on the products of the light-dependent reaction.) It takes place in the stroma of the chloroplast — see Figure 3. Here, the ATP and reduced NADP from the light-dependent reaction supply the energy and hydrogen to make glucose from CO_2.

Tip: See pages 67-69 for loads more information on the Calvin cycle.

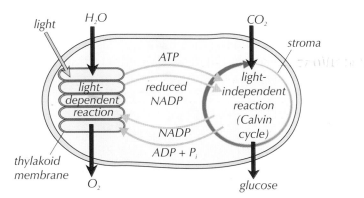

Figure 3: How the light-dependent and light-independent reactions link together in a chloroplast.

Tip: The light-independent reaction can take place in the dark. However, it needs the products of the light-dependent reaction (ATP and reduced NADP) so in reality it only continues for a little while after it gets dark.

The light-dependent reaction

In the light-dependent reaction, the light energy absorbed by the photosystems is used for three things:

1. Making ATP from ADP and inorganic phosphate. This is called **photophosphorylation** — it's the process of adding phosphate to a molecule using light.

2. Making reduced NADP from NADP.

3. Splitting water into protons (H⁺ ions), electrons and oxygen. This is called **photolysis** — it's the splitting (lysis) of a molecule using light (photo) energy.

The light-dependent reaction actually includes two types of photophosphorylation — non-cyclic and cyclic. Each of these processes has different products and is explained on the next couple of pages.

Photosynthesis Map

The light-dependent reaction

You are here

The light-independent reaction

Non-cyclic photophosphorylation

Non-cyclic photophosphorylation produces ATP, reduced NADP and oxygen (O_2). To understand the process you need to know that the photosystems (in the thylakoid membranes) are linked by **electron carriers**. Electron carriers are proteins that transfer electrons. The photosystems and electron carriers form an **electron transport chain** — a chain of proteins through which excited electrons flow. There are several processes going on all at once in non-cyclic photophosphorylation — they're shown in the diagrams below and on the next page.

Tip: To remind yourself what photosystems are, take a look back at page 62.

Tip: Not all of the electron carriers are shown in these diagrams.

1. Light energy excites electrons in chlorophyll

Light energy is absorbed by PSII. The light energy excites electrons in chlorophyll. The electrons move to a higher energy level (i.e. they have more energy — see Figure 4). These high-energy electrons move along the electron transport chain to PSI.

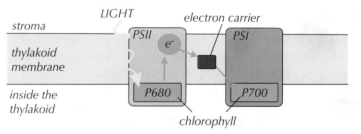

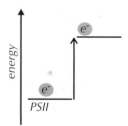

Figure 4: *Light energy excites electrons in PSII, moving them to a higher energy level.*

2. Photolysis of water produces protons, electrons and oxygen

As the excited electrons from chlorophyll leave PSII to move along the electron transport chain, they must be replaced. Light energy splits water into protons (H⁺ ions), electrons and oxygen. (So the oxygen in photosynthesis comes from water.) The reaction is: $H_2O \longrightarrow 2H^+ + \frac{1}{2}O_2$

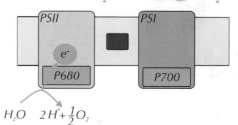

Tip: The O_2 produced from the photolysis of water is really important. It diffuses out of the chloroplast and eventually into the atmosphere for us to breathe. Good old plants.

3. Energy from the excited electrons makes ATP

The excited electrons lose energy as they move along the electron transport chain (see Figure 5). This energy is used to transport protons (H^+ ions) into the thylakoid so that the thylakoid has a higher concentration of protons than the stroma. This forms a proton gradient across the membrane. Protons move down their concentration gradient, into the stroma, via an enzyme called ATP synthase. The energy from this movement combines ADP and inorganic phosphate (Pi) to form ATP.

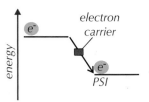

Figure 5: *The excited electrons lose energy as they pass down the electron transport chain.*

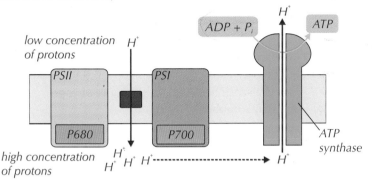

Tip: Chemiosmosis is the name of the process where the movement of protons (H^+ ions) across a membrane generates ATP. This process also occurs in respiration (see p. 81).

4. Energy from the excited electrons generates reduced NADP

Light energy is absorbed by PSI, which excites the electrons again to an even higher energy level (see Figure 6). Finally, the electrons are transferred to NADP, along with a proton from the stroma, to form reduced NADP.

Tip: Remember a 'proton' is just another word for a hydrogen ion (H^+).

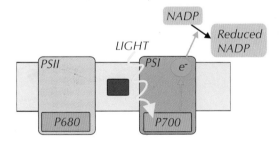

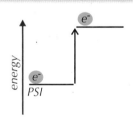

Figure 6: *Light energy excites electrons in PSI to an even higher energy level.*

Cyclic photophosphorylation

Cyclic photophosphorylation produces ATP and only uses PSI. It's called 'cyclic' because the electrons from the chlorophyll molecule aren't passed onto NADP, but are passed back to PSI via electron carriers. This means the electrons are recycled and can repeatedly flow through PSI. This process doesn't produce any reduced NADP or oxygen — it only produces small amounts of ATP.

Tip: The ATP and reduced NADP made here in the light-dependent reaction are really important for use later on in the light-independent reaction (see page 67).

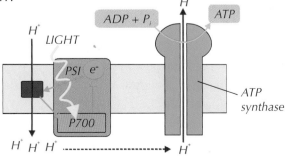

Tip: ATP is formed in the same way in cyclic photophosphorylation as in non-cyclic photophosphorylation — by the movement of protons across the thylakoid membrane.

Practice Questions — Application

This diagram on the right shows a process in the light-dependent reaction.

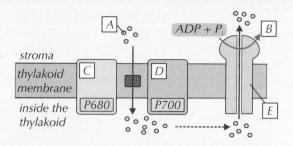

Q1 The object labelled A in the diagram is transported across the thylakoid membrane, so that its concentration is higher in the thylakoid than in the stroma.

   a) What is the name of object A?

   b) Explain why it is important that the concentration of object A is higher inside the thylakoid than in the stroma.

Q2 What is the name of structure C?

Q3 Which structure, C or D, is involved in cyclic photophosphorylation?

Q4 What does cyclic photophosphorylation produce?

Tip: Tempting as it is, you need to be able to answer this question without looking back at the last couple of pages.

Practice Questions — Fact Recall

Q1 The diagram on the right shows a chloroplast. Label the parts A-F.

Q2 a) What are photosynthetic pigments?

   b) Name the primary photosynthetic pigment in most chloroplasts.

Q3 Describe and explain three ways in which chloroplasts are adapted for their function.

Q4 NADP is a coenzyme used in photosynthesis. What chemical group does it transfer between molecules?

Q5 Where in the chloroplast does the light-dependent reaction occur?

Q6 Which products of the light-dependent reaction are needed in the light-independent reaction?

Q7 What is photophosphorylation?

Q8 What is the electron transport chain?

Q9 a) Name the products of the photolysis of water.

   b) What is the purpose of photolysis in the light-dependent reaction?

Q10 Name the photosystem(s) involved in and the product(s) of:

   a) non-cyclic photophosphorylation,

   b) cyclic photophosphorylation.

Tip: Make sure you get your head round what happens in cyclic and non-cyclic phosphorylation (see previous two pages) — don't get them mixed up.

3. Light-independent Reaction

The light-independent reaction is the second (and final, phew) stage of photosynthesis. It uses the products of the light-dependent reaction (ATP and reduced NADP) to make organic substances for the plant.

The Calvin cycle

The light-independent reaction is also called the Calvin cycle. It takes place in the stroma of the chloroplasts. It makes a molecule called **triose phosphate** from carbon dioxide (CO_2) and **ribulose bisphosphate** (a 5-carbon compound). Triose phosphate can be used to make glucose and other useful organic substances. There are a few steps in the cycle, and it needs ATP and H^+ ions to keep it going. The reactions are linked in a cycle (see Figure 1), which means the starting compound, ribulose bisphosphate, is regenerated.

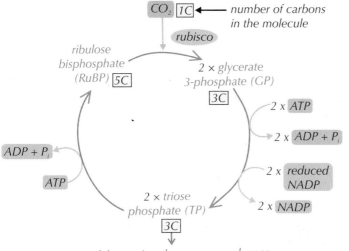

Figure 1: *One turn of the Calvin cycle.*

Here's what happens at each stage in the cycle:

1. Formation of glycerate 3-phosphate

Carbon dioxide enters the leaf through the stomata and diffuses into the stroma of the chloroplast. Here, it's combined with ribulose bisphosphate (RuBP), a 5-carbon compound. This gives an unstable 6-carbon compound, which quickly breaks down into two molecules of a 3-carbon compound called **glycerate 3-phosphate** (GP). **Ribulose bisphosphate carboxylase** (rubisco) catalyses the reaction between carbon dioxide and RuBP.

$$RuBP\ (5C) + CO_2 \xrightarrow{\ \ rubisco\ \ } unstable\ 6C\ compound \longrightarrow 2 \times GP\ (3C)$$

2. Formation of triose phosphate

The 3-carbon compound GP is reduced to a different 3-carbon compound called triose phosphate (TP). ATP (from the light-dependent reaction) provides the energy to do this. The H^+ ions come from reduced NADP (also from the light-dependent reaction). Reduced NADP is recycled to NADP. Triose phosphate is then converted into many useful organic compounds, e.g. glucose (see pages 68-69).

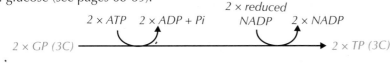

Tip: The Calvin cycle is also called carbon fixation, because carbon from CO_2 is 'fixed' into an organic molecule.

Photosynthesis Map

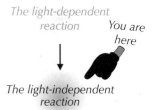

The light-dependent reaction

You are here

The light-independent reaction

3. Regeneration of ribulose bisphosphate

Five out of every six molecules of TP produced in the cycle aren't used to make useful organic compounds, but to regenerate RuBP. Regenerating RuBP uses the rest of the ATP produced by the light-dependent reaction.

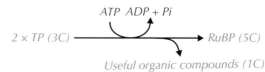

$$2 \times TP\ (3C) \xrightarrow{\quad ATP\quad ADP + Pi\quad} RuBP\ (5C)$$

Useful organic compounds (1C)

Hexose sugars

A hexose sugar is a monosaccharide that has six carbon atoms, e.g. glucose (see Figure 2). One hexose sugar is made by joining two molecules of triose phosphate (TP) together. Hexose sugars can be used to make larger carbohydrates (see next page).

The Calvin cycle needs to turn six times to make one hexose sugar. The reason for this is that three turns of the cycle produces six molecules of triose phosphate (because two molecules of TP are made for every one CO_2 molecule used). Five out of six of these TP molecules are used to regenerate ribulose bisphosphate (RuBP). This means that for three turns of the cycle only one TP is produced that's used to make a hexose sugar.

As a hexose sugar has six carbons, two TP molecules are needed to form one hexose sugar. This means the cycle must turn six times to produce two molecules of TP that can be used to make one hexose sugar — see Figure 3. Six turns of the cycle need 18 ATP and 12 reduced NADP from the light-dependent reaction.

This might seem a bit inefficient, but it keeps the cycle going and makes sure there's always enough RuBP ready to combine with carbon dioxide taken in from the atmosphere.

Tip: Useful organic compounds have more than one carbon atom, e.g. glucose has six carbon atoms. This means the cycle has to turn more than once to make them — see below.

Tip: It's really important that RuBP is regenerated. If it wasn't then glycerate 3-phosphate wouldn't be formed, the Calvin cycle would stop and photosynthesis would be unable to continue.

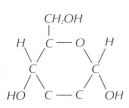

Figure 2: The structure of glucose, a hexose sugar.

Exam Tip
If you're asked in the exam to work out how many turns of the Calvin cycle are needed to produce a certain number of hexose sugars you need to remember that five out of every six TP molecules are used to regenerate RuBP.

Tip: Six turns of the Calvin cycle produce 12 GP molecules because one turn produces 2 GP, so 6 × 2 = 12 GP.

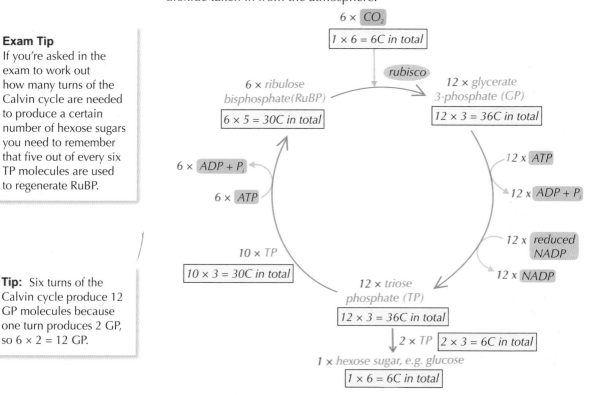

Figure 3: Six turns of the Calvin cycle.

Carbohydrates, lipids and amino acids

The Calvin cycle is the starting point for making all the organic substances a plant needs. Triose phosphate (TP) and glycerate 3-phosphate (GP) molecules are used to make carbohydrates, lipids and amino acids:

- **Carbohydrates** — hexose sugars are made from two triose phosphate molecules (see the previous page) and larger carbohydrates (e.g. sucrose, starch, cellulose — see Figure 4) are made by joining hexose sugars together in different ways.

- **Lipids** — these are made using glycerol, which is synthesised from triose phosphate, and fatty acids, which are synthesised from glycerate 3-phosphate.

- **Amino acids** — some amino acids are made from glycerate 3-phosphate.

Figure 4: *Cellulose strands in a plant cell wall made from hexose sugars.*

Practice Questions — Application

The diagram on the right shows a simplified version of the Calvin cycle.

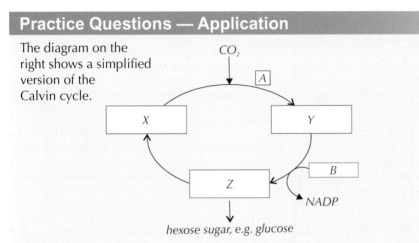

Q1 Name the molecules X, Y and Z.

Q2 Name enzyme A and coenzyme B.

Q3 Copy the diagram and draw on where ATP is used in the Calvin cycle (including how many molecules of ATP are used).

Practice Questions — Fact Recall

Q1 What is the role of carbon dioxide in the Calvin cycle?

Q2 a) Write out a word equation to show the formation of two molecules of triose phosphate.

   b) Is this reaction an oxidation or reduction reaction?

Q3 Describe the role of ATP in the Calvin cycle.

Q4 If six molecules of triose phosphate (TP) are produced by the Calvin cycle, how many of these will be used to regenerate ribulose bisphosphate?

Q5 To make one hexose sugar:

   a) How many turns of the Calvin cycle are needed?

   b) How many molecules of ATP are needed?

   c) How many molecules of reduced NADP are needed?

Q6 Describe how the products of the Calvin cycle are used to make the following organic substances:
   a) large carbohydrates,   b) lipids,   c) some amino acids.

Tip: The Calvin cycle can be summarised as follows:

Inputs

CO_2
ATP
Reduced NADP

↓ .

Outputs
Organic substances
RuBP

Exam Tip
Don't panic if you get a diagram of the Calvin cycle in the exam that doesn't look exactly the same as the one on the previous page (e.g. it might have extra or fewer stages) — as long as you remember the key points then you'll be fine.

Exam Tip
If you're asked to 'discuss the fate' of a molecule in the Calvin cycle, you just need to write about what happens to it.

- Be able to discuss·
  limiting factors in
  photosynthesis with·
  reference to light
  intensity, temperature
  and carbon dioxide
  concentration.
- Be able to describe
  how to investigate
  experimentally the
  factors that affect the
  rate of photosynthesis.
- Be able to describe
  the effect on the rate
  of photosynthesis,
  and on levels of
  GP, RuBP and TP,
  of changing light
  intensity, temperature
  and carbon dioxide
  concentration.

  **Specification
  Reference 4.3.1**

Tip: If you exposed a plant to only green light, there would be little or no photosynthesis because most of the green light is reflected rather than being absorbed. This is why plants look green.

4. Limiting Factors in Photosynthesis

Plants have optimum conditions for photosynthesis. If you're a budding gardener then these pages are for you...

Optimum conditions for photosynthesis

The ideal conditions for photosynthesis vary from one plant species to another, but the conditions below would be ideal for most plant species in temperate climates like the UK.

1. High light intensity of a certain wavelength

Light is needed to provide the energy for the light-dependent reaction — the higher the intensity of the light, the more energy it provides. Only certain wavelengths of light are used for photosynthesis. The photosynthetic pigments chlorophyll a, chlorophyll b and carotene only absorb the red and blue light in sunlight (see Figure 1).

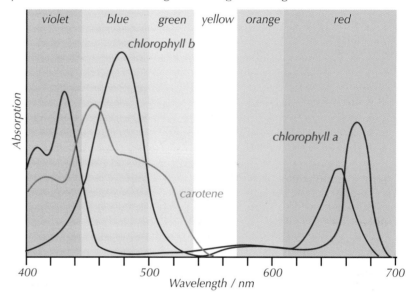

Figure 1: *The wavelengths of light absorbed by chlorophylls a and b, and carotene.*

2. Temperature around 25 °C

Photosynthesis involves enzymes (e.g. ATP synthase, rubisco). If the temperature falls below 10 °C the enzymes become inactive, but if the temperature is more than 45 °C they may start to **denature** (lose structure and function). Also, at high temperatures stomata close to avoid losing too much water. This causes photosynthesis to slow down because less carbon dioxide enters the leaf when the stomata are closed.

3. Carbon dioxide at 0.4%

Carbon dioxide makes up 0.04% of the gases in the atmosphere. Increasing this to 0.4% gives a higher rate of photosynthesis, but any higher and the stomata start to close.

4. Water

Plants also need a constant supply of water — too little and photosynthesis has to stop but too much and the soil becomes waterlogged (reducing the uptake of minerals such as magnesium, which is needed to make chlorophyll a).

Tip: At AS you learnt that stomata are pores in the epidermis of a plant leaf which allow gas exchange.

Limiting factors of photosynthesis

Light, temperature and carbon dioxide can all limit photosynthesis. All three of these things need to be at the right level to allow a plant to photosynthesise as quickly as possible. If any one of these factors is too low or too high, it will limit photosynthesis (slow it down). Even if the other two factors are at the perfect level, it won't make any difference to the speed of photosynthesis as long as that factor is at the wrong level.

Examples

- On a warm, sunny, windless day, it's usually carbon dioxide that's the limiting factor.
- At night it's usually the light intensity that's the limiting factor.

However, any of these factors could become the limiting factor, depending on the environmental conditions. The graphs below show the effect of each limiting factor on the rate of photosynthesis:

Examples

Light intensity

Between points A and B, the rate of photosynthesis is limited by the light intensity. So as the light intensity increases, so can the rate of photosynthesis. Point B is the **saturation point** — increasing light intensity after this point makes no difference, because something else has become the limiting factor. The graph now levels off.

Temperature

Both these graphs level off when light intensity is no longer the limiting factor. The graph at 25 °C levels off at a higher point than the one at 15 °C, showing that temperature must have been a limiting factor at 15 °C.

Carbon dioxide concentration

Both these graphs level off when light intensity is no longer the limiting factor. The graph at 0.4% carbon dioxide (CO_2) levels off at a higher point than the one at 0.04%, so carbon dioxide concentration must have been a limiting factor at 0.04% carbon dioxide. The limiting factor here isn't temperature because it's the same for both graphs (25 °C).

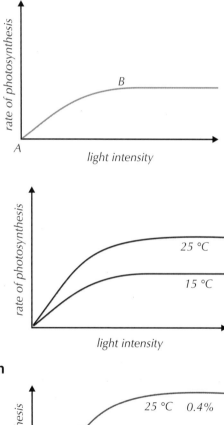

Tip: A limiting factor is a variable that can slow down the rate of a reaction.

Figure 2: *As night falls, light intensity begins to limit the rate of photosynthesis.*

Tip: The saturation point is where a factor is no longer limiting the reaction — something else has become the limiting factor.

Tip: As each of the graphs level off, it doesn't mean that photosynthesis has stopped — it means that the rate of photosynthesis is not increasing anymore.

Investigating the rate of photosynthesis

Canadian pondweed (*Elodea*) can be used to measure the effect of light intensity, temperature and CO_2 concentration on the rate of photosynthesis. The rate at which oxygen is produced by the pondweed can be easily measured and this corresponds to the rate of photosynthesis.

Tip: Don't forget — photosynthesis produces glucose and oxygen (see page 60).

Examples

The apparatus below is used to measure the effect of light intensity on photosynthesis.

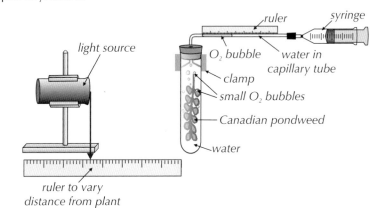

Figure 3: *A beaker of pondweed that could be used to investigate the effect of limiting factors on the rate of photosynthesis.*

Here's how the experiment works:

1. A source of white light is placed at a specific distance from the pondweed.

2. The pondweed is left to photosynthesise for a set amount of time. As it photosynthesises, the oxygen released will collect in the capillary tube.

3. At the end of the experiment, the syringe is used to draw the gas bubble in the tube up alongside a ruler and the length of the gas bubble is measured. This is proportional to the volume of O_2 produced.

4. Any variables that could affect the results should be controlled, e.g. temperature, the time the weed is left to photosynthesise.

5. The experiment is repeated and the average length of gas bubble is calculated, to make the results more reliable.

6. The whole experiment is then repeated with the light source placed at different distances from the pondweed.

Tip: To work out the exact volume of O_2 produced you also need to know the radius of the capillary tube.

Tip: Not all the O_2 released by the pondweed will be collected in the capillary tube, e.g. because some O_2 dissolves in water and some is used in respiration. Also, the tube will contain other gases, such as CO_2 from respiration.

The apparatus above can be altered to measure the effect of temperature and CO_2 on photosynthesis, e.g. the test tube of pondweed is put into a beaker of water at a set temperature and CO_2 is bubbled into the test tube (then the experiment's repeated with different temperatures of water / concentrations of CO_2).

Increasing plant growth

Commercial growers (e.g. farmers) know the factors that limit photosynthesis and therefore limit plant growth. This means they can create an environment where plants get the right amount of everything that they need, which increases growth and so increases yield. Growers create optimum conditions in **glasshouses**, as shown in Figure 4 on the next page.

Tip: A greenhouse is the same thing as a glasshouse.

Limiting Factor	Management in Glasshouse
Carbon dioxide concentration	Carbon dioxide is added to the air, e.g. by burning a small amount of propane in a carbon dioxide generator.
Light	Light can get in through the glass. Lamps provide light at night time.
Temperature	Glasshouses trap heat energy from sunlight, which warms the air. Heaters and cooling systems can also be used to keep a constant optimum temperature.

Figure 4: *Techniques used by growers to create optimum conditions in a glasshouse.*

Figure 5: *Lamps in greenhouses provide light at night.*

Limiting factors and the Calvin cycle

Light intensity, temperature and CO_2 concentration all affect the rate of photosynthesis, which means they affect the levels of glycerate 3-phosphate (GP), ribulose bisphosphate (RuBP) and triose phosphate (TP) in the Calvin cycle.

Tip: See pages 67-68 for how GP, TP and RuBP are made in the Calvin cycle.

Light intensity

In low light intensities, the products of the light-dependent stage (reduced NADP and ATP) will be in short supply (see Figure 6). This means that conversion of GP to TP and RuBP is slow. So the level of GP will rise as it's still being made, but it isn't being used up as quickly. The levels of TP and RuBP will fall as they're used up to make GP, but aren't being remade as quickly — see Figure 7.

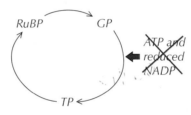

Figure 6: *The effect of low light intensity on the Calvin cycle.*

Tip: Light intensity doesn't affect the Calvin cycle directly because light isn't needed for the reactions of the Calvin cycle. However, the Calvin cycle does depend on the products from the light-dependent reaction, so it is indirectly affected by light intensity.

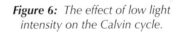

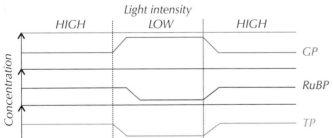

Figure 7: *The effect of light intensity on the levels of GP, RuBP and TP.*

Temperature

All the reactions in the Calvin cycle are catalysed by enzymes (e.g. rubisco). At low temperatures, all of the reactions will be slower as the enzymes work more slowly. This means the levels of RuBP, GP and TP will fall. GP, TP and RuBP are affected in the same way at very high temperatures, because the enzymes will start to denature (see Figure 8).

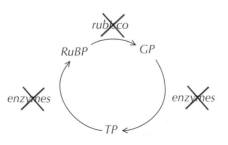

Figure 8: *The effect of temperature on the Calvin cycle.*

Tip: Unlike light intensity, temperature does affect the Calvin cycle directly because it affects enzyme activity.

Carbon dioxide concentration

At low CO_2 concentrations, conversion of RuBP to GP is also slow as there's less CO_2 to combine with RuBP to make GP — see Figure 9. So the level of RuBP will rise as it's still being made, but isn't being used up. The levels of GP and TP will fall as they're used up to make RuBP, but aren't being remade.

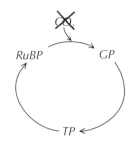

Figure 9: *The effect of low CO_2 concentration on the Calvin cycle.*

Practice Questions — Application

Q1 A farmer grows two tomato crops — one in a greenhouse and the other outside.
He records the average plant height each week for seven weeks.
The results are shown on the right.

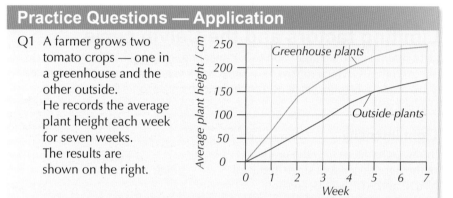

a) For each tomato crop, calculate the percentage difference in the average plant height between week two and week five.

b) Describe three ways in which the farmer may have created ideal conditions in the greenhouse in order to increase photosynthesis.

Q2 a) Jen has two house plants. She puts plant A under a light with a wavelength of 520 nm and plant B under a light with a wavelength of 480 nm. All other conditions the two plants are kept in are the same. After 4 weeks she measures the height of both plants. Which plant do you think was tallest? Explain your answer.

b) Jen keeps another house plant in her conservatory, which gets sun throughout the day and can reach temperatures of 40°C. She regularly waters the plant but it's beginning to die. Suggest why this might be and explain your answer.

Tip: Have a look back at the graph on page 70 to see which colours different wavelengths of light correspond to.

Practice Questions — Fact Recall

Q1 Describe an experiment involving pondweed that could be used to determine the effect of light intensity on the rate of photosynthesis. (Make sure you include a brief description of the apparatus.)

Q2 Explain why a low light intensity decreases the rate of the Calvin cycle, even though it's a light-independent reaction.

Q3 Describe how the following would affect the concentration of RuBP in the Calvin cycle:

a) low light intensity,

b) low temperature,

c) low concentration of CO_2.

Exam-style Questions

1   Plants use photosynthesis to produce glucose.

(a)   What name is given to an organism that is able to produce its own food?

(1 mark)

(b)   Photosynthesis occurs in the chloroplasts.
Fig 1.1 shows the structure of a chloroplast.

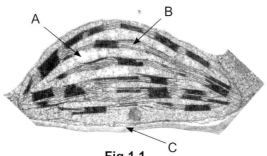

Fig 1.1

(i)   Identify the structures labelled **A – C**.

(3 marks)

(ii)   Explain how structures **B** and **C** enable the chloroplast to carry out photosynthesis efficiently.

(2 marks)

(iii)   Which of the structures **A – C** is the site of the light-independent reaction of photosynthesis?

(1 mark)

(c)   Glucose is synthesised from a 3-carbon compound produced in the light-independent reaction of photosynthesis.

(i)   Describe how this 3-carbon compound is produced.

In your answer, you should use appropriate technical terms, spelled correctly.

(6 marks)

(ii)   Only one out of six of the 3-carbon compounds produced in the light-independent reaction is converted into glucose. Describe what happens to the other five.

(2 marks)

(d)   The glucose generated in photosynthesis is used to make ATP.
Name the process in which glucose is used to make ATP.

(1 mark)

2 DNIP is an artificial hydrogen acceptor that can be used to measure the rate of photosynthesis. When DNIP is reduced it turns from blue to colourless. In the presence of NADP, DNIP is reduced first. A scientist used DNIP to investigate the rate of photosynthesis in plant chloroplasts under three different conditions. The results are shown below.

Tube	Condition	Colour after 24 hours
A	Unboiled chloroplasts kept in the dark	blue
B	Unboiled chloroplasts kept in the light	colourless
C	Boiled chloroplasts kept in the light	blue

(a) Explain the result for tube B.

(3 marks)

(b) Explain the results for tubes A and C.

(2 marks)

(c) Describe the role of reduced NADP in the light-independent reaction of photosynthesis.

(2 marks)

3 A student carried out a study into the effect of different factors on the rate of photosynthesis in a certain species of plant. He calculated the rate of photosynthesis by measuring how much oxygen was released by the plants over a period of time.

(a) Is this an accurate way of calculating the rate of photosynthesis? Explain your answer.

(1 mark)

(b) The student carried out three experiments in his study — the results of which are shown in Fig 3.1. In each experiment the plants had an adequate supply of water.

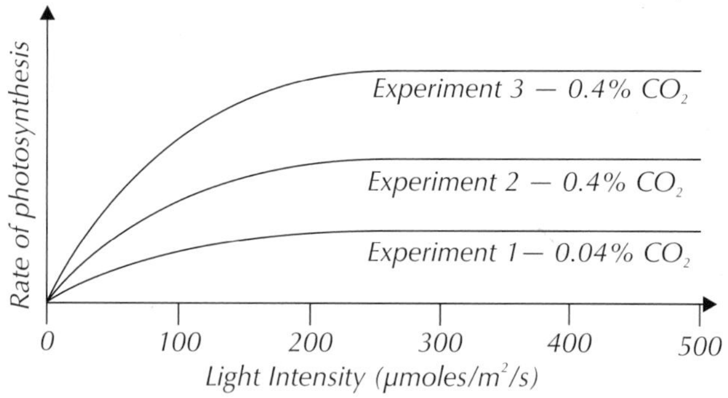

Rate of photosynthesis (y-axis)

Experiment 3 — 0.4% CO_2

Experiment 2 — 0.4% CO_2

Experiment 1— 0.04% CO_2

0   100   200   300   400   500

Light Intensity (μmoles/m²/s)

Fig 3.1

(i) Describe and explain the results of experiment 1.

(3 marks)

(ii) What is the limiting factor of photosynthesis in experiment 2? Explain your answer.

(2 marks)

(c) The student extended experiment 2 by measuring the amount of RuBP and TP produced by the plant over time. After 5 minutes, the student lowered the CO_2 concentration of the plants to 0.04%. Describe and explain what effect the lowering of CO_2 concentration had on the levels of RuBP and TP in the plants.

(2 marks)

5. Aerobic Respiration

Respiration is the process that allows cells to produce ATP from glucose. The next few pages are about aerobic respiration — respiration using oxygen.

Mitochondria

Most of the reactions in respiration take place in the mitochondria. You covered the mitochondrial structure at AS, but you might want to refresh your memory of it before you start this page — see Figure 1.

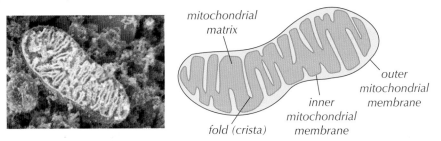

mitochondrial matrix

outer mitochondrial membrane

inner mitochondrial membrane

fold (crista)

Figure 1: *A mitochondrion in a nerve cell (left) and mitochondrial structure (right).*

Adaptations for respiration

Mitochondria are adapted to their function in the following ways:

- The inner mitochondrial membrane is folded into cristae, which increases the membrane's surface area to maximise respiration.

- There are lots of ATP synthase molecules in the inner mitochondrial membrane to produce lots of ATP in the final stage of respiration (see below).

- The mitochondrial matrix contains all the reactants and enzymes needed for the Krebs cycle (see below) to take place.

Coenzymes

As you saw in photosynthesis, a coenzyme is a molecule that aids the function of an enzyme by transferring a chemical group from one molecule to another. Coenzymes used in respiration include **NAD**, **coenzyme A** and **FAD**. NAD and FAD transfer hydrogen from one molecule to another. This means they can reduce (give hydrogen to) or oxidise (take hydrogen from) a molecule. Coenzyme A transfers acetate between molecules (see page 79).

Aerobic respiration

There are four stages in aerobic respiration:

1. Glycolysis.
2. The link reaction.
3. The Krebs cycle.
4. Oxidative phosphorylation.

The first three stages are a series of reactions. The products from these reactions are used in the final stage to produce loads of ATP. The first stage happens in the cytoplasm of cells and the other three stages take place in the mitochondria.

All cells use glucose to respire, but organisms can also break down other complex organic molecules (e.g. fatty acids, amino acids), which can then be respired.

Learning Objectives:

- Be able to explain, with the aid of diagrams and electron micrographs, how the structure of mitochondria enables them to carry out their functions.

- Be able to explain the importance of coenzymes in respiration.

- Know that glycolysis takes place in the cytoplasm.

- Be able to outline the process of glycolysis.

- Know that, during aerobic respiration in animals, pyruvate is actively transported into mitochondria.

- Know that the link reaction takes place in the mitochondrial matrix.

- Be able to outline the link reaction.

- Know that the Krebs cycle occurs in the mitochondrial matrix.

- Be able to outline the Krebs cycle.

- Be able to explain that during the Krebs cycle, decarboxylation and dehydrogenation occur, NAD and FAD are reduced and substrate-level phosphorylation occurs.

- Be able to outline the processes of oxidative phosphorylation and chemiosmosis.

- Know that oxygen is the final electron acceptor in aerobic respiration.

- Be able to explain why the theoretical maximum yield of ATP per molecule of glucose is rarely, if ever, achieved in aerobic respiration.

Specification Reference 4.4.1

Respiration Map

Glycolysis

↓

Link
Reaction

You are
here

↓

Krebs
Cycle

↓

Oxidative
Phosphorylation

Stage 1 — Glycolysis

Glycolysis makes **pyruvate** from glucose. Glycolysis involves splitting one molecule of glucose (with 6 carbons — 6C) into two smaller molecules of pyruvate (3C). The process happens in the cytoplasm of cells.
Glycolysis is the first stage of both aerobic and anaerobic respiration and doesn't need oxygen to take place — so it's an anaerobic process.

There are two stages in glycolysis — phosphorylation and oxidation. First, ATP is used to phosphorylate glucose to triose phosphate. Phosphorylation is the process of adding phosphate to a molecule. Then triose phosphate is oxidised, releasing ATP. Overall there's a net gain of 2 ATP.

1. Phosphorylation

Glucose is phosphorylated by adding a phosphate from a molecule of ATP. This creates one molecule of hexose phosphate and a molecule of ADP. Hexose phosphate is phosphorylated by ATP to form hexose bisphosphate and another molecule of ADP. Then, hexose bisphosphate is split up into 2 molecules of triose phosphate.

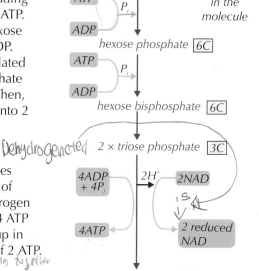

number of
carbons
in the
molecule

2. Oxidation

Triose phosphate is oxidised (loses hydrogen), forming 2 molecules of pyruvate. NAD collects the hydrogen ions, forming 2 reduced NAD. 4 ATP are produced, but 2 were used up in stage one, so there's a net gain of 2 ATP.

Tip: Remember the first part of OILRIG, (page 63) — oxidation is loss, so when triose phosphate is oxidised it loses hydrogen.

Tip: Glycolysis takes place in the cytoplasm of cells because glucose can't cross the outer mitochondrial membrane. Pyruvate can cross this membrane, so the rest of the reactions in respiration occur within the mitochondria.

The products of glycolysis

Here's what happens to all the products of glycolysis...

Products from glycolysis	Where it goes
2 reduced NAD	To oxidative phosphorylation
2 pyruvate	To the link reaction
2 ATP (net gain)	Used for energy

Practice Questions — Application

The diagram below is a simplified representation of glycolysis:

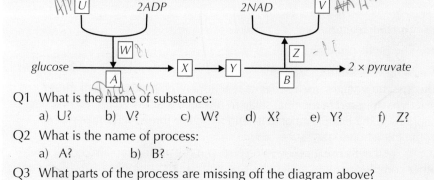

Q1 What is the name of substance:
   a) U?   b) V?   c) W?   d) X?   e) Y?   f) Z?

Q2 What is the name of process:
   a) A?   b) B?

Q3 What parts of the process are missing off the diagram above?

Stage 2 — The link reaction

Pyruvate is actively transported into the matrix of the mitochondria. Here, the link reaction converts pyruvate to acetyl coenzyme A. Pyruvate is **decarboxylated**, so one carbon atom is removed from pyruvate in the form of carbon dioxide. NAD is reduced — it collects hydrogen from pyruvate, changing pyruvate into acetate. Acetate is combined with coenzyme A (CoA) to form acetyl coenzyme A (acetyl CoA). No ATP is produced in this reaction.

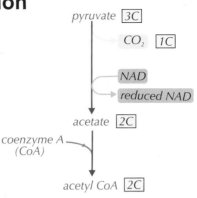

pyruvate 3C

CO_2 1C

NAD
reduced NAD

acetate 2C

coenzyme A (CoA)

acetyl CoA 2C

Tip: Decarboxylation is the removal of carbon dioxide from a molecule.

Respiration Map

Glycolysis

You are here

Link Reaction

Krebs Cycle

Oxidative Phosphorylation

The products of the link reaction

Two pyruvate molecules are made for every glucose molecule that enters glycolysis. This means the link reaction and the third stage (the Krebs cycle) happen twice for every glucose molecule.

Here's what happens to the products of two link reactions (i.e. for one glucose molecule):

Products from two link reactions	Where it goes
2 acetyl coenzyme A	To the Krebs cycle
2 carbon dioxide	Released as a waste product
2 reduced NAD	To oxidative phosphorylation

Stage 3 — The Krebs cycle

The Krebs cycle produces reduced coenzymes and ATP. It involves a series of oxidation-reduction reactions, which take place in the matrix of the mitochondria. The cycle happens once for every pyruvate molecule, so it goes round twice for every glucose molecule.

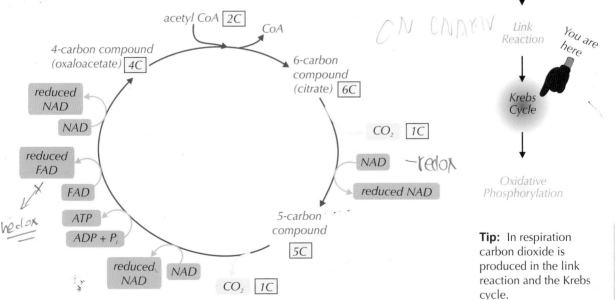

acetyl CoA 2C

CoA

4-carbon compound (oxaloacetate) 4C

reduced NAD

NAD

reduced FAD

FAD

ATP

ADP + P_i

reduced NAD   NAD

CO_2 1C

6-carbon compound (citrate) 6C

CO_2 1C

NAD

reduced NAD

5-carbon compound 5C

Figure 2: One turn of the Krebs cycle.

Respiration Map

Glycolysis

Link Reaction

You are here

Krebs Cycle

Oxidative Phosphorylation

Tip: In respiration carbon dioxide is produced in the link reaction and the Krebs cycle.

Here's what happens at each stage in the Krebs cycle:

1. Formation of citrate

Acetyl CoA from the link reaction combines with oxaloacetate to form citrate. Coenzyme A goes back to the link reaction to be used again.

oxaloacetate (4C) + acetyl CoA (2C) — *CoA* → *citrate (6C)*

2. Formation of a 5-carbon compound

The 6C citrate molecule is converted to a 5C molecule. Decarboxylation occurs, where carbon dioxide is removed. **Dehydrogenation** also occurs. The hydrogen is used to produce reduced NAD from NAD.

citrate (6C) — CO_2 *NAD reduced NAD* → *5-carbon compound*

3. Regeneration of oxaloacetate

The 5C molecule is then converted to a 4C molecule. (There are some intermediate compounds formed during this conversion, but you don't need to know about them.) Decarboxylation and dehydrogenation occur, producing one molecule of reduced FAD and two of reduced NAD. ATP is produced by the direct transfer of a phosphate group from an intermediate compound to ADP. When a phosphate group is directly transferred from one molecule to another it's called **substrate-level phosphorylation**. Citrate has now been converted into oxaloacetate.

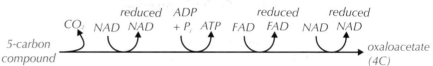

5-carbon compound — CO_2 *reduced NAD NAD   ADP + P_i ATP   reduced FAD FAD   reduced NAD NAD* → *oxaloacetate (4C)*

The products of the Krebs cycle

Some products of the Krebs cycle are reused, some are released and others are used for the next stage of respiration — oxidative phosphorylation.

Product from one Krebs cycle	Where it goes
1 coenzyme A	Reused in the next link reaction
Oxaloacetate	Regenerated for use in the next Krebs cycle
2 carbon dioxide	Released as a waste product
1 ATP	Used for energy
3 reduced NAD	To oxidative phosphorylation
1 reduced FAD	To oxidative phosphorylation

Tip: Coenzyme A transfers acetate between molecules (see page 63 for a reminder on coenzymes).

Tip: Dehydrogenation is the removal of hydrogen from a molecule.

Tip: See previous page if you can't remember what decarboxylation is.

Tip: Reduced NAD and reduced FAD may also be written as NADH and FADH$_2$. Don't worry, they still mean the same thing.

Tip: The table only shows the products of <u>one</u> turn of the Krebs cycle. The cycle turns <u>twice</u> for one glucose molecule, so one glucose molecule produces twice as much as what's shown in the table.

Tip: Remember that the Krebs cycle is just that... a cycle — some of its products need to be recycled for the process to continue.

Practice Questions — Application

Q1 The diagram below shows part of the Krebs cycle:

oxaloacetate → *citrate* → *5C-intermediate*

a) How many carbon atoms do oxaloacetate and citrate each have?

b) What happens to turn the 5C-intermediate back into oxaloacetate?

Q2 If six molecules of glucose were respired, how many molecules of CO_2 would be produced from the Krebs cycle?

Q3 Fats can be broken down and converted into acetyl coenzyme A. Explain how this allows fats to be respired.

Stage 4 — Oxidative phosphorylation

Oxidative phosphorylation is the process where the energy carried by electrons, from reduced coenzymes (reduced NAD and reduced FAD), is used to make ATP. (The whole point of the previous stages is to make reduced NAD and reduced FAD for the final stage.) Oxidative phosphorylation involves two processes — the **electron transport chain** and **chemiosmosis**.

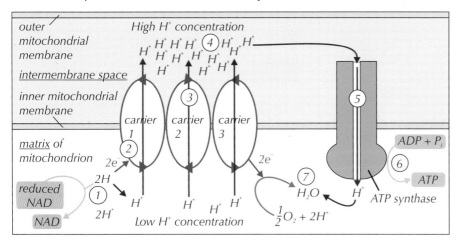

The numbers of the steps below correspond to the circled numbers in the diagram above.

1. Hydrogen atoms are released from reduced NAD and reduced FAD as they're oxidised to NAD and FAD. The hydrogen atoms split into protons (H$^+$) and electrons (e$^-$).

2. The electrons move along the electron transport chain (made up of three electron carriers), losing energy at each carrier (see Figure 3).

3. This energy is used by the electron carriers to pump protons from the mitochondrial matrix into the intermembrane space (the space between the inner and outer mitochondrial membranes).

4. The concentration of protons is now higher in the intermembrane space than in the mitochondrial matrix — this forms an electrochemical gradient (a concentration gradient of ions).

5. Protons move down the electrochemical gradient, back into the mitochondrial matrix, via ATP synthase.

6. This movement drives the synthesis of ATP from ADP and inorganic phosphate (P$_i$). The movement of H$^+$ ions across a membrane, which generates ATP, is called chemiosmosis.

7. In the mitochondrial matrix, at the end of the transport chain, the protons, electrons and oxygen (from the blood) combine to form water. Oxygen is said to be the **final electron acceptor**.

Practice Questions — Application

Antimycin A inhibits carrier 2 in the electron transport chain of oxidative phosphorylation.

Q1 If antimycin A was added to isolated mitochondria, what state (oxidised or reduced) would carriers 1 and 3 be in after its addition? Explain your answers.

Q2 Suggest why antimycin A can be used as a fish poison.

Respiration Map

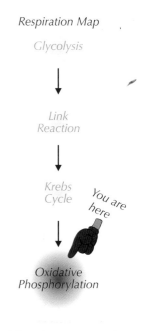

Tip: The regenerated coenzymes from the electron transport chain are reused in the Krebs cycle.

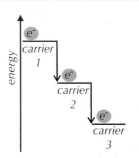

Figure 3: *As electrons move along the electron transport chain, they lose energy.*

Exam Tip
Don't write that protons move into or out of the inner mitochondrial membrane — they move across it.

Tip: The job of a carrier is to transfer electrons. When a carrier receives electrons it's reduced and when it passes on electrons it becomes oxidised again.

Stages of aerobic respiration

Glycolysis, the link reaction and the Krebs cycle are basically a series of reactions which produce ATP, reduced NAD, reduced FAD and CO_2. The reduced coenzymes (NAD and FAD) are then used in oxidative phosphorylation, to produce loads more ATP. The overall process is shown below:

Tip: Don't forget oxygen's role in respiration. It's the final electron acceptor in the electron transport chain in oxidative phosphorylation (see previous page).

Tip: Remember that the whole purpose of respiration is to produce ATP to fuel biological processes. That's why it's happening continuously in plant and animal cells.

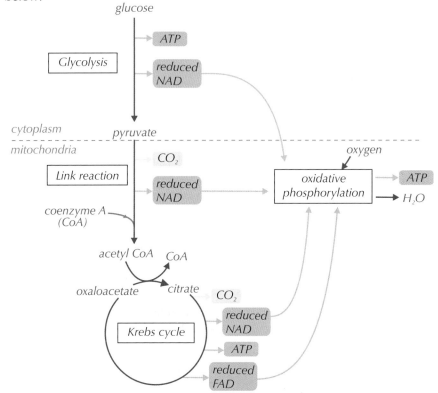

Aerobic respiration and ATP

As you know, oxidative phosphorylation makes ATP using energy from the reduced coenzymes — 2.5 ATP are made from each reduced NAD and 1.5 ATP are made from each reduced FAD.

The table below shows that a cell can make 32 ATP from one molecule of glucose in aerobic respiration. (Remember, one molecule of glucose produces 2 pyruvate, so the link reaction and Krebs cycle happen twice.)

Tip: The number of ATP produced per reduced NAD or reduced FAD was thought to be 3 and 2, but new research has shown that the figures are nearer 2.5 and 1.5.

Tip: For each molecule of glucose, 28 molecules of ATP are produced by oxidative phoshorylation (i.e. that's the ATP made from reduced NAD and reduced FAD).

Stage of respiration	Molecules produced	Number of ATP molecules
Glycolysis	2 ATP	**2**
Glycolysis	2 reduced NAD	$2 \times 2.5 = $ **5**
Link Reaction (×2)	2 reduced NAD	$2 \times 2.5 = $ **5**
Krebs cycle (×2)	2 ATP	**2**
Krebs cycle (×2)	6 reduced NAD	$6 \times 2.5 = $ **15**
Krebs cycle (×2)	2 reduced FAD	$2 \times 1.5 = $ **3**
		Total ATP = **32**

Actual yield of ATP

In theory, aerobic respiration can make 32 ATP per glucose molecule (see previous page). But in reality the actual yield is lower because:

- Some of the reduced NAD formed during the first three stages of aerobic respiration is used in other reduction reactions in the cell instead of in oxidative phosphorylation.

- Some ATP is used up by actively transporting substances into the mitochondria during respiration, e.g. pyruvate (formed at the end of glycolysis), ADP and phosphate (both needed for making ATP).

- The inner mitochondrial membrane is leaky — some protons may leak into the matrix without passing through ATP synthase and without making ATP.

Practice Questions — Fact Recall

Q1 Describe and explain three ways in which mitochondria are adapted for respiration.

Q2 Where in the cell does glycolysis take place?

Q3 What is ATP used for in glycolysis?

Q4 How is pyruvate transported into the mitochondria?

Q5 Where in the mitochondria does the link reaction take place?

Q6 a) In the link reaction, pyruvate is converted into acetate. Describe how this happens.

b) The second stage of the link reaction relies on coenzyme A. What is the role of coenzyme A in the link reaction?

c) State what happens to the products of the link reaction.

Q7 During the Krebs cycle ATP is produced by the direct transfer of a phosphate group from an intermediate compound to ADP. What name is given to this process?

Q8 After each turn of the Krebs cycle, what happens to:

a) coenzyme A?   b) oxaloacetate?

Q9 During oxidative phosphorylation, what happens to electrons as they move down the electron transport chain?

Q10 What is said to be the final electron acceptor in oxidative phosphorylation?

Q11 Give one example of a decarboxylation reaction in respiration.

Q12 Draw out the table below and fill it in with crosses to show where the following substances are made in respiration.

Substance	Glycolysis	Link reaction	Krebs cycle	Oxidative phosphorylation
ATP				
reduced NAD				
reduced FAD				
CO_2				

Q13 Give three reasons why the actual yield of ATP from aerobic respiration is less than the predicted theoretical yield.

Exam Tip
You really need to know this stuff for your exam. If you find you're struggling to answer a question go back to the relevant page and make sure you really understand what's going on.

Learning Objective:

■ Be able to evaluate the experimental evidence for the theory of chemiosmosis.

Specification Reference 4.4.1

6. Respiration Experiments

Everything we know about respiration and how it works comes from experiments. Here are a few experiments you need to know about...

Investigating the rate of respiration

The volume of oxygen taken up or the volume of carbon dioxide produced indicates the rate of respiration. A **respirometer** (see Figure 1 below) measures the rate of oxygen being taken up — the more oxygen taken up, the faster the rate of respiration.

Tip: It's easy to remember what a respirometer is for. 'Respiro' means breath, and a 'meter' is a piece of equipment that measures something (e.g. a water meter) — so a respirometer measures breathing.

---- Example --

The respirometer below is set up to measure the volume of oxygen taken up by some woodlice:

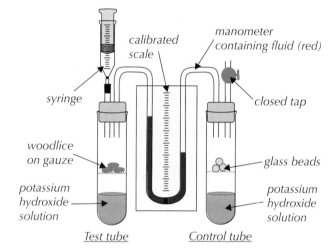

Figure 1: A respirometer.

Figure 2: A respirometer set up to measure the rate of respiration by germinating peas (left). Glass beads are being used as a control (right).

Each tube contains potassium hydroxide solution (or soda lime), which absorbs carbon dioxide. The control tube is set up in exactly the same way as the test tube, but without the woodlice, to make sure the results are only due to the woodlice respiring (e.g. it contains beads that have the same mass as the woodlice).

Here's how the experiment works:

1. The syringe is used to set the fluid in the manometer to a known level.

2. The respirometer is left for a set period of time (e.g. 20 minutes). During that time there'll be a decrease in the volume of the air in the test tube, due to oxygen consumption by the woodlice (all the CO_2 produced is absorbed by the potassium hydroxide). The decrease in the volume of the air will reduce the pressure in the tube and cause the coloured liquid in the manometer to move towards the test tube.

3. The distance moved by the liquid in a given time is measured. This value can then be used to calculate the volume of oxygen taken in by the woodlice per minute.

4. Any variables that could affect the results are controlled, e.g. temperature, volume of potassium hydroxide solution in each test tube.

5. To produce more reliable results the experiment is repeated and a mean volume of O_2 is calculated.

Tip: You'd calculate the rate of respiration (volume of oxygen taken up per minute) by dividing the volume of oxygen used by the number of minutes the respirometer was left for.

Evidence for chemiosmosis

Before the 1960s, scientists didn't understand the connection between the electron transport chain and ATP synthesis in respiration. One idea was that energy lost from electrons moving down the electron transport chain creates a proton gradient (a concentration gradient of H⁺ ions), which is then used to synthesise ATP — this is called the **chemiosmotic theory**. Nowadays, there's quite a lot of experimental evidence supporting this theory:

HOW SCIENCE WORKS

Tip: Gathering evidence to support or disprove a theory is an important part of how science works — see page 2 for more.

Examples

Experiment one — low pH

The pH of the intermembrane space in mitochondria was found to be lower than the pH of the matrix. A lower pH means the intermembrane space is more acidic — it has a higher concentration of H⁺ ions. This observation shows that a proton gradient exists between the intermembrane space and the matrix of mitochondria (see Figure 3).

Tip: The chemiosmotic theory is the most widely accepted theory for linking the electron transport chain to ATP synthesis.

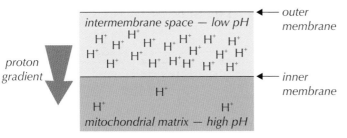

Figure 3: The proton gradient in mitochondria.

Tip: Mitochondria are far too small to use a pH probe to measure the pH inside them, so scientists have to use other methods to work out the pH.

Experiment two — artificial vesicles

Artificial vesicles were created from phospholipid bilayers to represent the inner mitochondrial membrane. Proton pumps from bacteria and ATP synthase were added to the vesicle membranes.

The proton pumps are activated by light, so when light was shone onto these vesicles they started to pump protons. The pH inside the vesicles decreased — protons were being pumped into the vesicle from outside. When ADP and P_i were added to the solution outside the vesicles, ATP was synthesised — see Figure 4. This artificial system shows that a proton gradient can be used to synthesise ATP (but doesn't show that this happens in mitochondria).

Tip: Bacteria don't have mitochondria but they do have proton pumps in their membranes that are very similar to proton pumps found in mitochondria.

Figure 4: The production of ATP from a proton gradient in an artificial vesicle.

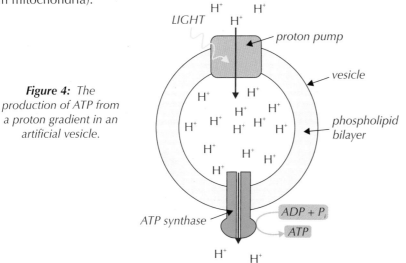

Tip: You have to be very careful with the conclusions you draw from an experiment. For example, experiment two didn't show that proton gradients are used to generate ATP <u>in mitochondria</u> because the experiment was carried out in an artificial system, not in mitochondria.

Experiment three — mitochondria

Mitochondria were put into a slightly alkaline solution (pH 8). They were left until the whole of each mitochondrion (matrix and intermembrane space) became pH 8. When these mitochondria were given ADP and P_i no ATP was produced.

Then the mitochondria were transferred to a more acidic solution of pH 4 (i.e. one with a higher concentration of protons). The outer membrane of the mitochondrion is permeable to protons — the protons moved into the intermembrane space, creating a proton gradient across the inner mitochondrial membrane. In the presence of ADP and P_i, ATP was produced. This experiment shows that a proton gradient can be used by mitochondria to make ATP — see Figure 5.

Tip: Moving the mitochondria from one pH to a different pH is a way of artificially creating a proton gradient across the inner membrane.

Tip: Experiment three goes a step further than experiment two and shows that a proton gradient can be used to generate ATP in mitochondria. However, it still doesn't prove that this is what happens during respiration because the proton gradient has been generated artificially.

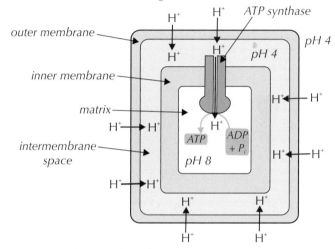

Figure 5: The production of ATP from a proton gradient in a mitochondrion.

Experiment four — uncouplers

Uncouplers are substances that destroy the proton gradient across the inner mitochondrial membrane. An uncoupler was added to mitochondria, along with reduced NAD, and ADP and P_i. No ATP was made. This experiment shows that a proton gradient is required to synthesise ATP in mitochondria.

Practice Question — Application

Q1 Dicyclohexylcarbodiimide (DCC) is an inhibitor that binds to ATP synthase and prevents protons moving through it. When mitochondria are treated with DCC they stop synthesising ATP. Explain how this provides evidence for the chemiosmotic theory.

Practice Questions — Fact Recall

Q1 In a respirometer, what is the function of the potassium hydroxide solution?

Q2 If you were using a respirometer to measure the oxygen consumed by a mouse with a mass of 20 g, what mass of glass beads would you have in the control tube?

Q3 What is the chemiosmotic theory?

7. Anaerobic Respiration

How cells respire aerobically is covered on pages 77 - 83. This page is all about how cells respire anaerobically.

What is anaerobic respiration?

Anaerobic respiration is a type of respiration that doesn't use oxygen. Like aerobic respiration, it starts with glycolysis. However, unlike aerobic respiration it doesn't involve the link reaction, the Krebs cycle or oxidative phosphorylation.

There are two types of anaerobic respiration — alcoholic fermentation and lactate fermentation. These two processes are similar, because they both take place in the cytoplasm, they both produce two ATP per molecule of glucose and they both start with glycolysis (which produces pyruvate). They differ in which organisms they occur in and what happens to the pyruvate (see below).

Lactate fermentation

Lactate fermentation occurs in mammals and produces lactate. Reduced NAD (from glycolysis) transfers hydrogen to pyruvate to form lactate and NAD — see Figure 1. NAD can then be reused in glycolysis. The production of lactate regenerates NAD. This means glycolysis can continue even when there isn't much oxygen around, so a small amount of ATP can still be produced to keep some biological processes going... clever.

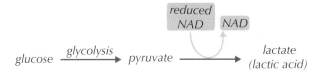

Figure 1: *The reactions of lactate fermentation.*

Alcoholic fermentation

Alcoholic fermentation occurs in yeast cells and produces ethanol. CO_2 is removed from pyruvate to form ethanal. Reduced NAD (from glycolysis) transfers hydrogen to ethanal to form ethanol and NAD — see Figure 2. NAD can then be reused in glycolysis. The production of ethanol also regenerates NAD so glycolysis can continue when there isn't much oxygen around.

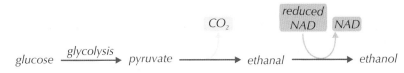

Figure 2: *The reactions of alcoholic fermentation.*

Anaerobic respiration and ATP

The ATP yield from anaerobic respiration is always lower than from aerobic respiration. This is because anaerobic respiration only includes one energy-releasing stage (glycolysis), which only produces 2 ATP per glucose molecule. The energy-releasing reactions of the Krebs cycle and oxidative phosphorylation need oxygen, so they can't occur during anaerobic respiration.

Learning Objectives:

- Be able to compare and contrast anaerobic respiration in mammals and in yeast.
- Be able to explain why anaerobic respiration produces a much lower yield of ATP than aerobic respiration.

Specification Reference 4.4.1

Tip: Some bacteria carry out lactate fermentation too.

Tip: Remember, NAD is needed to oxidise triose phosphate to pyruvate in glycolysis — see page 78.

Tip: Alcoholic fermentation also occurs in plants.

Figure 3: *Yeast cells can respire anaerobically using alcoholic fermentation.*

Tip: Aerobic respiration produces 32 ATP per molecule of glucose — see page 82.

Q1 Kate is competing in a 100 m sprint. Towards the end of the race her body cannot supply oxygen to the muscle cells in her legs quickly enough.

   a) Will Kate's muscle cells begin respiring aerobically or anaerobically towards the end of the race?

   b) How many molecules of ATP are produced per molecule of glucose by this type of respiration?

   c) Write out the word equation for this reaction.

Q2 The diagram below shows the two fates of glucose in anaerobic conditions.

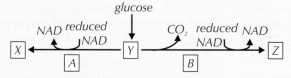

   a) What is the name of substance:

   i) X?   ii) Y?   iii) Z?

   b) Which process, A or B:

   i)   is lactate fermentation?

   ii) happens in plant cells?

   iii) can happen in bacterial cells?

   c) How many molecules of ATP are made by each of these processes?

Q3 Janus Green B is an artificial hydrogen acceptor. It is a useful redox reaction indicator as it is a blue colour when oxidised and turns to a pink colour when reduced. A scientist adds Janus Green B and pyruvate to a suspension of yeast cells under anaerobic conditions. He then records the colour of the mixture after 5 minutes. Suggest what colour the mixture should be. Explain your answer.

Tip: Artificial hydrogen acceptors can accept hydrogen and become reduced. This means they can be used to model the function of some coenzymes, e.g. NAD.

Practice Questions — Fact Recall

Q1 Where in the cell does anaerobic respiration take place?

Q2 Give one similarity between aerobic respiration and anaerobic respiration.

Q3 In which organisms do the following occur:

   a) lactate fermentation?   b) alcoholic fermentation?

Q4 Describe what happens to pyruvate in lactate fermentation.

Q5 Describe what happens to ethanal in alcoholic fermentation.

Q6 a) If aerobic respiration produces 32 ATP per molecule of glucose, how many fewer ATP molecules does anaerobic respiration produce?

   b) Explain why anaerobic respiration gives a lower yield of ATP than aerobic respiration.

8. Respiratory Substrates

Most of the time we talk about glucose being used in respiration, but glucose isn't the only molecule that can be respired...

Learning Objectives:

- Be able to define the term 'respiratory substrate'.

- Be able to explain the difference in relative energy values of carbohydrate, lipid and protein respiratory substrates.

Specification Reference 4.4.1

What is a respiratory substrate?

Any biological molecule that can be broken down in respiration to release energy is called a respiratory substrate. Cells respire glucose, but they also respire other carbohydrates, lipids and proteins — these are all respiratory substrates. Different respiratory substrates enter respiration at different points. Glucose enters right at the beginning — at the start of glycolysis. Proteins and lipids enter respiration at the Krebs cycle.

Respiratory quotients

When an organism respires a specific respiratory substrate, the respiratory quotient (RQ) can be worked out. The respiratory quotient is the volume of carbon dioxide produced when that substrate is respired, divided by the volume of oxygen consumed, in a set period of time. You calculate it using these equations:

$$RQ = \frac{\text{Volume of } CO_2 \text{ released}}{\text{Volume of } O_2 \text{ consumed}} \quad \text{or} \quad RQ = \frac{\text{Molecules of } CO_2 \text{ released}}{\text{Molecules of } O_2 \text{ consumed}}$$

Exam Tip:
The two equations on the left mean the same thing. The volume of gas is equal to the number of molecules of that gas. In the exam you'll get the equation written in terms of volumes, but the other equation may be easier to use, as shown below.

--- Example ---

You can work out the RQ for cells that only respire glucose.

First you need the basic equation for aerobic respiration:

$$C_6H_{12}O_6 + 6O_2 \rightarrow 6CO_2 + 6H_2O + \text{energy}$$

From the equation you can see that for every six molecules of oxygen consumed, six molecules of carbon dioxide are released.
So, you just need to plug these numbers into the RQ equation:

$$\text{RQ for glucose} = \frac{\text{Molecules of } CO_2 \text{ released}}{\text{Molecules of } O_2 \text{ released}} = \frac{6}{6} = 1$$

Exam Tip
Make sure you know how to calculate a respiratory quotient — it could come up in the exam.

Respiratory quotients have been worked out for the respiration of other respiratory substrates — see Figure 1. Lipids and proteins have an RQ value lower than one because more oxygen is needed to oxidise fats and lipids than to oxidise carbohydrates.

Respiratory substrate	RQ
Lipids (triglycerides)	*0.7*
Proteins or amino acids	*0.9*
Carbohydrates	*1*

Figure 1: The respiratory quotients of different respiratory substrates.

--- Example ---

Oleic acid ($C_{18}H_{34}O_2$) is a fatty acid that can be respired. The equation for aerobic respiration using oleic acid is:

$$2C_{18}H_{34}O_2 + 51O_2 \rightarrow 36CO_2 + 34H_2O + \text{energy}$$

So, the RQ for oleic acid $= \dfrac{\text{Molecules of } CO_2 \text{ released}}{\text{Molecules of } O_2 \text{ released}} = \dfrac{36}{51} = 0.71$

Tip: Oleic acid is a fatty acid. Fatty acids make up triglycerides (lipids), so you would expect oleic acid to have an RQ of about 0.7 looking at Figure 1. Like other lipids, oleic acid enters respiration at the Krebs cycle.

Figure 2: This equipment measures O_2 intake and CO_2 output, which could be used to calculate the RQ of the man during exercise.

Tip: Don't forget, carbohydrates have an RQ of 1, lipids have an RQ of about 0.7 and proteins have an RQ of around 0.9.

Tip: The equation for calculating RQ is:

$$\frac{\text{Volume of } CO_2 \text{ released}}{\text{Volume of } O_2 \text{ consumed}}$$

Tip: Don't forget — you can use either the volumes of CO_2 and O_2, or the number of molecules of these gases, to work out the RQ.

Uses of the respiratory quotient

You can work out the respiratory quotient for a whole organism as well as a particular substrate. The respiratory quotient for a whole organism is an average of all the respiratory quotients for all the different molecules the organism is respiring. You can work it out by directly measuring the volume of oxygen consumed and the volume of carbon dioxide released, and then putting these figures into the equation on the previous page.

The respiratory quotient for an organism is useful because it tells you what kind of respiratory substrate an organism is respiring and what type of respiration it's using (aerobic or anaerobic).

Examples

- Under normal conditions the usual RQ for humans is between 0.7 and 1.0. An RQ in this range shows that some fats (lipids) are being used for respiration, as well as carbohydrates like glucose. Protein isn't normally used by the body for respiration unless there's nothing else.

- High RQs (greater than 1) mean that an organism is short of oxygen, and is having to respire anaerobically as well as aerobically.

- Plants sometimes have a low RQ. This is because the CO_2 released in respiration is used for photosynthesis (so it's not measured).

Practice Questions — Application

Q1 Lactose ($C_{12}H_{22}O_{11}$) is a sugar. The equation for the respiration of lactose is:

$$C_{12}H_{22}O_{11} + 12O_2 \rightarrow 12CO_2 + 11H_2O$$

Calculate the respiratory quotient of lactose.

Q2 Palmitic acid ($C_{16}H_{32}O_2$) is a fatty acid commonly found in plants and animals. The equation for the respiration of palmitic acid is:

$$C_{16}H_{32}O_2 + 23O_2 \rightarrow 16CO_2 + 16H_2O$$

Calculate the respiratory quotient of palmitic acid.

Q3 The equation for the respiration of a mystery molecule is:

$$C_{57}H_{104}O_6 + 80O_2 \rightarrow 57CO_2 + 52H_2O$$

a) Calculate the respiratory quotient of the mystery molecule.

b) Suggest whether this molecule is a carbohydrate, a protein or a lipid. Explain your answer.

Q4 Robert consumes about 250 ml of O_2 per minute and releases around 180 ml of CO_2.

a) Calculate Robert's respiratory quotient.

b) Robert eats a bowl of pasta for lunch. After lunch, Robert's respiratory quotient increases to nearly 1. Suggest why.

Practice Questions — Fact Recall

Q1 What is a respiratory substrate?

Q2 Which have the highest RQ — lipids, proteins or carbohydrates?

Q3 Why are the respiratory quotients of organisms useful?

Section Summary

Make sure you know...

- That plants and animals need energy to power biological processes (e.g. photosynthesis, active transport, DNA replication, cell division, muscle contraction and maintenance of body temperature).

- That autotrophs are organisms that can produce their own food and heterotrophs are organisms that can't produce their own food.

- That in photosynthesis, light energy is used to produce complex organic molecules such as glucose.

- That plants and animals release energy from the products of photosynthesis by respiration.

- That ATP is the immediate source of energy in a cell. It is used to carry out biological processes.

- That ATP consists of the base adenine, a ribose sugar and three phosphate groups.

- That photosynthesis takes place in the chloroplasts of plants.

- That a photosynthetic pigment is a coloured substance that absorbs light energy in photosynthesis.

- How the structure of a chloroplast is adapted for photosynthesis.

- That photosynthesis has two stages — the light-dependent reaction (which takes place in the thylakoid membranes) and the light-independent reaction (which takes place in the stroma).

- That the light-dependent reaction includes non-cyclic photophosphorylation and cyclic photophosphorylation. In both processes, light energy is absorbed by the chlorophyll in photosystems and used to excite electrons. As the electrons move down the electron transport chain they lose energy, which is used to generate a proton gradient across the thylakoid membrane. The subsequent movement of protons down their concentration gradient is used to produce ATP. In non-cyclic photophosphorylation reduced NADP is also produced.

- That the protons and electrons needed for the light-dependent reaction come from the photolysis of water — the splitting of water using light, which also produces oxygen. It happens in non-cyclic photophosphorylation.

- That in the light-independent reaction carbon dioxide (CO_2) enters the Calvin cycle, where it is combined with ribulose bisphosphate (RuBP) to form two molecules of glycerate 3-phosphate (GP). These two molecules of GP are then reduced to two molecules of triose phosphate (TP), using ATP and reduced NADP from the light-dependent reaction. Five out of every six molecules of TP are used to regenerate RuBP, (allowing the Calvin cycle to continue), while the remaining TP is used to produce organic substrates such as carbohydrates, lipids and amino acids.

- That a limiting factor is a variable that can slow down the rate of a reaction. The limiting factors of photosynthesis are light intensity, temperature and carbon dioxide concentration.

- How the limiting factors of photosynthesis affect the rate of photosynthesis and how this can be investigated experimentally.

- How the limiting factors of photosynthesis affect the concentrations of GP, RuBP and TP in the Calvin cycle.

- How the structure of a mitochondrion is adapted for respiration.

- That NAD and FAD are coenzymes that transfer hydrogen between molecules during respiration and that coenzyme A is a coenzyme that transfers acetate between molecules during respiration.

- That there are four stages of aerobic respiration — glycolysis, the link reaction, the Krebs cycle and oxidative phosphorylation.

- That glycolysis happens in the cytoplasm of a cell, and that the link reaction and the Krebs cycle occur in the mitochondrial matrix.

- That in glycolysis, ATP is used to phosphorylate glucose to hexose bisphosphate. Hexose bisphosphate then splits into two molecules of triose phosphate, which are then oxidised to pyruvate. There is a net gain of two ATP and two reduced NAD, per molecule of glucose.

- That the pyruvate formed during glycolysis is actively transported into mitochondria.
- That in the link reaction, pyruvate is converted to acetate (via decarboxylation and the reduction of NAD). Then acetate is combined with coenzyme A to form acetyl coenzyme A.
- That in the Krebs cycle, acetyl coenzyme A (a 2C molecule) combines with oxaloacetate (4C) to produced citrate (6C). Citrate is decarboxylated and dehydrogenated to produce a 5-carbon compound, which is then used to regenerate oxaloacetate. During these reactions reduced NAD, reduced FAD, ATP and CO_2 are produced.
- That ATP is produced in the Krebs cycle by substrate-level phosphorylation — a phosphate group is directly transferred from an intermediate molecule to ADP.
- That oxidative phosphorylation uses electrons from reduced NAD and reduced FAD to make ATP. Electrons travel down the electron transport chain (which is made up of three electron carriers), losing energy at each carrier. This energy is used to form a proton gradient across the inner mitochondrial membrane, which is used to make ATP by chemiosmosis.
- That oxygen is the final electron acceptor in aerobic respiration.
- That aerobic respiration doesn't always produce the theoretical maximum yield of ATP and the reasons for this.
- How to investigate an organism's respiration rate using a respirometer.
- What the chemiosmotic theory is and be able to evaluate evidence for or against it.
- That there are two types of anaerobic respiration (lactate fermentation and alcoholic fermentation) and the similarities between them — they both happen in the cytoplasm, they both produce 2 ATP per glucose molecule and they both start with glycolysis.
- The differences between lactate fermentation and alcoholic fermentation — lactate fermentation occurs in mammals and produces lactate, and alcoholic fermentation occurs in yeast cells and produces ethanol.
- That anaerobic respiration produces a much lower yield of ATP than aerobic respiration because it only includes one energy releasing stage (glycolysis), which only produces 2 ATP per glucose molecule.
- That a respiratory substrate is any molecule that can be broken down in respiration to release energy.
- How to calculate respiratory quotients.
- That lipids, carbohydrates and proteins have different respiratory quotients.
- How to use the respiratory quotient of a whole organism to determine what respiratory substrates the organism is respiring or what type of respiration it is using.

Exam-style Questions

1   Petite mutants are yeast cells that have mutations in genes that are important for mitochondrial function. They are called petite mutants because they grow and divide to form unusually small colonies when grown in medium with a low glucose concentration. Fig. 1.1 below shows the structure of a mitochondrion from a normal yeast cell and Fig. 1.2 shows a mitochondrion from a petite mutant.

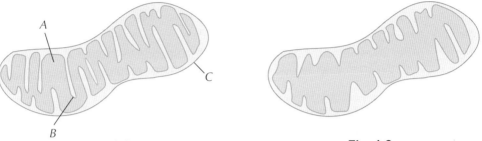

Fig. 1.1   **Fig. 1.2**

(a) (i)   Name structures **A**, **B** and **C** in Fig. 1.1.

(3 marks)

  (ii)   State how the structure of the mitochondrion in Fig. 1.2 differs from that in Fig. 1.1.

(1 mark)

(b) (i)   Petite mutants lack functioning mitochondria but they can still produce ATP by glycolysis. Explain why.

(1 mark)

  (ii)   Hexose bisphosphate is an intermediate compound in glycolysis. Describe how hexose bisphosphate is formed from a molecule of glucose.

(3 marks)

  (iii)   Describe the role of coenzyme NAD in glycolysis.

(2 marks)

(c)   Normal yeast cells can respire a range of different respiratory substrates, including glycerol ($C_3H_8O_3$). The equation for the respiration of glycerol is:

$$2C_3H_8O_3 + 7O_2 \rightarrow 6CO_2 + 8H_2O$$

The respiratory quotient (RQ) is defined as:

$$RQ = \frac{\text{Volume of } CO_2 \text{ released}}{\text{Volume of } O_2 \text{ consumed}}$$

Calculate the respiratory quotient of glycerol.

(2 marks)

2　A scientist carried out an experiment on respiration in yeast cells. She put some yeast into a test tube containing glucose solution and added a layer of oil. The rest of the apparatus was set up as shown in Fig. 2.1.

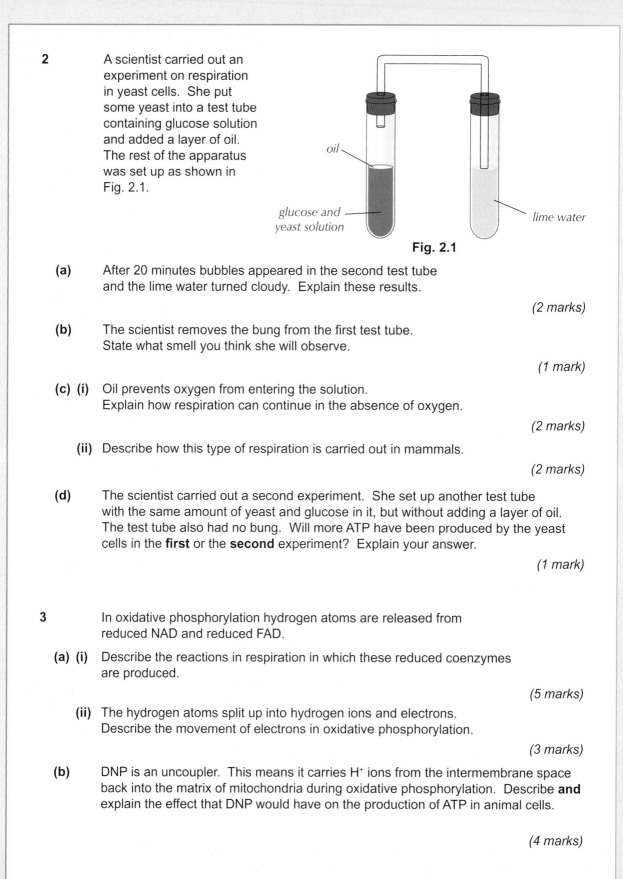

Fig. 2.1

(a)　After 20 minutes bubbles appeared in the second test tube and the lime water turned cloudy. Explain these results.

(2 marks)

(b)　The scientist removes the bung from the first test tube. State what smell you think she will observe.

(1 mark)

(c) (i)　Oil prevents oxygen from entering the solution. Explain how respiration can continue in the absence of oxygen.

(2 marks)

　　(ii)　Describe how this type of respiration is carried out in mammals.

(2 marks)

(d)　The scientist carried out a second experiment. She set up another test tube with the same amount of yeast and glucose in it, but without adding a layer of oil. The test tube also had no bung. Will more ATP have been produced by the yeast cells in the **first** or the **second** experiment? Explain your answer.

(1 mark)

3　In oxidative phosphorylation hydrogen atoms are released from reduced NAD and reduced FAD.

(a) (i)　Describe the reactions in respiration in which these reduced coenzymes are produced.

(5 marks)

　　(ii)　The hydrogen atoms split up into hydrogen ions and electrons. Describe the movement of electrons in oxidative phosphorylation.

(3 marks)

(b)　DNP is an uncoupler. This means it carries H^+ ions from the intermembrane space back into the matrix of mitochondria during oxidative phosphorylation. Describe **and** explain the effect that DNP would have on the production of ATP in animal cells.

(4 marks)

1. DNA, RNA and Protein Synthesis

You learnt about DNA, RNA and protein synthesis at AS, but you need to cover them again for A2. There's a bit more to get your head around this time though...

Learning Objectives:

- Know that genes code for polypeptides, including enzymes.
- Be able to explain the meaning of the term 'genetic code'.
- Be able to describe, with the aid of diagrams, the way in which a nucleotide sequence codes for the amino acid sequence in a polypeptide.
- Be able to describe the roles of messenger RNA and transfer RNA.

Specification Reference 5.1.1

DNA structure

Remember, DNA is a double-helix — it's formed from two separate strands which are coiled around each other to form a spiral (see Figure 1). The strands are polynucleotides. They're made up of lots of nucleotides joined together in a long chain.

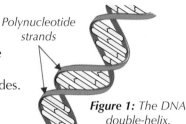

Polynucleotide strands

Figure 1: *The DNA double-helix.*

Nucleotide structure

Each nucleotide is made from a phosphate group, a pentose sugar (with 5 carbon atoms) and a nitrogenous base — see Figure 2.

The sugar in DNA nucleotides is a deoxyribose sugar. Each nucleotide has the same sugar and phosphate. The base on each nucleotide can vary though. There are four possible bases — adenine (A), thymine (T), cytosine (C) and guanine (G).

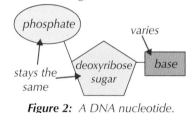

phosphate

stays the same

deoxyribose sugar

base

varies

Figure 2: *A DNA nucleotide.*

> **Tip:** Make sure you're familiar with the structure of DNA. It'll help you understand the rest of this section.

Polynucleotide strands

Many nucleotides join together to form the polynucleotide strands. The nucleotides join up between the phosphate group of one nucleotide and the sugar of another, creating a sugar-phosphate backbone (see Figure 3).

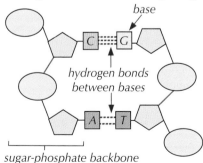

base

hydrogen bonds between bases

sugar-phosphate backbone

Figure 3: *A section of a DNA molecule.*

Complementary base pairing

Two DNA polynucleotide strands join together by hydrogen bonds between the bases. Each base can only join with one particular partner — this is called complementary base pairing. Adenine always pairs with thymine (A - T) and guanine always pairs with cytosine (G - C) — see Figure 3.

> **Tip:** You might remember from AS that adenine and guanine are purine bases, whereas cytosine and thymine are pyrimidine bases. Purines always pair with pyrimidines.

Genes

Genes are sections of DNA. They're found on chromosomes. Genes code for proteins (polypeptides), including enzymes — they contain the instructions to make them.

Proteins are made from amino acids. Different proteins have a different number and order of amino acids. It's the order of bases in a gene that determines the order of amino acids in a particular protein. Each amino acid is coded for by a sequence of three bases (called a **triplet** or a **codon**) in a gene. Different sequences of bases code for different amino acids — this is the **genetic code**.

┌─ Examples ─────────────────────────────

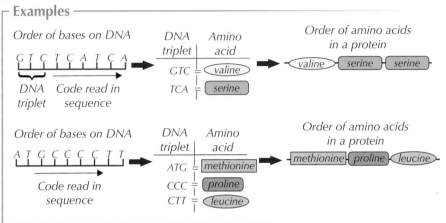

└──

Some amino acids are coded for by more than one triplet.

┌─ Examples ─────────────────────────────
The amino acid proline (often shortened to 'Pro') can be coded for by four different base triplets: CCT, CCC, CCA, and CCG. Glutamine (Gln) can be coded for by two different triplets: CAA and CAG.
└──

Tip: There are 64 triplets, but only 20 amino acids — which is why most triplets code for more than one amino acid.

Other triplets are used to tell the cell when to start and stop production of the protein — these are called **start** and **stop codons**. They're found at the beginning and end of the gene.

┌─ Examples ─────────────────────────────
AUG is a start codon, which also codes for the amino acid methionine.
TAG is a stop codon. It doesn't code for an amino acid.
└──

Tip: Stop codons are also called stop signals.

Tip: Stop codons don't code for an amino acid — this is what stops the production of the protein.

RNA and protein synthesis

DNA molecules are found in the nucleus of the cell, but the organelles for protein synthesis (ribosomes) are found in the cytoplasm. DNA is too large to move out of the nucleus, so a section is copied into RNA. This process is called **transcription**.

RNA is a single polynucleotide strand — it contains the sugar ribose, and uracil (U) replaces thymine as a base. Uracil always pairs with adenine during protein synthesis. The RNA leaves the nucleus and joins with a ribosome in the cytoplasm, where it can be used to synthesise a protein. This process is called **translation**. Figure 4 summarises this.

Tip: There's more on transcription and translation on pages 98-100.

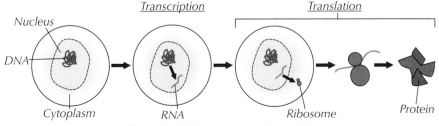

Figure 4: Making a protein from DNA.

RNA

There are two types of RNA you need to know about:

Messenger RNA (mRNA)

mRNA is a single polynucleotide strand (see Figure 5). It's made in the nucleus during transcription. mRNA carries the genetic code from the DNA in the nucleus to the cytoplasm, where it's used to make a protein during translation. In mRNA, groups of three adjacent bases are usually called **codons**.

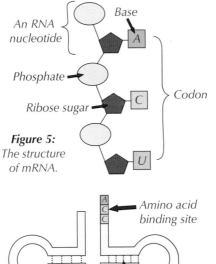

Figure 5:
*The structure
of mRNA.*

Tip: mRNA is copied from DNA — so its sequence is complementary to the DNA sequence. See next page for more.

Transfer RNA (tRNA)

tRNA is a single polynucleotide strand that's folded into a clover shape (see Figure 6). Hydrogen bonds between specific base pairs hold the molecule in this shape. Every tRNA molecule has a specific sequence of three bases at one end called an **anticodon**. They also have an amino acid binding site at the other end. tRNA is found in the cytoplasm where it's involved in translation. It carries the amino acids that are used to make proteins to the ribosomes.

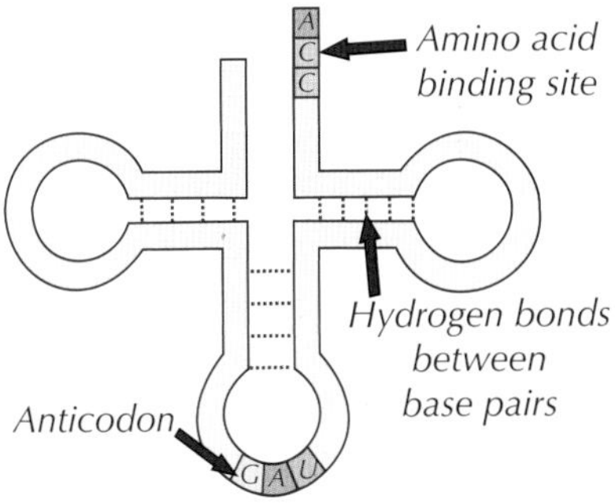

Figure 6: *The structure of tRNA.*

Tip: Codons and anticodons are sometimes referred to as triplets.

Tip: Transfer RNA is so called because it transfers amino acids to the ribosomes. There's more about this on page 99.

Practice Questions — Application

The table below shows six amino acids and some of the triplets that code for them:

Amino Acid:	His	Arg	Gly	Tyr	Cys	Asp
DNA triplet:	CAT/ CAC	AGA/ AGG	GGC/ GGT	TAC/ TAT	TGC/ TGT	GAC/ GAT

Q1 Use the table to determine the amino acid sequence coded for by the following DNA sequences:
   a) CATTACTACAGAGGCTGCCATAGAGGC
   b) AGGTACGACGACTGTCACGGTTATCAC

Q2 Use the table to determine a DNA sequence that could code for the following amino acid sequence:
   Asp - Tyr - Cys - Arg - Arg - Gly - Cys - Gly - Tyr - His - Gly - Asp

Exam Tip
You won't always get information about DNA triplets and amino acids presented in a table like this in the exam, e.g. it could be in the form of a graph or diagram. Don't let that throw you though. The trick is to read the question carefully, then apply what you know.

Practice Questions — Fact Recall

Q1 a) What is a DNA triplet? b) Describe the function of DNA triplets.
Q2 What is the genetic code?
Q3 Name the molecule responsible for:
   a) carrying the genetic code from the nucleus to the cytoplasm.
   b) carrying the amino acids used to make proteins to the ribosomes.

Learning Objective:

- Be able to describe, with the aid of diagrams, how the sequence of nucleotides within a gene is used to construct a polypeptide, including the roles of messenger RNA, transfer RNA and ribosomes.

Specification Reference 5.1.1

2. Transcription and Translation

Proteins are synthesised (made) using the instructions in DNA.
Protein synthesis involves two main stages: transcription and translation.

Transcription

Transcription is the first stage of protein synthesis. During transcription an mRNA copy of a gene (a section of DNA) is made in the nucleus. Here's how:

1. RNA polymerase attaches to the DNA

Transcription starts when **RNA polymerase** (an enzyme) attaches to the DNA double helix at the beginning of a gene.
The hydrogen bonds between the two DNA strands in the gene break, separating the strands, and the DNA molecule uncoils at that point. One of the strands is then used as a template to make an mRNA copy — see Figure 1.

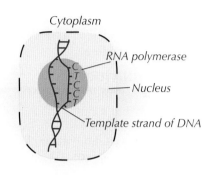

Figure 1: RNA polymerase attaches to the DNA double helix.

Tip: When RNA polymerase attaches to the DNA double helix, it binds to a specific DNA sequence called a <u>promoter</u> (see page 101). There's a promoter near the beginning of each gene.

2. Complementary mRNA is formed

The RNA polymerase lines up free RNA nucleotides alongside the template strand. Complementary base pairing means that the mRNA strand ends up being a complementary copy of the DNA template strand (except the base T is replaced by U in RNA). Once the RNA nucleotides have paired up with their specific bases on the DNA strand they're joined together, forming an mRNA molecule — see Figure 2.

Tip: The DNA template strand is also called the antisense strand.

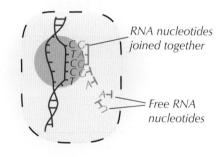

Figure 2: A complementary mRNA molecule starts to form.

Tip: Free RNA nucleotides aren't bound to anything in the nucleus — they're just floating freely.

3. RNA polymerase moves down the DNA strand

The RNA polymerase moves along the DNA, separating the strands and assembling the mRNA strand. The hydrogen bonds between the uncoiled strands of DNA re-form once the RNA polymerase has passed by and the strands coil back into a double helix — see Figure 3.

Tip: It's easy to remember that <u>RNA</u> polymerase is involved in the making of <u>mRNA</u>. Don't confuse it with DNA polymerase, which is involved in the making of DNA (see p. 168).

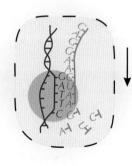

Figure 3: RNA polymerase moves down the DNA strand.

4. mRNA leaves the nucleus

When RNA polymerase reaches a particular sequence of DNA called a **stop codon**, it stops making mRNA and detaches from the DNA. The mRNA moves out of the nucleus through a nuclear pore and attaches to a ribosome in the cytoplasm, where the next stage of protein synthesis takes place (see below).

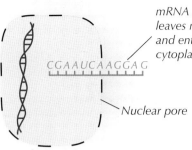

mRNA strand leaves nucleus and enters the cytoplasm

CGAAUCAAGGAG

Nuclear pore

Figure 4: *mRNA leaves the nucleus.*

Tip: Stop codons are particular DNA triplets, see page 96 for more.

Practice Question — Application

Q1 α–amanitin is a deadly toxin produced by some mushrooms. It works by inhibiting RNA polymerase. What effect will this have on protein synthesis? Explain your answer.

Translation

Translation is the second stage of protein synthesis. It takes place at the ribosomes in the cytoplasm. During translation, amino acids are joined together by a ribosome to make a polypeptide chain (protein), following the sequence of codons carried by the mRNA. Here's how it works:

The mRNA attaches itself to a ribosome and transfer RNA (tRNA) molecules carry amino acids to the ribosome.

Tip: See page 97 for more on the structures of mRNA and tRNA.

tRNA carrying an amino acid

amino acid

C A C

A U G A U U A G C C U A

mRNA

Ribosome

A tRNA molecule, with an anticodon that's complementary to the first codon on the mRNA, attaches itself to the mRNA by complementary base pairing. A second tRNA molecule attaches itself to the next codon on the mRNA in the same way.

Figure 5: *mRNA (turquoise) attached to a bacterial ribosome.*

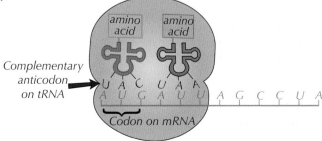

Complementary anticodon on tRNA

amino acid   amino acid

U A C   U A A

A U G A U U   A G C C U A

Codon on mRNA

Tip: Ribosomes are actually complexes made up of rRNA (ribosomal RNA) and loads of different proteins.

The two amino acids attached to the tRNA molecules are joined by a peptide bond. The first tRNA molecule moves away, leaving its amino acid behind.

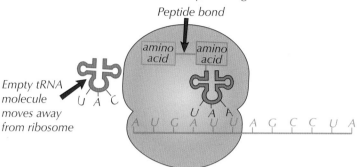

Tip: Once the amino acids are lined up in the correct order, the ribosome joins them together.

A third tRNA molecule binds to the next codon on the mRNA. Its amino acid binds to the first two and the second tRNA molecule moves away. This process continues, producing a chain of linked amino acids (a polypeptide chain), until there's a stop codon on the mRNA molecule.

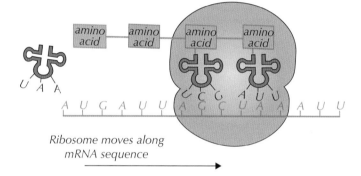

Ribosome moves along mRNA sequence

Tip: Protein synthesis happens this way in all eukaryotic cells (e.g. plants, animals and fungi). It's a bit different in prokaryotes (bacteria).

The polypeptide chain (protein) then moves away from the ribosome and translation is complete.

Tip: Protein synthesis is also called polypeptide synthesis as it makes a polypeptide (protein).

Tip: A mutation is any change to the DNA base sequence. See page 106 for more.

Practice Questions — Application

Q1 Diamond-Blackfan anaemia is an inherited condition caused by one of several gene mutations. The mutations can affect the function of the proteins that make up ribosomes. What effect could this have on protein synthesis? Explain your answer.

Q2 An error occurs during transcription that accidentally inserts a stop codon into the middle of an mRNA sequence. What effect could this have on the protein that is eventually produced? Explain your answer.

Practice Questions — Fact Recall

Q1 What is RNA polymerase? Describe its role in protein synthesis.

Q2 Describe the function of a ribosome.

Q3 a) Explain how tRNA molecules pair up with mRNA.

  b) During which stage of protein synthesis does this happen?

3. Control of Protein Synthesis and Protein Activation

Protein synthesis and protein activation are both tightly controlled. When you think about it, they need to be — proteins are responsible for everything from the structure of a cell (as structural proteins), to cell signalling (as hormones) and the regulation of cellular reactions (as enzymes).

Learning Objectives:
- Be able to explain genetic control of protein production in a prokaryote using the *lac* operon.
- Know that cyclic AMP activates proteins by altering their three-dimensional structure.

Specification Reference 5.1.1

How is protein synthesis controlled?

Protein synthesis can be controlled at the genetic level by starting or stopping the transcription of genes. Not all genes are transcribed in all cells or at all times. Genes that aren't being transcribed are said to be **switched off**. The proteins they code for aren't produced. Genes that are being transcribed are said to be **switched on**.

Tip: Transcription is covered on pages 98-99.

Operons

Genetic control of protein production in prokaryotes (e.g. bacteria) often involves operons. An operon is a section of DNA that contains **structural genes**, **control elements** and sometimes a **regulatory gene** — see Figure 1.

The structural genes code for useful proteins, such as enzymes — they're all transcribed together. The control elements include a **promoter** (a DNA sequence located before the structural genes that RNA polymerase binds to) and an **operator** (a DNA sequence that proteins called transcription factors bind to). The regulatory gene codes for a **transcription factor** (see below).

Exam Tip
Make sure you know the differences between structural genes, control elements and regulatory genes — you could be asked to explain them in the exam.

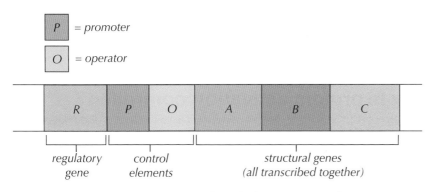

P = promoter

O = operator

R	P	O	A	B	C

regulatory gene   control elements   structural genes (all transcribed together)

Figure 1: *Diagram to show the basic structure of a prokaryotic operon.*

Transcription factors

A transcription factor is a protein that binds to DNA and switches genes on or off by starting or stopping transcription. Factors that start transcription are called **activators** and those that stop transcription are called **repressors**.

The shape of a transcription factor determines whether it can bind to DNA or not, and can be altered by the binding of some molecules, e.g. hormones and sugars. This means the amount of some molecules in an environment or a cell can control the synthesis of some proteins by affecting transcription factor binding.

Tip: It's easy to remember what activators and repressors do — it's all in the name. Activators <u>activate</u> transcription and repressors <u>repress</u> transcription.

Tip: By binding
to the operator, the
lac repressor blocks
RNA polymerase
from binding to the
promoter and beginning
transcription.

Figure 2: *Molecular model
of the lac repressor (pink)
binding to DNA.*

Example — the *lac* operon in *E. coli*

E. coli is a bacterium that respires glucose, but it can use lactose if
glucose isn't available. The genes that produce the enzymes needed to
respire lactose are found on an operon called the *lac* operon. The *lac*
operon has a regulatory gene (lacI) and three structural genes — lacZ,
lacY and lacA. The structural genes produce proteins that help the
bacteria digest lactose (including β-**galactosidase** and **lactose permease**).
Here's how it works:

Lactose NOT present
The regulatory gene (lacI) produces the lac repressor, which binds to the
operator site when there's no lactose present and blocks transcription.

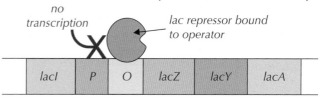

lacZ, lacY and lacA aren't transcribed

Lactose present
When lactose is present, it binds to the repressor, changing the repressor's
shape so that it can no longer bind to the operator site. RNA polymerase
can now begin transcription of the structural genes.

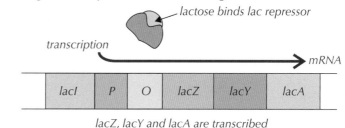

lacZ, lacY and lacA are transcribed

How is protein activation controlled?

Some proteins produced by protein synthesis aren't active — they have to be
activated to work. Like protein synthesis, protein activation is also controlled
by molecules, e.g. hormones and sugars.

cAMP

Some molecules that control protein activation work by binding to cell
membranes and triggering the production of cyclic AMP (cAMP) inside the
cell. cAMP then activates proteins inside the cell by altering their three-
dimensional (3D) structure. For example, altering the 3D structure can change
the active site of an enzyme, making it active or inactive.

Tip: The control
molecules (e.g.
hormones) bind
to specific protein
receptors in the cell
membrane.

Tip: cAMP is a
secondary messenger
— it relays the message
from the control
molecule to the inside of
the cell (see page 23).

Example — activation of protein kinase A (PKA) by cAMP

PKA is an enzyme made of four
subunits. When cAMP isn't bound,
the four units are bound together
and are inactive. When cAMP
binds, it causes a change in the
enzyme's 3D structure, releasing the
active subunits — PKA is now active.

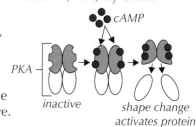

Practice Questions — Application

In the presence of lactose, normal *E. coli* produce the enzyme β-galactosidase, which is coded for by a structural gene on the *lac* operon. In the absence of lactose, β-galactosidase is not produced.

An experiment was carried out in which different *E. coli* mutants were isolated and grown in media containing either lactose or glucose. The mutants had mutations (changes in their DNA base sequence), which meant they behaved differently to normal *E. coli*.

To detect whether the bacteria produced working β-galactosidase, a chemical that turns yellow in the presence of active β-galactosidase was added to the medium. The bacteria were left for some time, after which the colour was recorded and the production of mRNA (that codes for β-galactosidase) was measured. The results are shown in the table below.

Tip: There's more on mutations on p. 106.

Medium	Mutant	mRNA	Colour
Glucose	Normal	No	No yellow
Lactose	Normal	Yes	Yellow
Glucose	Mutant 1	Yes	Yellow
Lactose	Mutant 1	Yes	Yellow
Glucose	Mutant 2	No	No yellow
Lactose	Mutant 2	Yes	No yellow

Q1 Suggest three variables that should have been controlled in this experiment.

Q2 Explain why normal *E. coli* bacteria were included in this test.

Q3 Describe and suggest an explanation for:

　　a)　the Mutant 1 results,

　　b)　the Mutant 2 results.

Q4 How could the scientists carrying out this experiment make sure that their results are reliable?

Tip: There's more on controlling variables on page 3 of How Science Works.

Practice Questions — Fact Recall

Q1 How is protein synthesis controlled at the genetic level?

Q2 Describe the function of the following parts of an operon:

　　a)　structural genes,

　　b)　control elements,

　　c)　a regulatory gene.

Q3 State the two types of transcription factor and explain how they work.

Q4 Describe how the *lac* operon controls protein production in *E. coli*.

Q5 Describe the way in which molecules like hormones can control protein activation.

Learning Objectives:

- Be able to explain that the genes that control development of body plans are similar in plants, animals and fungi, with reference to homeobox sequences.

- Be able to outline how apoptosis (programmed cell death) can act as a mechanism to change body plans.

Specification Reference 5.1.1

Tip: *Drosophila* are 'model organisms' — scientists use them to study how genes control development, then apply their findings to other, more complex animals (like humans). *Drosophila* make great model organisms because they're easy to keep and breed, and have a short life cycle.

Figure 2: *A mutation in a homeotic gene has caused this* Drosophila *to grow legs in place of antennae. This shows that homeotic genes are important in development.*

4. Body Plans

The development of an organism follows a careful plan, controlled by proteins. Some of these proteins activate (start) or repress (stop) transcription of developmental genes. Other proteins cause unneeded cells to break down and die.

Body plans and homeotic genes

A body plan is the general structure of an organism.

┌─ **Example** ─────────────────────────────────────

The *Drosophila* fruit fly has various body parts (head, abdomen, etc.) that are arranged in a particular way — this is its body plan.

Proteins control the development of a body plan — they help set up the basic body plan so that everything is in the right place, e.g. legs grow where legs should grow. The proteins that control body plan development are coded for by genes called **homeotic genes**.

┌─ **Example** ─────────────────────────────────────

Two homeotic gene clusters control the development of the *Drosophila* body plan — one controls the development of the head and anterior thorax (yellow in Figure 1) and the other controls the development of the posterior thorax and abdomen (red in Figure 1).

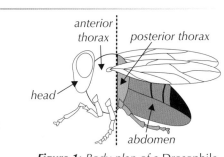

Figure 1: *Body plan of a* Drosophila.

Similar homeotic genes are found in animals, plants and fungi, which means that body plan development is controlled in a similar way in flies, mice, humans, etc.

How do homeotic genes control development?

Homeotic genes have regions called **homeobox sequences** that code for a part of the protein called the **homeodomain**. The homeodomain binds to specific sites on DNA, enabling the protein to work as a transcription factor (see page 101). The proteins bind to DNA at the start of developmental genes, activating or repressing transcription and so altering the production of proteins involved in the development of the body plan (see Figure 3).

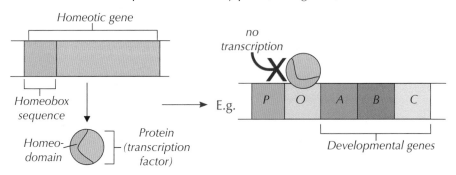

Figure 3: *Diagram to show how a transcription factor coded for by a homeotic gene may repress the transcription of developmental genes.*

Programmed cell death

Some cells die and break down as a normal part of development. This is a highly controlled process called **apoptosis**, or programmed cell death. Once apoptosis has been triggered the cell is broken down in a series of steps. These steps are shown in Figure 5.

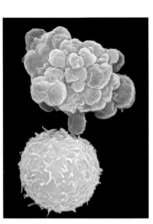

Figure 4: A normal white blood cell (bottom) and one undergoing apoptosis (top). The cell membrane of the apoptotic cell has formed blebs (round blobs).

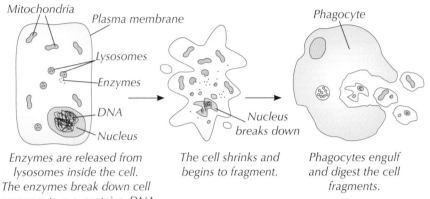

Enzymes are released from lysosomes inside the cell. The enzymes break down cell components, e.g. proteins, DNA.

The cell shrinks and begins to fragment.

Phagocytes engulf and digest the cell fragments.

Figure 5: The main steps in apoptosis.

The role of programmed cell death in development

Apoptosis is in involved the development of body plans — mitosis and differentiation create the bulk of the body parts and then apoptosis refines the parts by removing the unwanted structures.

Examples

- When hands and feet first develop the digits (fingers and toes) are connected. They're only separated when cells in the connecting tissue undergo apoptosis.
- As tadpoles develop into frogs their tail cells are removed by apoptosis.
- An excess of nerve cells are produced during the development of the nervous system. Nerve cells that aren't needed undergo apoptosis.

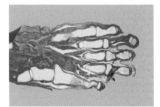

Figure 6: Light micrograph of a developing human hand. You can still see the connective tissue between the fingers that would eventually undergo apoptosis.

All cells contain genes that code for proteins that promote or inhibit apoptosis. During development, genes that control apoptosis are switched on and off in appropriate cells, so that some die and the correct body plan develops.

Figure 7: A developing tadpole. The tail will be lost as the cells undergo apoptosis.

Practice Questions — Fact Recall

Q1 What is a body plan?

Q2 Name the genes that control the development of a body plan.

Q3 Explain why development of body plans is similar in animals, plants and fungi.

Q4 Describe how the genes you named in Q2 control the development of a body plan.

Q5 a) Outline the process of apoptosis.

   b) Explain how apoptosis is involved in the development of body plans.

- Know that mutations cause changes to the sequence of nucleotides in DNA molecules.

- Be able to explain how mutations can have beneficial, neutral or harmful effects on the way a protein functions.

Specification Reference 5.1.1

5. Gene Mutations

Genes are pretty awesome. However, their base sequences can sometimes be mutated, changing the protein that gets produced.

What are mutations?

Any change to the base (nucleotide) sequence of DNA is called a **mutation**. The types of mutations that can occur include:

- **Substitution** — one base is swapped for another base, e.g. ATGCCT becomes ATTCCT (G is swapped for T).

- **Deletion** — one or more bases are removed, e.g. ATGCCT becomes ATCCT (G is removed).

- **Insertion** — one or more bases are added, e.g. ATGCCT becomes ATGACCT (A is added).

- **Duplication** — one or more bases are repeated, e.g. ATGCCT becomes ATGCCCCT (CC is repeated).

- **Inversion** — a sequence of bases is reversed, e.g. ATGCCT becomes ATCCGT (GCC is reversed to CCG).

The order of DNA bases in a gene determines the order of amino acids in a particular protein. If a mutation occurs in a gene, the primary structure (amino acid chain) of the protein it codes for could be altered.

Tip: Mutations can occur spontaneously (e.g. through errors in DNA replication), but exposure to mutagenic agents (e.g. UV light, ionising radiation and certain chemicals) may increase the rate at which mutations occur.

┌─ Example ──────────────────────────────

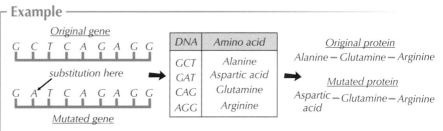

A change in the primary structure may change the final 3D shape of the protein so it doesn't work properly, e.g. active sites in enzymes may not form properly, meaning that substrates can't bind to them.

Tip: For a protein with a single polypeptide chain, the final 3D shape is called the tertiary structure.

Frameshift mutations

Some mutations have a huge effect on the base sequence of a gene. For example, adding or deleting a base changes the number of bases present, causing a shift in all the base triplets that follow. This is called a frameshift mutation — when an insertion or deletion changes the way the rest of the base sequence is read. The earlier a frameshift mutation appears in the base sequence, the more amino acids are affected and the greater the mutation's effect on the protein.

Tip: If the number of bases added or removed is a multiple of three, it won't cause a frameshift mutation because the triplets that follow the mutation will still be read correctly. So a deletion of three bases might actually affect a protein less seriously than the deletion of one base.

┌─ Examples ──────────────────────────────

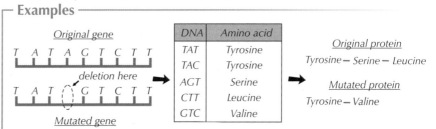

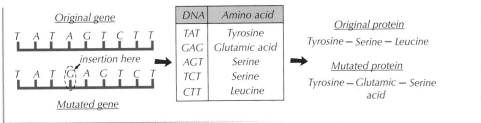

Exam Tip
You could be asked to predict how much a mutation will affect a protein's structure. Just remember that a frameshift mutation affects more amino acids than a substitution mutation, so it will have a bigger overall effect on the protein's structure.

Mutations that don't affect an organism

Different mutations affect proteins in different ways. Some mutations can have a neutral effect on a protein's function. They may have a neutral effect because:

- The mutation changes a base in a triplet, but the amino acid that the triplet codes for doesn't change. This happens because some amino acids are coded for by more than one triplet.

Example

Both TAT and TAC code for tyrosine, so if TAT is changed to TAC the amino acid won't change.

- The mutation produces a triplet that codes for a different amino acid, but the amino acid is chemically similar to the original so it functions like the original amino acid.

Example

Arginine (AGG) and lysine (AAG) are coded for by similar triplets — a substitution mutation can swap the amino acids. But this mutation would have a neutral effect on a protein as the amino acids are chemically similar.

- The mutated triplet codes for an amino acid not involved with the protein's function.

Example

If the affected amino acid is located far away from an enzyme's active site, the protein will work as it normally does.

A neutral effect on protein function won't affect an organism overall.

Tip: A substitution mutation is more likely to have a neutral effect on a protein than a frameshift mutation because it only affects one amino acid.

Mutations that do affect an organism

Some mutations do affect a protein's function — they can make a protein more or less active, e.g. by changing the shape of an enzyme's active site. If protein function is affected it can have a beneficial or harmful effect on the whole organism.

Mutations with beneficial effects

These have an advantageous effect on an organism, i.e. they increase its chance of survival.

Example

Some bacterial enzymes break down certain antibiotics. Mutations in the genes that code for these enzymes could make them work on a wider range of antibiotics. This is beneficial to the bacteria because antibiotic resistance can help them to survive.

Tip: Just to confuse things, some mutations alter a protein's function, but the effect is neither harmful nor beneficial to the whole organism. This means that the mutation doesn't affect the organism's chances of survival.

Mutations that are beneficial to the organism are passed on to future generations by the process of natural selection (see p. 138).

Mutations with harmful effects

These have a disadvantageous effect on an organism, i.e. they decrease its chance of survival.

> **Examples**
>
> - Cystic fibrosis (CF) can be caused by a deletion of three bases in the gene that codes for the CFTR (cystic fibrosis transmembrane conductance regulator) protein. The mutated CFTR protein folds incorrectly, so it's broken down. This leads to excess mucus production, which affects the lungs of CF sufferers.
> - Certain mutations in the BRCA1 gene can increase the risk of developing breast cancer. BRCA1 produces a protein that helps to repair breaks in DNA. But mutations in the BRCA1 gene itself can result in a very short protein that can't do its job. This may lead to uncontrolled cell division and the development of cancer.

Practice Questions — Application

The table below shows some amino acids and the base triplets that code for them. The following letters represent part of the DNA base sequence of a gene:

CTTCATGATACA

Look at the four mutated base sequences below.

Mutation A: CTCCATGATACA

Mutation B: CTTCATCATACA

Mutation C: CTTATGATACA

Mutation D: CTTCTTCATGATACA

Base Triplet(s)	Amino Acid
GAT	Asp
CAT	His
ATA	Ile
CTT/CTC	Leu
ATG	Met
ACA	Thr
TAT	Tyr

Q1 For each of the base sequences:

   a) State the type of mutation that has taken place.

   b) Give the amino acid sequence coded for by the mutated gene.

Q2 Explain which mutation is likely to have:

   a) the least serious effect on the structure of the protein produced,

   b) the most serious effect on the structure of the protein produced.

Practice Questions — Fact Recall

Q1 What is a mutation?

Q2 Give three ways in which a mutation may have a neutral effect on the protein produced by a gene.

Q3 Explain how a mutation may be:

   a) beneficial to an organism,

   b) harmful to an organism.

Exam Tip
If you're asked how a mutation affects protein structure in the exam, don't fall into the trap of only writing about how the mutation will change the base sequence. Make sure you make it clear how the altered base sequence will affect both the amino acid sequence and the protein's structure.

Section Summary

Make sure you know...

- That genes are sections of DNA that code for polypeptides (proteins), including enzymes.
- That the order of bases in a gene determines the order of amino acids in a particular protein.
- That each amino acid is coded for by a sequence of three bases called a triplet or a codon.
- That the sequence of bases which codes for amino acids is the genetic code.
- That transcription is the first stage of protein synthesis and involves the production of an mRNA copy of a gene in the nucleus.
- That during transcription the enzyme RNA polymerase attaches to the DNA double helix and the two DNA strands separate. RNA polymerase then lines up free RNA nucleotides alongside the DNA template strand and assembles the mRNA strand.
- That, once made, the mRNA leaves the nucleus and carries the genetic code to the ribosomes in the cytoplasm.
- That translation is the second stage of protein synthesis in which amino acids are joined together by ribosomes to make a polypeptide strand (protein) based on the order of codons in mRNA.
- That tRNA molecules carry amino acids to the ribosomes during translation.
- That protein synthesis can be controlled at the genetic level by starting or stopping transcription.
- That genetic control of protein production in prokaryotes (e.g. bacteria) often involves operons (sections of DNA that contain structural genes, control elements and sometimes a regulatory gene).
- How the *lac* operon in *E. coli* controls the production of the enzymes needed to respire lactose — the genes that code for the enzymes are only switched on (transcribed) in the presence of lactose.
- That some proteins need to be activated by cyclic AMP (cAMP) before they can work and that cAMP does this by altering their 3D structure.
- That a body plan is the general structure of an organism.
- That the development of the body plan in animals, plant and fungi is controlled in a similar way, by a similar group of genes called homeotic genes.
- How homeotic genes and the homeobox sequences they contain control the development of body plans by regulating transcription.
- How apoptosis (programmed cell death) can act as a mechanism to change body plans by removing unwanted structures.
- That mutations are changes to the base (nucleotide) sequence of DNA and that they can affect protein function by altering the amino acid sequence (primary structure).
- How mutations can have neutral, beneficial or harmful effects on an organism.

Exam-style Questions

1 Researchers have been studying a genetic disease with the aim of developing a treatment for it. The genetic disease is caused by the production of a specific enzyme.

(a) Part of the DNA sequence for the enzyme is shown in Fig. 1.1.

T	C	G	C	C	A	A	C	A	A	C	A	C	T	C

Fig. 1.1

State the complementary **mRNA** sequence to Fig. 1.1 **and** how many amino acids this DNA would sequence code for. (Assume there are no start or stop codons present).

(2 marks)

The researchers are exploring a possible treatment for the genetic disease that would involve disrupting the process of **translation**.

(b) (i) Name the organelle that mRNA attaches to for translation to take place.

(1 mark)

(ii) Once mRNA has attached to this organelle, translation begins.
Describe the process of translation from this point, including the role of **tRNA**.

In your answer, you should make the role of tRNA in translation clear.

(8 marks)

2 Glucagon is a hormone involved in the regulation of the blood glucose level in humans. It controls protein activation in a cell via the second messenger, cAMP.

(a) Glucagon is a protein.
How is the order of amino acids in glucagon determined?

(1 mark)

(b) Suggest how glucagon could control the activation of a protein via cAMP.

(3 marks)

(c) cAMP is also involved in the regulation of the *lac* operon in *E.coli*.

(i) Explain what is meant by the term 'operon'.

(2 marks)

(ii) When the concentration of glucose is low, cAMP activates the protein CRP. CRP helps RNA polymerase bind to the promoter at the start of the operon.

Explain how this helps *E. coli* to continue respiring when the concentration of glucose is low, but lactose is present.

(3 marks)

3   A mutation in the APC gene is found in the majority of colon cancers.
The mutation prevents the protein produced from carrying out its function.

(a) (i) Mutations that result in a non-functioning APC protein are usually caused by
base deletions.
Explain how the deletion of a single base could result in a non-functioning protein.

(3 marks)

(ii) Explain why a single-base **substitution** in a gene may have a less serious
effect on the gene's protein structure than a single-base deletion.

(2 marks)

(iii) Mutations in the APC gene that lead to the development of colon cancer
have a harmful effect on a person. Explain how other mutations may have
a **neutral effect** on an organism.

(4 marks)

(b)   During protein synthesis the APC gene must be **transcribed** into mRNA.
(i) Name the eukaryotic organelle where transcription takes place.

(1 mark)

(ii) Describe the process of transcription in detail.

In your answer, you should make the sequence of steps in transcription clear.

(7 marks)

4   Several studies have been carried out into the development of the plant,
Arabidopsis thaliana.

(a)   It has been found that a change to the base sequence of the ag-1 gene affects
flower development in *Arabidopsis thaliana* — the change causes petals to grow in
place of stamens (the long, thin structures that produce pollen).

(i) Using the information given above, explain why ag-1 is a classed as a
homeotic gene.

(2 marks)

(ii) Ag-1 contains a **homeobox sequence**. Explain how a homeobox sequence
helps to control an organism's development.

(4 marks)

(b)   Explain why studying *Arabidopsis thaliana* could help scientists to understand
development in a wide range of organisms, not just plants.

(2 marks)

(c)   It is thought that the process of **programmed cell death** may also play a role in
plant development.
(i) State what is meant by the term 'programmed cell death'.

(1 mark)

(ii) Suggest how programmed cell death may affect plant development.

(2 marks)

Learning Objectives:

- Describe, with the aid of diagrams and photographs, the behaviour of chromosomes during meiosis, and the associated behaviour of the nuclear envelope, cell membrane and centrioles. (Names of the main stages are expected.)

- Be able to explain the terms 'crossing-over' and 'linkage'.

- Be able to explain how meiosis and fertilisation can lead to variation through the independent assortment of alleles.

Specification Reference 5.1.2

1. Meiosis

Most cells in the body contain exactly the same genetic information. The one major exception to this rule are the gametes — the cells involved in sexual reproduction.

Gametes and fertilisation

Gametes are the sperm cells in males and egg cells in females. In sexual reproduction two gametes join together at fertilisation to form a **zygote**, which divides and develops into a new organism.

Normal body cells have the **diploid** number (2n) of chromosomes — meaning each cell contains two of each chromosome, one from the mum and one from the dad. Gametes have the **haploid** (n) number — there's only one copy of each chromosome. At fertilisation, a haploid sperm fuses with a haploid egg, making a cell with the normal diploid number of chromosomes (2n).

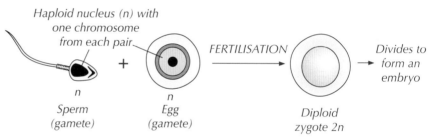

Figure 1: Diagram to show fertilisation.

What is meiosis?

Meiosis is a type of cell division that happens in the reproductive organs to produce gametes. Cells that divide by meiosis are diploid to start with, but the cells that are formed from meiosis are haploid — the chromosome number halves. Cells formed by meiosis are all genetically different because each new cell ends up with a different combination of chromosomes.

Interphase

Before meiosis, interphase happens — the cell's DNA unravels and replicates so there are two copies of each chromosome in each cell.

Tip: You'll have learnt a little bit about meiosis in your AS-Level course, but here it's covered in more detail.

Tip: You've come across interphase before — it also takes place before mitosis, which you learnt about at AS-Level.

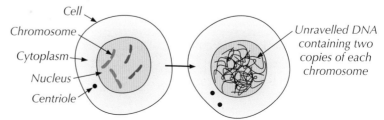

As meiosis begins, the chromosomes are made of two strands joined in the middle by a centromere. The separate strands are identical copies called chromatids. Two strands on the same chromosome are called sister chromatids — see Figure 2.

One chromatid ← ← *Centromere*

← *Sister chromatids*

Figure 2: *The structure of a double-stranded chromosome.*

Meiosis I

After interphase, the cells enter meiosis where they divide twice — the first division is called meiosis I and the second is called meiosis II. There are four similar stages to each division called prophase, metaphase, anaphase and telophase. Here's what happens during each of those stages in meiosis I:

Prophase I

The chromosomes condense, getting shorter and fatter. **Homologous chromosomes** pair up — number 1 with number 1, 2 with 2, 3 with 3 etc. Crossing-over occurs (see next page). Tiny bundles of protein called centrioles start moving to opposite ends of the cell, forming a network of protein fibres across it called the spindle. The nuclear envelope (the membrane around the nucleus) breaks down.

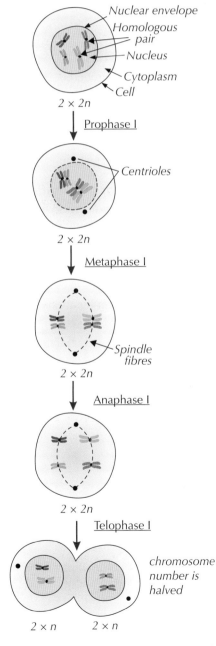

Nuclear envelope
Homologous pair
Nucleus
Cytoplasm
Cell

$2 \times 2n$

Prophase I

Centrioles

$2 \times 2n$

Metaphase I

$2 \times 2n$

Anaphase I

$2 \times 2n$

Telophase I

chromosome number is halved

$2 \times n$ $2 \times n$

Spindle fibres

Metaphase I

The homologous pairs line up across the centre of the cell and attach to the spindle fibres by their centromeres.

Anaphase I

The spindles contract, pulling the pairs apart (one chromosome goes to each end of the cell).

Telophase I

A nuclear envelope forms around each group of chromosomes and the cytoplasm divides so there are now two haploid daughter cells.

Tip: At AS-Level, you'll have learnt what a homologous pair of chromosomes is — it's a matching pair of chromosomes. It's also called a bivalent.

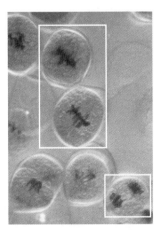

Figure 3: *Light micrograph of cells undergoing meiosis. The highlighted cells in the centre are in metaphase I. The bottom right cell is in anaphase I.*

Tip: We've only shown 4 chromosomes here for simplicity. Humans actually have 46 (23 homologous pairs).

Tip: Unlike in prophase I, there is no pairing up of homologous chromosomes in prophase II. This is because the pairs have already been split up by the end of meiosis I.

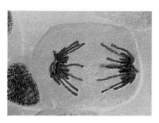

Figure 4: *Chromatids separating during meiosis II.*

Meiosis II

The two daughter cells undergo prophase II, metaphase II, anaphase II and telophase II — which are pretty much the same as the ones in meiosis I except with half the number of chromosomes. In anaphase II, the sister chromatids are separated — each new daughter cell inherits one chromatid from each chromosome. Four haploid daughter cells are produced.

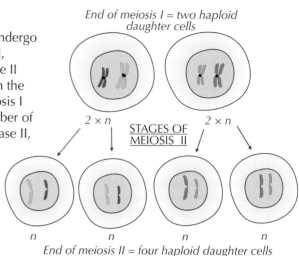

End of meiosis I = two haploid daughter cells

$2 \times n$ $\qquad$ $2 \times n$

STAGES OF MEIOSIS II

n $\qquad$ n $\qquad$ n $\qquad$ n

End of meiosis II = four haploid daughter cells

Genetic variation

Genetic variation is the differences that exist between individuals' genetic material. The reason meiosis is important is that it creates genetic variation — it makes gametes that are all genetically different. Then during fertilisation, any egg can fuse with any sperm, which also creates variation. This means new individuals have a new mixture of alleles, making them genetically unique.

Meiosis creates genetic variation in the following three ways:

1. Crossing-over of chromatids

Tip: Crossing-over is also known as recombination.

During prophase I, homologous chromosomes come together and pair up. In each pair, one chromosome is maternal (from your mum) and one is paternal (from your dad). They have the same genes but different versions of the genes, called alleles. The non-sister chromatids twist around each other and bits of the chromatids swap over (they break off their chromatid and join onto the other chromatid). The chromatids still contain the same genes but now have a different combination of alleles — see Figure 6.

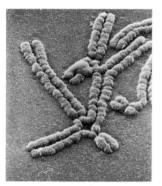

Figure 5: *Electron micrograph showing crossing-over occurring in cells.*

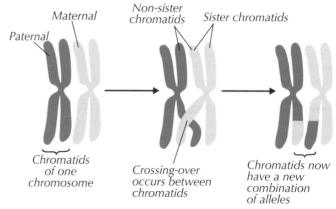

Figure 6: *Crossing-over.*

The crossing-over of chromatids during prophase I means that each of the four daughter cells formed from meiosis contains chromatids with a different combination of alleles.

2. Independent assortment of chromosomes (in metaphase I)

During meiosis I, different combinations of maternal and paternal chromosomes go into each cell (e.g. one cell gets maternal chromosomes 1 and 2 and paternal 3, the other cell gets paternal 1 and 2, and maternal 3). So each cell ends up with a different combination of alleles — see Figure 7. If alleles are on the same chromosome they'll go into the same cell, so are inherited together — this is called **linkage**.

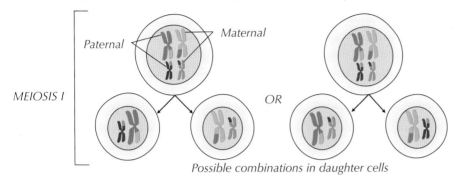

Figure 7: Independent segregation of chromosomes.

Tip: In any species there are 2^n possible combinations of maternal and paternal chromosomes (where n is the number of homologous pairs). This means that in humans (which have 23 homologous pairs) there are 2^{23} or 8388608 possible combinations of chromosomes.

Tip: Crossing-over, plus the independent assortment of chromosomes and chromatids during meiosis, means that gametes end up with a unique assortment of alleles (i.e. all the cells are genetically different).

3. Independent assortment of chromatids (in metaphase II)

During meiosis II, different combinations of chromatids go into each daughter cell. So each cell ends up with a different combination of alleles.

Practice Questions — Application

Q1 For each of the following cells, state which stage of meiosis I or II the cell is in (e.g. prophase I).

a)   b)   c)   d)

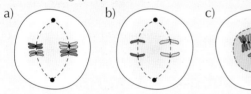

Tip: To answer Q1 you need to look at the number of chromosomes as well as what is happening to them in each cell.

Q2 The diagram to the right shows two homologous chromosomes. The red cross marks a point at which crossing-over can occur. Draw the chromosomes as they would be if crossing-over occurred at this point.

Practice Questions — Fact Recall

Q1 Are the following haploid or diploid:
   a) normal body cells?   b) gametes?   c) zygotes?

Q2 During meiosis I, describe what happens in:
   a) prophase,   b) metaphase,   c) anaphase,   d) telophase.

Q3 Briefly describe what happens during meiosis II.

Q4 a) What are the three main events in meiosis that lead to genetic variation?

   b) Describe how each of these processes works.

Q5 Explain what is meant by the term 'linkage'.

Learning Objective:

- Be able to explain the terms allele, locus, genotype, phenotype, dominant, recessive and codominant.

Specification Reference 5.1.2

2. Genetic Terms

Inheritance is all about how you got the genes you have and how likely you are to pass them on to your children. To help you understand the rest of this section, you really need to get to grips with the basic terms described below.

Basic terms and definitions

Genes and alleles

A **gene** is a sequence of bases on a DNA molecule that codes for a protein (polypeptide) which results in a characteristic.

You can have one or more versions of the same gene. These different versions are called **alleles**. The order of bases in each allele is slightly different — that's because each allele codes for different versions of the same characteristic. Alleles are represented using letters.

Tip: 'Codes for' means 'contains the instructions for'.

Tip: A base is a nitrogen-containing molecule that forms part of a DNA nucleotide.

> **Examples**
>
> - There are many different alleles for eye colour. The allele for brown eyes is shown using a B, and the allele for blue eyes uses b.
> - Pea plants have a gene for seed shape. The allele for a round seed shape is shown using a R, and the allele for wrinkled seed shape uses r.

Most plants and animals, including humans, have two alleles of each gene, one from each parent. That's because we inherit one copy of each chromosome of a pair from our parents. The allele of each gene is found at a fixed position, called a **locus**, on each chromosome in a pair (see Figure 1).

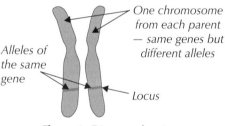

Alleles of the same gene

One chromosome from each parent — same genes but different alleles

Locus

Figure 1: *Diagram showing a locus on a pair of chromosomes.*

Genotype

The genotype of an organism is the alleles it has. This could be a list of all its alleles but usually it's just the alleles for one characteristic at a time.

> **Examples**
>
> - One person may have the genotype BB for eye colour and another person Bb.
> - One pea plant might have the genotype RR for seed shape and another pea plant rr.

Phenotype

The phenotype of an organism is the characteristics the alleles produce.

Tip: The phenotype of an organism can't always be seen. E.g. your metabolic rate (how fast your metabolic reactions are) is a phenotype but you can't see it.

> **Examples**
>
> - One person may have brown eyes and another may have blue eyes.
> - One pea plant may have round seeds and another may have wrinkled seeds.

Homozygous and heterozygous

If an organism carries two copies of the same allele it's said to be homozygous. If an organism carries two different alleles then it's heterozygous.

Dominant and recessive alleles

An allele whose characteristic appears in the phenotype even when there's only one copy is called a dominant allele. Dominant alleles are shown by a capital letter. Recessive alleles are those whose characteristics only appear in the phenotype if two copies are present. They're shown by lower case letters.

Examples

- The allele for brown eyes, B, is dominant, so if a person's genotype is Bb or BB they'll have brown eyes. The allele for blue eyes, b, is recessive, so a person will only have blue eyes if their genotype is bb.
- The allele for round seed shape, R, is dominant, so if a pea plant's genotype is Rr or RR it will have round seeds. The allele for wrinkled seed shape, r, is recessive, so a pea plant will only have wrinkled seeds if its genotype is rr.

Codominant alleles

Some alleles are both expressed in the phenotype because neither one is recessive. They are said to be codominant alleles.

Examples

- Snapdragon plants can have alleles for red flowers or white flowers. Neither allele is recessive so a snapdragon plant with one copy of each allele will have pink flowers.
- The alleles for haemoglobin are codominant because they're both expressed in the phenotype (see page 116).

Figure 2: A snapdragon plant — this plant has pink flowers so it must be heterozygous with one allele for red flowers and one allele for white flowers.

Carrier

A carrier is a person carrying an allele which is not expressed in the phenotype but that can be passed on to offspring.

Example

Cystic fibrosis is an inherited disease caused by a mutation in the CFTR gene. It's a recessive disease, so both CFTR alleles have to be mutated for someone to get the disease. If someone has one mutated CFTR allele and one normal CFTR allele, they won't have cystic fibrosis but they will be a carrier of the disease.

Tip: If two carriers of cystic fibrosis have a child, there's a 1 in 4 chance that the child will be born with cystic fibrosis.

Practice Questions — Application

Q1 In owl monkeys, the allele T codes for a tufted tail and t codes for a non-tufted tail. For each of the following genotypes, give the owl monkey's phenotype: A — Tt, B — TT, C — tt.

Q2 The yellow colour pea seed allele is dominant to the green allele.

   a) What would be the phenotype of a pea seed with the alleles Yy?

   b) Give the genotype of a homozygous pea seed that's yellow.

   c) Give the genotype of a green pea seed.

Learning Objective:

■ Be able to use genetic diagrams to solve problems involving codominance and sex linkage.

Specification Reference 5.1.2

3. Genetic Diagrams — Monohybrid Crosses

Genetic diagrams show how alleles could be passed on to the next generation.

What are genetic diagrams?

Individuals have two alleles for each gene. Gametes (sex cells) contain only one allele for each gene. When gametes from two parents fuse together, the alleles they contain form the genotype of the offspring produced.

Genetic diagrams show the possible genotypes of offspring, so they can be used to predict the genotypes and phenotypes of the offspring that would be produced if two parents are crossed (bred).

Monohybrid inheritance

Monohybrid inheritance is the inheritance of a single characteristic (gene) controlled by different alleles. **Monohybrid crosses** show the likelihood of alleles (and so different versions of the characteristic) being inherited by offspring of particular parents. The example below shows how wing length can be inherited in fruit flies.

Figure 1a: Photo of a fruit fly with normal wings.

Figure 1b: Photo of a fruit fly with vestigial wings.

Tip: The first set of offspring is called the F_1 generation.

Tip: A monohybrid cross with two homozygous parents will <u>always</u> produce <u>all heterozygous</u> offspring in the F_1 generation.

Example

The allele for normal wings is dominant, so it's shown by a capital letter N. Any flies that have even one N allele will have normal wings. The allele for vestigial (little) wings is recessive, so it's shown by the letter n. Only flies that have two n alleles will have vestigial wings.

The genetic diagram in Figure 2 shows a cross between one homozygous parent with normal wings (NN) and one homozygous parent with vestigial wings (nn). The normal winged parent can only produce gametes with the allele for normal wings (N). The vestigial winged parent can only produce gametes with the allele for vestigial wings (n).

Here's how to draw a genetic diagram for this cross:

Step 1: Make sure you're clear what the letters mean.

Step 2: Show the parents' genotype at the top.

Step 3: The middle circles show the possible gametes. Put one of each letter into a circle.

Step 4: The lines show all the possible ways the gametes could combine. Fill in the possible combinations in the bottom boxes.

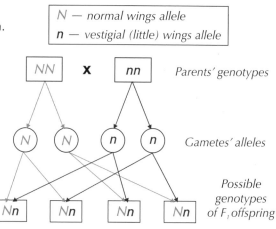

N — normal wings allele
n — vestigial (little) wings allele

Figure 2: Genetic diagram showing a single generation monohybrid cross between homozygous parents.

All offspring produced are heterozygous (Nn), as one allele is inherited from each parent.

The genetic diagram in Figure 3 shows a cross between two parents from the F_1 generation (both heterozygous). Just follow the same steps as on the previous page, but this time the gametes produced by each F_1 offspring may contain the allele for either normal (N) or vestigial wings (n).

Exam Tip
If you draw a genetic diagram in the exam and you use letters that haven't been given to you in the question, you'll need to include a key to explain what those letters mean.

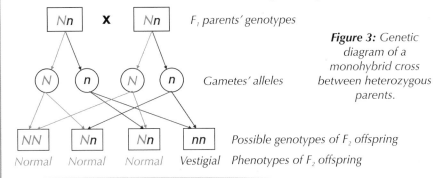

F₁ parents' genotypes

Gametes' alleles

Figure 3: *Genetic diagram of a monohybrid cross between heterozygous parents.*

Possible genotypes of F₂ offspring

Phenotypes of F₂ offspring

NN — *Normal* Nn — *Normal* Nn — *Normal* nn — *Vestigial*

Tip: The second set of offspring is called the F_2 generation.

Phenotypic ratios

The phenotypic ratio is the ratio of different phenotypes in the offspring. Genetic diagrams allow you to predict the phenotypic ratios in F_1 and F_2 offspring.

- **Example**

  Using the example above, there's a 75% chance the F_2 offspring will have the normal wings phenotype (genotype NN or Nn) and a 25% chance they'll have the vestigial wings phenotype (genotype nn). So you'd expect a 3 : 1 ratio of normal : vestigial wings in the offspring. This is the phenotypic ratio.

Usually whenever you do a monohybrid cross with two heterozygous parents you get a 3 : 1 ratio of dominant : recessive characteristic. However, sometimes you won't get the expected (predicted) phenotypic ratio. This can be because of epistasis (see page 124) or linkage (see page 115).

Punnett squares

A Punnett square is just another way of showing a genetic diagram. The Punnett squares below show the same crosses from p.118 and above.

- **Example — how to draw a Punnett square**

  Step 1: Work out the alleles the gametes would have.

  Parents' genotypes NN nn

  Gametes' alleles (N)(N) (n)(n)

  Gametes' alleles (N) (N)

	N	N
n	Nn	Nn
n	Nn	Nn

  Possible genotypes of F₁ offspring

  Step 2: Cross the parents' gametes to show the possible genotypes of the F_1 generation — all heterozygous, Nn.

  Gametes' alleles (N) (n)

	N	n
N	NN	Nn
n	Nn	nn

  Possible genotypes of F₂ offspring

  Normal : vestigial
  3 : 1
  Ratio of phenotypes in F₂ offspring

  Step 3: Cross the gametes of the F_1 generation to show the possible genotypes of the F_2 generation. The Punnett square shows a 75% chance that offspring will have normal wings and a 25% chance that they'll have vestigial wings, i.e. a 3 : 1 ratio.

Exam Tip
It's up to you whether you draw a diagram or a Punnett square in the exam, whichever you find easier. The steps are the same, so just take your time and go through it carefully.

Figure 4: A coloured scanning electron micrograph (SEM) of normal red blood cells (red) and sickle-shaped cells (pink).

Inheritance of codominant alleles

Occasionally, alleles show codominance — both alleles are expressed in the phenotype, and neither one is recessive. One example in humans is the allele for sickle-cell anaemia, a genetic disorder caused by a mutation in the haemoglobin gene. It causes red blood cells to be sickle (crescent) shaped.

Example

People who are homozygous for normal haemoglobin ($H^N H^N$) don't have the disease. People who are homozygous for sickle haemoglobin ($H^S H^S$) have sickle-cell anaemia — all their blood cells are sickle shaped. People who are heterozygous ($H^N H^S$) have an in-between phenotype, called the sickle-cell trait — they have some normal haemoglobin and some sickle haemoglobin. The two alleles are codominant because they're both expressed in the phenotype.

The genetic diagram in Figure 5 shows the possible offspring from crossing two parents with sickle-cell trait (heterozygous).

Figure 5: Genetic diagram showing a monohybrid cross of codominant alleles.

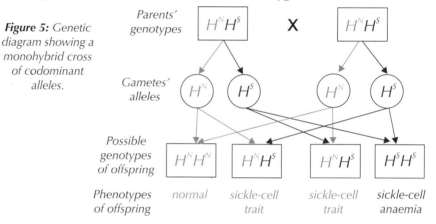

This cross has produced a 1 : 2 : 1 ratio of normal: sickle-cell trait: sickle-cell anaemia, or normal homozygous : heterozygous : disorder homozygous.

Usually, whenever you do a monohybrid cross involving codominant alleles with two heterozygous parents, you get a 1 : 2 : 1 phenotypic ratio of homozygous for one allele : heterozygous : homozygous for the other allele.

Tip: When alleles show codominance they're represented in a slightly different way to normal — you show the main gene as a normal capital letter (H) and then the alleles as superscript capitals (H^S or H^N), because neither is recessive.

Tip: A codominant cross where one parent is homozygous for one allele and the other parent homozygous for the other allele will produce all heterozygous offspring in the F_1 generation. E.g. for the sickle-cell trait:

	H^N	H^N
H^S	$H^N H^S$	$H^N H^S$
H^S	$H^N H^S$	$H^N H^S$

Inheritance of sex-linked characteristics

The genetic information for gender (sex) is carried on two sex chromosomes. In mammals, females have two X chromosomes (XX) and males have one X chromosome and one Y chromosome (XY).

Figure 6 is a genetic diagram that shows how gender is inherited. From this you can see that the probability of having male offspring is 50% and the probability of having female offspring is 50%.

Tip: In mammals, males are <u>heterogametic</u> — they have two different kinds of sex chromosomes (X and Y). Females are <u>homogametic</u> — they have only one kind of sex chromosome (X).

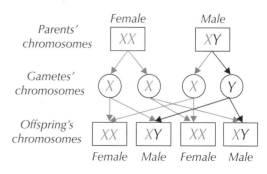

Figure 6: Genetic diagram showing the inheritance of gender.

Some characteristics are **sex-linked**. That means the alleles that code for them are located on a sex chromosome. The Y chromosome is smaller than the X chromosome and carries fewer genes. So most genes on the sex chromosomes are only carried on the X chromosome (called X-linked genes).

As males only have one X chromosome they often only have one allele for sex-linked genes. So because they only have one copy they express the characteristic of this allele even if it's recessive. This makes males more likely than females to show recessive phenotypes for genes that are sex-linked.

Genetic disorders caused by faulty alleles located on sex chromosomes include colour blindness and haemophilia. The faulty alleles for both of these disorders are carried on the X chromosome and so are called X-linked disorders. Y-linked disorders do exist but are less common.

Tip: Remember, a carrier is a person carrying an allele which is not expressed in the phenotype but that can be passed on to offspring. Males can't be carriers of X-linked disorders because they only have one copy of each chromosome, so if they have the allele they have the disease — whether it's recessive or not.

Example

Figure 7 below shows a genetic diagram for colour blindness. Colour blindness is a sex-linked disorder caused by a faulty allele carried on the X chromosome. As it's sex-linked both the chromosome and the allele are represented in the genetic diagram, e.g. X^n, where X represents the X chromosome and n the faulty allele for colour vision. The Y chromosome doesn't have an allele for colour vision so is just represented by Y.

Females would need two copies of the recessive allele to be colour blind, while males only need one copy. This means colour blindness is much rarer in women than men.

Here's how to draw a Punnett square for this sex-linked cross:

Step 1: Make sure you're clear what the letters mean. You need to show X and Y chromosomes too this time. You usually show them as a capital X and Y and then have the genes as superscript letters.

> *N* — normal colour vision allele
> *n* — faulty colour vision allele
> *X* — female   **Y** — male

Step 2: Work out the alleles the gametes would have.

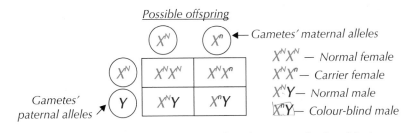

Step 3: Cross the parents' gametes to show the possible offspring.

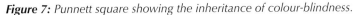

Figure 7: *Punnett square showing the inheritance of colour-blindness.*

Tip: The faulty allele for colour vision is represented by a lower case 'n', so you know it's a recessive allele.

Exam Tip
You need to be able to work out genetic diagrams for codominant alleles and sex-linked characteristics.

Exam Tip
Always read the question carefully — if it only asks you for the F_1 genotypes, don't write about anything else in your answer. It wastes time and you might lose marks.

Tip: This cross isn't any harder than the simple monohybrid ones you saw on pages 118-119. Just follow the same steps to work out all the possible combinations of gametes and what they would mean.

Q1 The allele for tall pea plants is dominant over the allele for dwarf pea plants. Give the possible genotype(s) of offspring produced if a homozygous tall pea plant is crossed with a homozygous dwarf pea plant. Show your working.

Q2 A couple decide to have a child. One of the couple has sickle-cell anaemia (genotype H^SH^S) and the other is homozygous normal for the sickle-cell gene (genotype H^NH^N).

    a) Draw a genetic diagram to show that the child will be a carrier of the sickle-cell allele (H^NH^S).

    b) The child grows up and has children with an individual with the sickle-cell trait. What is the probability that any of these children will have sickle-cell anaemia? Show your working.

Q3 In one organism, the alleles for skin colour show codominance. Any organisms that are homozygous with blue alleles are blue in colour. Organisms that are homozygous with yellow alleles are yellow in colour. Heterozygous organisms are yellow and blue striped. What colour ratio of organisms would be produced if a heterozygous parent was crossed with a homozygous blue parent? Show your working.

Q4 Fragile X syndrome is an X-linked dominant disorder. A male sufferer and a heterozygous female sufferer have a child. Give the possible genotypes and phenotypes of the child.

Q5 Duchenne muscular dystrophy is a form of muscular dystrophy that causes muscle breakdown and difficulties walking and breathing. It is caused by a recessive X-linked allele. What is the probability of having a child with Duchenne muscular dystrophy if a normal male has a child with a carrier female?

Q6 Hypertrichosis pinnae (extremely hairy ears) was once thought to be a Y-linked characteristic. If this were true, why might a father with 'bald' ears whose child has hairy ears, be suspicious of his wife?

Practice Questions — Fact Recall

Q1 Define the term 'phenotypic ratio'.

Q2 Predict the phenotypic ratio for:

    a) a monohybrid cross <u>not</u> involving codominant alleles with two heterozygous parents,

    b) a monohybrid cross involving codominant alleles with two heterozygous parents.

Q3 Give the chromosomes that determine sex in a male and a female.

Q4 What is the probability of having a female child?

Q5 Some characteristics are sex-linked. What does this mean?

Q6 Why are X-linked disorders more common in males than females?

4. Dihybrid Crosses and Epistasis

Learning Objectives:
- Be able to describe the interactions between loci (epistasis).
- Be able to predict phenotypic ratios in problems involving epistasis.

Specification Reference 5.1.2

If you want to, you can use genetic diagrams to look at the inheritance of two characteristics simultaneously. You can also use them to predict what will happen when different genes interact to produce the phenotype...

Dihybrid crosses

Dihybrid inheritance is the inheritance of two characteristics, which are controlled by different genes. Each of the two genes will have different alleles. **Dihybrid crosses** can be used to show the likelihood of offspring inheriting certain combinations of the two characteristics from particular parents. The example below is a dihybrid cross showing how wing size and colour are inherited in fruit flies.

> **Tip:** Monohybrid crosses (see p. 118) look at the inheritance of one characteristic only.

> **Tip:** The colour ebony is a very dark brown or black.

Example

As you saw on page 118, the gene for wing size has two alleles. The allele for normal wings (N) is dominant and the allele for vestigial wings (n) is recessive. The body colour gene also has two alleles. The allele for a grey body (G) is dominant and the allele for an ebony body (g) is recessive.

The genetic diagram in Figure 1 shows a cross between two heterozygous gametes — both have normal wings and grey bodies (NnGg).

Here's how to draw a genetic diagram for this cross:

> **Tip:** See page 117 for a reminder of what dominant and recessive alleles are.

Step 1: Make sure you're clear what the letters mean.

N — normal wings	G — grey body
n — vestigial (little) wings	g — ebony body

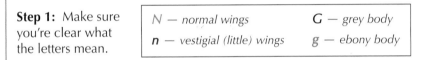

Parents' genotypes   NnGg   **x**   NnGg

Step 2: Work out the alleles the gametes would have.

Gametes' alleles   NG Ng nG ng   NG Ng nG ng

> **Tip:** You could never get a gamete that contained both the alleles for a particular gene (e.g. Nn or Gg) because the homologous chromosomes that contain these alleles are separated during meiosis — see page 113.

Step 3: Cross the parents' gametes to show the possible offspring.

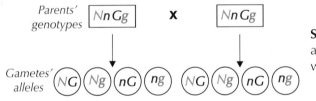

	NG	Ng	nG	ng
NG	NNGG	NNGg	NnGG	NnGg
Ng	NNGg	NNgg	NnGg	Nngg
nG	NnGG	NnGg	nnGG	nnGg
ng	NnGg	Nngg	nnGg	nngg

Normal wings and grey body
= NNGG, NnGG, NnGg, NNGg = 9

Normal wings and ebony body
= NNgg, Nngg = 3

Vestigial wings and grey body
= nnGG, nnGg = 3

Vestigial wings and ebony body
= nngg = 1

Phenotypic ratio: 9 : 3 : 3 : 1

Figure 1: *Genetic diagram showing a dihybrid cross between two heterozygous parents.*

> **Tip:** A dihybrid cross between a homozygous dominant parent and a homozygous recessive parent (e.g. NNGG × nngg) will produce all heterozygous offspring in the F$_1$ generation.

Usually, whenever you do a dihybrid cross with two heterozygous parents you get a 9 : 3 : 3 : 1 phenotypic ratio of dominant both : dominant first, recessive second : recessive first, dominant second : recessive both.

Epistasis

Many different genes can control the same characteristic — they interact to form the phenotype. This can be because the allele of one gene masks (blocks) the expression of the alleles of other genes — this is called **epistasis**.

Figure 2: A man with a widow's peak (a V-shaped hair growth). If this man were bald, you wouldn't be able to tell whether he had a widow's peak or not.

Tip: Epistatic genes are usually at different loci (different positions on chromosomes).

Example 1 — Widow's peak

In humans a widow's peak (see Figure 2) is controlled by one gene and baldness by others. If you have the alleles that code for baldness, it doesn't matter whether you have the allele for a widow's peak or not, as you have no hair. The baldness genes are epistatic to the widow's peak gene, as the baldness genes mask the expression of the widow's peak gene.

Example 2 — Flower colour

Flower pigment in a plant is controlled by two genes. Gene 1 codes for a yellow pigment (Y is the dominant yellow allele) and gene 2 codes for an enzyme that turns the yellow pigment orange (R is the dominant orange allele). If you don't have the Y allele it won't matter if you have the R allele or not as the flower will be colourless. Gene 1 is epistatic to gene 2 as it can mask the expression of gene 2.

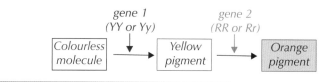

Phenotypic ratios for epistatic genes

Crosses involving epistatic genes don't result in the expected phenotypic ratios, e.g. if you cross two heterozygous orange flowered plants (YyRr) from the example above you wouldn't get the expected 9 : 3 : 3 : 1 phenotypic ratio for a normal dihybrid cross.

The phenotypic ratio you would expect to get from a dihybrid cross involving an epistatic allele depends on whether the epistatic allele is recessive or dominant.

Recessive epistatic alleles

If the epistatic allele is recessive then two copies of it will mask (block) the expression of the other gene. If you cross a homozygous recessive parent with a homozygous dominant parent you will produce a 9 : 3 : 4 phenotypic ratio of dominant both : dominant epistatic, recessive other : recessive epistatic in the F_2 generation.

Tip: Remember the F_1 generation is the first generation and the F_2 generation is the second generation.

Example

The flower colour example above is an example of a recessive epistatic allele. If a plant is homozygous recessive for the epistatic gene (yy) then it will be colourless, masking the expression of the orange gene. So if you cross homozygous parents you should get a 9 : 3 : 4 ratio of orange : yellow : white in the F_2 generation. You can check the phenotypic ratio is right using a genetic diagram:

Key:

Y — *yellow pigment*	R — *orange pigment*
y — *no yellow pigment*	r — *no orange pigment*

F₁ cross:

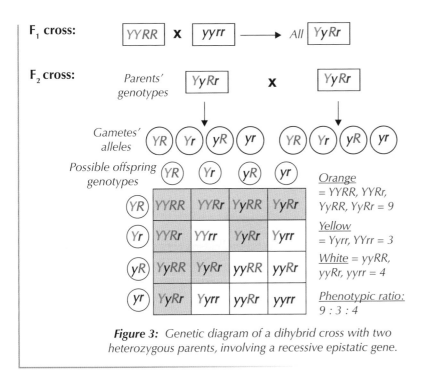

Figure 3: Genetic diagram of a dihybrid cross with two heterozygous parents, involving a recessive epistatic gene.

Tip: All of the F₁ offspring have to have the genotype YyRr because the only gametes you can get from the parents are YR and yr.

Tip: You should be familiar with Punnett squares by now but if not, see page 119 for a recap.

Tip: This is a dihybrid cross because you're looking at the inheritance of two genes.

Dominant epistatic alleles

If the epistatic allele is dominant, then having at least one copy of it will mask (block) the expression of the other gene. Crossing a homozygous recessive parent with a homozygous dominant parent will produce a 12 : 3 : 1 phenotypic ratio of dominant epistatic : recessive epistatic, dominant other : recessive both in the F₂ generation.

Exam Tip:
Make sure you know the difference between dominant and recessive epistatic alleles. The phenotypic ratios you'd expect to get are different for each.

Example

Squash colour is controlled by two genes — the colour epistatic gene (W/w) and the yellow gene (Y/y). The no-colour, white allele (W) is dominant over the coloured allele (w), so WW or Ww will be white and ww will be coloured. The yellow gene has the dominant yellow allele (Y) and the recessive green allele (y). So if the plant has at least one W, then the squash will be white, masking the expression of the yellow gene.

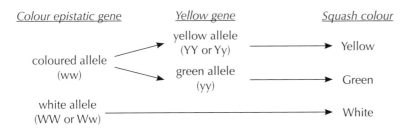

Figure 4: Diagram to show how squash colour is controlled by two genes.

Figure 5: These squash are yellow in colour so they must have the genotype wwYY or wwYy.

So if you cross wwyy with WWYY, you'll get a 12 : 3 : 1 ratio of white : yellow : green in the F₂ generation. Here's a genetic diagram to prove it:

Key: | W — white   **w** — coloured   Y — yellow   **y** — green |

F₁ cross: WWYY x wwyy ⟶ All WwYy

F₂ cross:

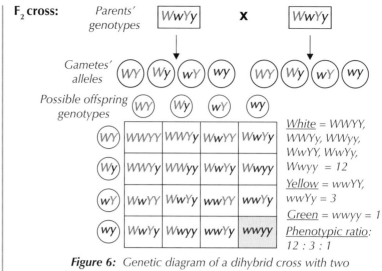

Figure 6: *Genetic diagram of a dihybrid cross with two heterozygous parents, involving a dominant epistatic gene.*

Figure 7: *Chocolate and black coated Labrador retrievers.*

Practice Questions — Application

Q1 Coat colour in Labrador retrievers is controlled by two genes. Gene 1 controls whether the dog can express dark pigment in its coat (E) or not (e). Gene 1 is epistatic over gene 2, which controls whether the dark pigment is black (B) or chocolate (b). Dogs that can't express dark pigment in their coat are yellow (golden) in colour.

  a) Write down all the possible genotypes for:

    i) a black Labrador,   ii) a chocolate Labrador,

    iii) a yellow Labrador.

  b) Describe and explain the phenotypic ratio produced in the F₂ generation if a black Labrador retriever (EEBB) breeds with a yellow Labrador retriever (eebb).

Q2 Petal colour in a species of flower is controlled by this pathway:

Gene 1 codes for a protein that prevents the formation of the red pigment. This means the dominant allele for gene 1 (W) causes the petals to be white and the recessive allele (w) causes red pigment to be made. Gene 2 codes for a protein that turns the red pigment into purple pigment. This means the dominant allele for gene 2 (P), causes the petals to be purple and the recessive allele (p) causes the petals to stay red. When a white flower (WWPP) is crossed with a red flower (wwpp), 48 white flowers, 12 purple flowers and 4 red flowers are produced in the F₂ generation.

  a) Is this an example of dominant or recessive epistasis?

  b) Explain the phenotypic ratio shown by the cross.

  c) Draw a genetic diagram to show this cross.

5. The Chi-Squared Test

Ok, it's time for a bit of maths. The chi-squared test can be a bit tricky to get your head around, but it might pop up in the exam so make sure you spend some time working through the next few pages.

What is the chi-squared test?

The chi-squared (χ^2) test is a statistical test that's used to see if the results of an experiment support a theory. First, the theory is used to predict a result — this is called the expected result. Then, the experiment is carried out and the actual result is recorded — this is called the observed result.

To see if the results support the theory you have to make a hypothesis called the **null hypothesis**. The null hypothesis is always that there's no significant difference between the observed and expected results. Your experimental result will usually be a bit different from what you expect, but you need to know if the difference is just due to chance, or because your theory is wrong. The χ^2 test is then carried out and the outcome either supports or rejects the null hypothesis.

Tip: A theory is a possible explanation for something and a hypothesis is a specific testable statement. See page 1 for more on this.

Using the chi-squared test

You can use the χ^2 test in genetics to test theories about the inheritance of characteristics.

Tip: See pages 118-119 for a recap on monohybrid inheritance.

--- Example — inheritance of wing length experiment ---

Theory: Wing length in fruit flies is controlled by a single gene with two alleles (monohybrid inheritance). The dominant allele (N) gives normal wings, and the recessive allele (n) gives vestigial wings.

Expected results: With monohybrid inheritance, if you cross a homozygous dominant parent with a homozygous recessive parent, you'd expect a 3 : 1 phenotypic ratio of normal : vestigial wings in the F_2 generation.

Observed results: The experiment (of crossing a homozygous dominant parent with a homozygous recessive parent) is carried out on fruit flies and the number of offspring with normal and vestigial wings is counted.

Null hypothesis: There's no significant difference between the observed and expected results.

Chi-squared test: To find out if the results are significant you first need to calculate the **chi-squared value** (see below) and then compare it to the **critical value** (see page 129). If the χ^2 test shows the observed and expected results are not significantly different the null hypothesis is accepted — the data supports the theory that wing length is controlled by monohybrid inheritance.

Figure 1: Karl Pearson — the English statistician who developed the chi-squared test.

Calculating the chi-squared value

Chi-squared (χ^2) is calculated using this formula:

$$\chi^2 = \sum \frac{(O - E)^2}{E}$$

O = observed result

E = expected result

Σ = the sum of...

Exam Tip
You don't need to learn the formula for chi-squared — it'll be given to you in the exam.

The best way to understand the χ^2 test is to work through an example — on page 128 there's one for testing the wing length of fruit flies, as explained above.

1. First the number of offspring expected (E) for each phenotype (out of a total of 160) is worked out using this equation:

$$E = \text{total no. of offspring} \div \text{ratio total} \times \text{predicted ratio}$$

A 3 : 1 phenotypic ratio of normal : vestigial wings is expected (see previous page), so the ratio total is 3 + 1 = 4. Here are the expected results:

Tip: This isn't the only way to work out the expected results. If you're taught a different way in class, stick with whichever method you find easiest.

Phenotype	Ratio	Expected result (E)
Normal wings	3	$160 \div 4 \times 3 = 120$
Vestigial wings	1	$160 \div 4 \times 1 = 40$

2. Then the actual number of offspring observed with each phenotype (out of the 160 offspring) is recorded, e.g. 111 with normal wings:

Phenotype	Ratio	Expected result (E)	Observed result (O)
Normal wings	3	120	111
Vestigial wings	1	40	49

3. The results are used to work out χ^2, taking it one step at a time:

   a. First calculate O – E (subtract the expected result from the observed result) for each phenotype.

Phenotype	Ratio	Expected result (E)	Observed result (O)	O – E
Normal wings	3	120	111	$111 - 120 = -9$
Vestigial wings	1	40	49	$49 - 40 = 9$

   b. Then the resulting numbers are squared:

Tip: Don't forget — if you multiply a negative number by a negative number you get a positive number. So -9^2 (-9×-9) is 81 and not -81.

Phenotype	Ratio	Expected result (E)	Observed result (O)	O – E	$(O - E)^2$
Normal wings	3	120	111	-9	$-9^2 = 81$
Vestigial wings	1	40	49	9	$9^2 = 81$

   c. These figures are divided by the expected results:

Exam Tip
Make sure you divide $(O - E)^2$ by E and not O. It's easy to get these two mixed up when you're under pressure in the exam.

Phenotype	Ratio	Expected result (E)	Observed result (O)	O – E	$(O - E)^2$	$\dfrac{(O - E)^2}{E}$
Normal wings	3	120	111	-9	81	$81 \div 120 = 0.675$
Vestigial wings	1	40	49	9	81	$81 \div 40 = 2.025$

   d. Finally, the numbers are added together to get χ^2.

Tip: Remember you need to work out $(O - E)^2 \div E$ for each phenotype first, then add all the numbers together.

Phenotype	Ratio	Expected result (E)	Observed result (O)	O – E	$(O - E)^2$	$\dfrac{(O - E)^2}{E}$
Normal wings	3	120	111	-9	81	0.675
Vestigial wings	1	40	49	9	81	2.025

$$\sum \frac{(O - E)^2}{E} = 0.675 + 2.025 = \boxed{2.7}$$

The critical value

To find out if there is no significant difference between your observed and expected results you need to compare your χ^2 value to a critical value. The critical value is the value of χ^2 that corresponds to a 0.05 (5%) level of probability that the difference between the observed and expected results is due to chance.

Finding the critical value

In the exam you might be given the critical value or asked to work it out from a table.

--- Example — wing length experiment continued ---

Figure 2 below is a chi-squared table — this shows a range of probabilities that correspond to different critical values for different **degrees of freedom** (explained below). Biologists normally use a **probability level** of 0.05 (5%), so you only need to look in that column.

degrees of freedom	no. of classes	Critical values					
1	2	0.46	1.64	2.71	3.84	6.64	10.83
2	3	1.39	3.22	4.61	5.99	9.21	13.82
3	4	2.37	4.64	6.25	7.82	11.34	16.27
4	5	3.36	5.99	7.78	9.49	13.28	18.47
probability that result is due to chance only		0.50 (50%)	0.20 (20%)	0.10 (10%)	0.05 (5%)	0.01 (1%)	0.001 (0.1%)

Figure 2: A chi-squared table.

In order to find the critical value for the wing length experiment:

▪ First, the degrees of freedom for the experiment are worked out — this is the number of classes (number of phenotypes) minus one. There were two phenotypes, so the degrees of freedom = 2 – 1 = 1.

▪ Next, the critical value corresponding to the degrees of freedom (1 in this case) and a probability level of 0.05 is found in the table. By following the arrows in Figure 2 you can see that the critical value is 3.84.

Comparing the χ^2 value to the critical value

If your χ^2 value is smaller than the critical value then there is no significant difference between the observed and expected results — the null hypothesis is accepted. If your χ^2 value is larger than the critical value then there is a significant difference between the observed and expected results (something other than chance is causing the difference) — the null hypothesis is rejected. This is shown in Figure 3.

χ^2 value < critical value = null hypothesis accepted
χ^2 value > critical value = null hypothesis rejected

Figure 3: Possible outcomes of a chi-squared test.

--- Example — wing length experiment continued ---

The chi-squared value of 2.7 is smaller than the critical value of 3.84. This means that there's no significant difference between the observed and expected results. This means the theory that wing length in fruit flies is controlled by monohybrid inheritance is supported.

Exam Tip
The chi-squared table you get given in the exam might look a bit different to this, but don't panic. It'll still contain all the information you need to answer the question.

Tip: Remember, the two phenotypes for the wing length experiment are normal wings and vestigial wings.

Tip: Don't forget — < means 'less than' and > means 'greater than'.

Tip: If the χ^2 value had been bigger than 3.84 then something else must have been affecting wing length — like epistasis or sex linkage.

For these questions, you may need to use the equation shown below:

$$\chi^2 = \sum \frac{(O - E)^2}{E}$$

Q1 The critical value for a chi-squared test is 5.99. Explain whether or not the difference between the observed and expected results would be significant if the calculated chi-squared value was:

a) 6.20,

b) 4.85.

Q2 Fruit flies can have grey bodies or ebony bodies. The allele for grey bodies is dominant over the allele for ebony bodies. If two heterozygous parents are crossed, you would expect a 3 : 1 phenotypic ratio of grey : ebony offspring. When this cross was carried out, 64 offspring were produced, 45 of which had grey bodies and the rest were ebony. Copy and complete the table below to calculate the chi-squared value for this experiment.

Exam Tip
You won't always be told the observed number of offspring for both phenotypes. You can work out the number of offspring for the phenotype you don't know by taking the number you do know away from the total.

Phenotype	Ratio	Expected result (E)	Observed result (O)	O − E	(O − E)^2	$\frac{(O - E)^2}{E}$
Grey body	3		45			
Ebony body	1					
					$\chi^2 =$	

For the following questions, you may need to use the χ^2 table below:

Degrees of freedom	Probability (p)					
	0.50	0.20	0.10	0.05	0.01	0.001
1	0.46	1.64	2.71	3.84	6.64	10.83
2	1.39	3.22	4.61	5.99	9.21	13.82
3	2.37	4.64	6.25	7.82	11.34	16.27
4	3.36	5.99	7.78	9.49	13.28	18.47

← probability levels

critical values

Q3 A student is looking at the inheritance of pea shape (round vs. wrinkled) and pea colour (green vs. yellow) in pea plants. His theory is that this is a simple case of dihybrid inheritance with no linkage or epistasis involved. He predicts that if this is the case, when two heterozygous plants are crossed, there will be a 9 : 3 : 3 : 1 ratio in the offspring. To test his theory, the student carries out this cross and looks at the phenotypes of the 128 offspring produced. Some of his results are shown in the table below. His null hypothesis is that there is no significant difference between the observed and expected results.

a) Copy and complete the table to calculate χ^2 for this experiment:

Exam Tip
In the exam, you could be given a table like this to fill in. If you're not given a table, the easiest way to calculate χ^2 would be to draw a table like this yourself and work through it step by step.

Phenotype	Ratio	Expected result (E)	Observed result (O)	O − E	(O − E)^2	$\frac{(O - E)^2}{E}$
Round, green	9		74			
Round, yellow	3		21			
Wrinkled, green	3					
Wrinkled, yellow	1		7			
					$\chi^2 =$	

b) Find the critical value for this experiment and explain whether the null hypothesis can be accepted or rejected.

Q4 A scientist comes up with the following theory:

> 'Height in plants is controlled by a single gene with two alleles. The dominant allele gives tall plants. The recessive allele gives dwarf plants.'

The scientist predicts that if this theory is true, when a homozygous recessive plant is crossed with a homozygous dominant plant you will get a 3 : 1 ratio of tall : dwarf in the F_2 generation. The scientist then comes up with a null hypothesis and carries out the cross. Of the 52 F_2 offspring produced, 9 were dwarf.

a) What should the scientist's null hypothesis be?

b) Use the chi-squared test to explain whether or not the results of the scientist's experiment support his theory.

Q5 A flower can have red, white or pink flowers. If this is an example of codominance and two heterozygous plants were crossed, you would expect a 1 : 2 : 1 ratio of red : pink : white flowers in the offspring. This cross was performed and of the 160 offspring produced, 92 had pink flowers, 24 had red flowers and 44 had white flowers. The null hypothesis is that there is no significant difference between the observed and expected results.

a) Use the chi-squared test to show that this is not an example of codominance.

b) If the determination of flower colour in this plant involved recessive epistasis a 9 : 3 : 4 phenotypic ratio of pink flowers : red flowers : white flowers would be expected. Using the chi-squared test, show that recessive epistasis is involved. (The null hypothesis is that there is no significant difference between the observed and expected results.)

Tip: Remember to use the table on the previous page if you need to work out the critical value for an experiment.

Tip: Remember to check whether the ratio and number of offspring of each phenotype in the question refer to the F_1 or the F_2 generation.

Exam Tip
You can take a calculator in the exam to help you do these kinds of questions.

Tip: There's more about recessive epistasis on pages 124-125.

Section Summary

Make sure you know...

- What happens in the four stages of meiosis I (prophase, metaphase, anaphase and telophase).
- That during meiosis II, prophase, anaphase, metaphase and telophase are repeated, this time separating the sister chromatids to form four haploid daughter cells.
- That genetic variation is generated during meiosis via crossing-over, the independent assortment of chromosomes and the independent assortment of chromatids, and after meiosis by random fertilisation.
- That crossing-over happens in prophase I and is where chromatids twist around each other and bits of chromatid swap over.
- That the independent assortment of chromosomes happens in metaphase I and is where different combinations of maternal and paternal chromosomes end up in each cell.
- That linkage is when alleles on the same chromosome end up in the same daughter cell, so are inherited together.
- That the independent assortment of chromatids happens in metaphase II and is where different combinations of chromatids go into each daughter cell.
- That there can be one or more versions of the same gene and that these are called alleles.
- That most plants and animals have two alleles for each gene and that each one is found at a fixed position (called a locus) on each chromosome in a pair.
- That the genotype of an organism is what alleles it has and that the phenotype of an organism is the characteristics the alleles produce.
- That if an organism has two different alleles for the same characteristic it's heterozygous, but if it has two copies of the same allele it's homozygous.
- That an allele can be dominant (its characteristic is always shown in the phenotype), recessive (its characteristic is only shown in the phenotype if there are two copies of it) or codominant (where two alleles are both shown in the phenotype).
- That a carrier is a person carrying an allele which is not expressed in the phenotype but that can be passed on to offspring.
- That the phenotypic ratio is the ratio of phenotypes in the offspring.
- That the typical phenotypic ratio for a monohybrid cross between two heterozygous parents is 3 : 1 of dominant : recessive characteristic and the typical phenotypic ratio for a cross between two heterozygous parents involving codominant alleles is 1 : 2 : 1 of homozygous for one allele : heterozygous : homozygous for the other allele.
- How to use genetic diagrams to show the inheritance of codominant alleles and sex-linked characteristics (the alleles that code for them are located on sex chromosomes).
- That a typical phenotypic ratio for a dihybrid cross between two heterozygous parents is 9 : 3 : 3 : 1 (dominant both : dominant first, recessive second : recessive first, dominant second : dominant both).
- That epistasis is when the allele of one gene masks the expression of the alleles of other genes.
- What recessive epistasis is and that when the epistatic allele is recessive, crossing a homozygous recessive parent with a homozygous dominant parent will produce a 9 : 3 : 4 phenotypic ratio of dominant both : dominant epistatic, recessive other : recessive epistatic in the F_2 generation.
- What dominant epistasis is and that when the epistatic allele is dominant, crossing a homozygous recessive parent with a homozygous dominant parent will produce a 12 : 3 : 1 phenotypic ratio of dominant epistatic : recessive epistatic, dominant other : recessive both in the F_2 generation.
- How to calculate the chi-squared (χ^2) value for an experiment, how to find the critical value from a chi-squared table and how to use these values to determine whether the difference between observed and expected results is significant or not.

1   Fig. 1.1 shows the average DNA content of a group of cells that are undergoing meiosis.

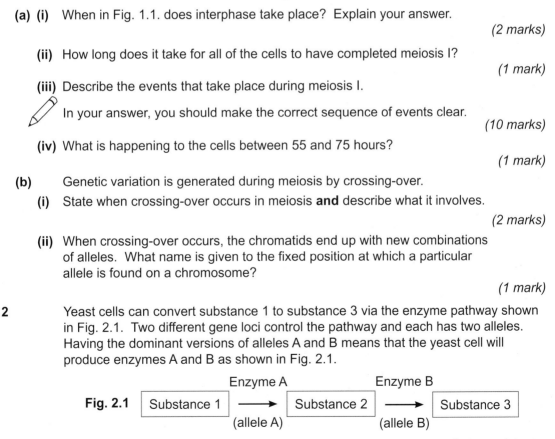

Fig. 1.1

(a) (i)   When in Fig. 1.1. does interphase take place? Explain your answer.

(2 marks)

(ii)   How long does it take for all of the cells to have completed meiosis I?

(1 mark)

(iii)   Describe the events that take place during meiosis I.

   In your answer, you should make the correct sequence of events clear.

(10 marks)

(iv)   What is happening to the cells between 55 and 75 hours?

(1 mark)

(b)   Genetic variation is generated during meiosis by crossing-over.

(i)   State when crossing-over occurs in meiosis **and** describe what it involves.

(2 marks)

(ii)   When crossing-over occurs, the chromatids end up with new combinations of alleles. What name is given to the fixed position at which a particular allele is found on a chromosome?

(1 mark)

2   Yeast cells can convert substance 1 to substance 3 via the enzyme pathway shown in Fig. 2.1. Two different gene loci control the pathway and each has two alleles. Having the dominant versions of alleles A and B means that the yeast cell will produce enzymes A and B as shown in Fig. 2.1.

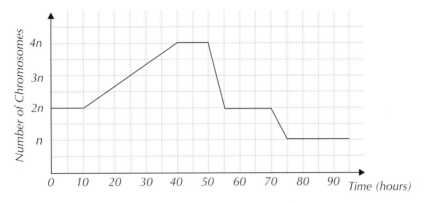

Yeast cells that lack either enzyme A or enzyme B cannot convert substance 1 to substance 3 and so cannot grow in media containing substance 1.

(a) Complete Table 2.1 by putting a tick (✓) or a cross (✗) in the correct boxes below to show whether or not yeast cells with the following genotypes could grow on substance 1. The first one has been done for you

Table 2.1

Genotype	Growth on substance 1
AaBb	✓
aaBb	
AAbb	
AABb	

(3 marks)

(b) Some of the cells that could not grow on substance 1 will grow if supplied with substance 2. Suggest why (with reference to their genotype).

(3 marks)

(c) Yeast cells with genotype AAbb are homozygous dominant for allele A and homozygous recessive for allele B.

Define the following terms: homozygous, dominant, recessive.

(3 marks)

3 Haemophilia is sex-linked genetic disorder. It is caused by a faulty allele on the X-chromosome. The faulty allele (X^h) is recessive to the normal allele (X^H). A study was carried out into the inheritance of haemophilia. The phenotypes of children in families where the mother was a carrier of the disease (genotype $X^H X^h$) and the father was a haemophiliac (genotype $X^h Y$) were recorded.

(a) Draw a genetic diagram to show why a 1 : 1 : 1 : 1 phenotypic ratio of haemophiliac male : haemophiliac female : carrier female : normal male was expected in the results of this study.

(3 marks)

(b) Of the 272 children in this study, 130 were boys and 142 were girls.
61 of the boys and 70 of the girls had haemophilia.
A chi-squared test was used to analyse the results.

(i) Calculate the chi-squared value (χ^2) for this study.

$$\chi^2 = \sum \frac{(O - E)^2}{E}$$

degrees of freedom = n − 1

O = observed result
E = expected result
$\sum$ = the sum of...
n = number of classes

(3 marks)

(ii) Use your calculated value of χ^2 and Table 3.1 to determine whether or not the difference between the observed and expected results is significant.

Degrees of freedom	Probability (p)					
	0.50	0.20	0.10	0.05	0.01	0.001
1	0.46	1.64	2.71	3.84	6.64	10.83
2	1.39	3.22	4.61	5.99	9.21	13.82
3	2.37	4.64	6.25	7.82	11.34	16.27

Table 3.1

(1 mark)

1. Variation

You've already come across variation at AS level — but the examiners think it's important enough to cover again at A2. This time though, you need to know a little bit more detail...

What is variation?

Variation is the differences that exist between individuals. Every individual organism is unique — even clones (such as identical twins) show some variation. It can occur:

Within species

Variation within a species is called **intraspecific** variation.

┌─ Example ────────────────────────────────────
Individual English oak trees (*Quercus robur*) vary in things like height, trunk diameter and number of leaves.

Between species

The variation between different species is called **interspecific** variation.

┌─ Example ────────────────────────────────────
The smallest species of tree is the dwarf willow, which grows to a maximum of around 6 cm high. The tallest species of tree is the coast redwood, which has been recorded growing up to a whopping 115.55 m high (that's nearly 2000 times as tall as the dwarf willow).

Continuous variation

Continuous variation is when the individuals in a population vary within a range — there are no distinct categories.

┌─ Examples ────────────────────────────────────

- Height — humans can be any height within a range (e.g. 139 cm, 175 cm, 185.9 cm, etc.), not just tall or short — see Figure 1.

- Waist circumference — humans can have any waist size within a range.

- Fur length — dogs can have any length of fur within a range.

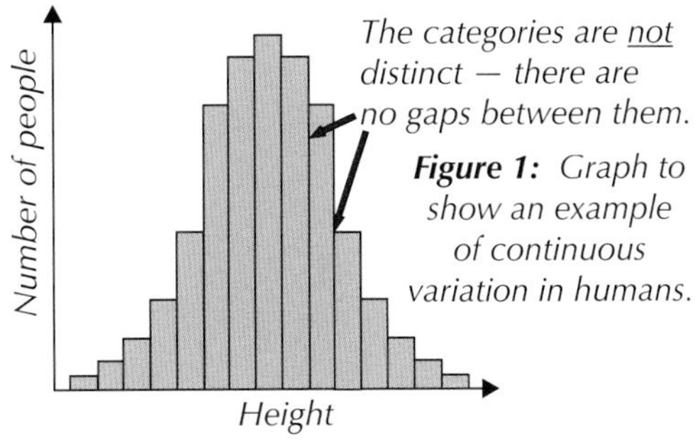

The categories are <u>not</u> distinct — there are no gaps between them.

Figure 1: *Graph to show an example of continuous variation in humans.*

Discontinuous variation

Discontinuous variation is when there are two or more distinct categories — each individual falls into only one of these categories, there are no intermediates.

Learning Objectives:

- Be able to describe the differences between continuous and discontinuous variation.

- Be able to explain the basis of continuous and discontinuous variation by reference to the number of genes which influence the variation.

- Be able to explain that both genotype and environment contribute to phenotypic variation. (No calculations of heritability will be expected.)

Specification Reference 5.1.2

Tip: Continuous variation can be shown by continuous data. Continuous data is <u>quantitative</u> — this means it has values that can be measured with a number.

Tip: Discontinuous variation can be shown by <u>qualitative</u> data — this is data that doesn't contain any numbers.

Figure 3: *Tongue-rolling ability is an example of a characteristic that shows discontinuous variation.*

Tip: Characteristics are sometimes described as phenotypic traits.

Tip: 'Poly' means 'many' and 'mono' means 'one' — so 'polygenic' means 'many genes' and 'monogenic' means 'one gene'. Simple.

Tip: Blood group is also a monogenic characteristic. It's only controlled by one gene (there just happen to be a few different alleles of that gene).

┌─ **Examples** ─────────────

- Blood group — humans can be group A, B, AB or O (see Figure 2).

- Sex — animals can be male or female.

- Tongue-rolling ability — you can either roll your tongue or you can't.

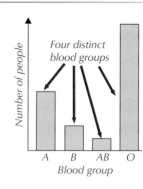

Figure 2: *Graph to show an example of discontinuous variation in humans.*

Phenotypic variation

Phenotypic variation is the variation in an organism's **phenotype** (i.e. the characteristics it displays, see page 116). Phenotypic variation is influenced by different factors:

1. Genotype

Different species have different genes. Individuals of the same species have the same genes, but different **alleles** (versions of genes). The alleles an organism has make up its genotype (see page 116). Differences in genotype result in phenotypic variation.

┌─ **Example** ─────────────

Human blood group — there are three different blood group alleles, which result in four different blood groups.

Inherited characteristics that show continuous variation are usually influenced by many genes — these characteristics are said to be **polygenic**.

┌─ **Example** ─────────────

Human height is polygenic — it's influenced by many genes and can take any value within a range.

Inherited characteristics that show discontinuous variation are usually influenced by only one gene (or a small number of genes). Characteristics controlled by only one gene are said to be **monogenic**.

┌─ **Example** ─────────────

Violet flower colour (either coloured or white) is controlled by only one gene.

2. The environment

Phenotypic variation can also be caused by differences in the environment, e.g. climate, food, lifestyle. Characteristics controlled by environmental factors can change over an organism's life.

┌─ **Examples** ─────────────

- Accent — this is determined by environmental factors only, including where you live now, where you grew up and the accents of people around you.

- Pierced ears — this is also only determined by environmental factors, e.g. fashion, peer pressure.

3. Genotype and the environment

Genotype tends to influence the characteristics an organism is born with, but environmental factors can influence how some characteristics develop. Most phenotypic variation is caused by the combination of genotype and environmental factors. Phenotypic variation influenced by both usually shows continuous variation.

Example 1 — height of pea plants

Pea plants come in tall and dwarf forms (discontinuous variation, see Figure 4), which is determined by genotype. However, the exact height of the tall and dwarf plants varies (continuous variation) because of environmental factors (e.g. light intensity and water availability affect how tall a plant grows).

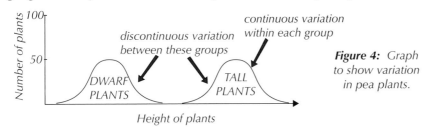

Figure 4: Graph to show variation in pea plants.

Example 2 — human body mass

Human body mass is partly genetic (large parents often have large children), but it's also strongly influenced by environmental factors, like diet and exercise. Body mass varies within a range, so it's continuous variation.

Practice Questions — Application

Q1 MAOA is an enzyme that breaks down monoamines in humans. Low levels of MAOA have been linked to mental health problems. MAOA production is controlled by a single gene, but taking anti-depressants or smoking tobacco can reduce the amount produced.

a) Is MAOA production monogenic or polygenic?

b) Patient X has mental health problems linked to low MAOA levels. Are these problems likely to be due to the patient's genotype, the environment or both? Explain your answer.

Tip: Monoamines are a type of chemical with one amine group (NH_2).

Q2 A study was conducted into how smoking during pregnancy affects the birth mass of newborn babies, depending on the genotype of the mother. The results showed that women who smoked during the entire pregnancy had babies with a mean reduction in birth mass of 377 grams. But the reduction was as much as 1285 grams among women with certain genotypes.

What can be concluded about the influence of genotype and environmental factors on birth mass? Give evidence from the study to support your answer.

Tip: There's more on drawing conclusions about scientific data on page 5.

Practice Questions — Fact Recall

Q1 Are traits that show continuous variation usually monogenic or polygenic?

Q2 What type of variation do traits that are influenced by both genotype and the environment tend to show?

- Be able to explain why variation is essential in selection.
- Be able to explain, with examples, how environmental factors can act as stabilising or evolutionary forces of natural selection.
- Be able to explain how genetic drift can cause large changes in small populations.

Specification Reference 5.1.2

Tip: A population is a group of organisms of the same species living in a particular area.

Tip: Variation is generated by meiosis (see pages 112-115) and mutations.

Tip: A selection pressure is anything that affects an organism's chance of survival and reproduction.

Exam Tip
If you're asked to describe the process of natural selection in the exam, it's important to make it clear that it takes place <u>over many generations</u>.

2. Evolution by Natural Selection and Genetic Drift

Evolution is another familiar topic from AS. It's caused by the variation in alleles within a species.

Alleles and evolution

The complete range of alleles present in a population is called the **gene pool**. How often an allele occurs in a population is called the **allele frequency**. It's usually given as a percentage of the total population, e.g. 35%, or a decimal, e.g. 0.35. The frequency of an allele in a population changes over time — this is evolution.

Evolution by natural selection

Evolution may take place by the process of natural selection. Here's how it works:

- Individuals within a population vary because they have different alleles. New alleles are usually generated by **mutations** in genes.
- Predation, disease and competition (selection pressures) create a struggle for survival.
- Because individuals vary, some are better adapted to the selection pressures than others.
- Individuals that have an allele that increases their chance of survival (a beneficial allele) are more likely to survive, reproduce and pass on the beneficial allele, than individuals with different alleles.
- This means that a greater proportion of the next generation inherit the beneficial allele.
- They, in turn, are more likely to survive, reproduce and pass on their genes. So the frequency of the beneficial allele increases from generation to generation.

Evolution and the environment

Whether the environment is changing or stable affects which characteristics are selected for by natural selection.

Selection in a stable environment

When the environment isn't changing much, individuals with alleles for characteristics towards the middle of the range are more likely to survive and reproduce. This is called **stabilising selection** and it reduces the range of possible phenotypes.

┌─ **Example** ─────────────────────────────────

In any mammal population there's a range of fur length. In a stable climate, having fur at the extremes of this range reduces the chances of surviving as it's harder to maintain the right body temperature, so mammals with very short or very long fur have a selective disadvantage. Mammals with alleles for average fur length are the most likely to survive, reproduce and pass on their alleles. These mammals have a selective advantage, so these alleles for average fur length increase in frequency.

Over time, the proportion of the population with average fur length increases and the range of fur lengths decreases — as shown in Figure 1. In the offspring graph the range of fur lengths has decreased, which results in a narrower graph. The proportion with average length fur has increased, resulting in a taller graph in the average fur length region.

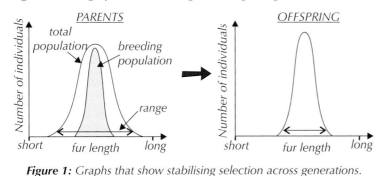

Figure 1: Graphs that show stabilising selection across generations.

Tip: The breeding population is just the animals that are surviving, reproducing and passing on their alleles.

Exam Tip
Here the data is shown as a graph, but you could be given a table of data in your exam.

Selection in a changing environment

When there's a change in the environment, individuals with alleles for characteristics of an extreme type are more likely to survive and reproduce. This is called **directional selection**.

Example

If the environment becomes very cold, individual mammals with alleles for long fur length will find it easier to maintain the right body temperature than animals with short fur length. They have a selective advantage, so they're more likely to survive, reproduce and pass on their alleles. Over time the frequency of alleles for long fur length increases — see Figure 2. In the offspring graph, the average fur length (dotted line) has moved towards the extreme, longer end.

Tip: With data that shows <u>stabilising</u> selection, the mean <u>stays</u> in the middle. With data that shows <u>directional</u> selection, the mean moves in one <u>direction</u> or the other.

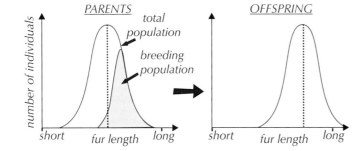

Figure 2: Graphs that show directional selection across generations.

Evolution via genetic drift

Natural selection is just one process by which evolution occurs. Evolution also occurs due to genetic drift — this just means that instead of environmental factors affecting which individuals survive, breed and pass on their alleles, chance dictates which alleles are passed on.
Here's how it works:

- Individuals within a population show variation in their genotypes (e.g. A and B, see Figure 3, next page).

- By chance, the allele for one genotype (B) is passed on to the offspring more often than others. So the number of individuals with the allele increases.

- If by chance the same allele is passed on more often again and again, it can lead to evolution as the allele becomes more common in the population.

genotype A (4)
genotype B (4) → genotype A (3)
genotype B (5) → genotype A (1)
genotype B (7)

Figure 3: *Diagram to show genetic drift in a population.*

Genetic drift and population size

Natural selection and genetic drift work alongside each other to drive evolution, but one process can drive evolution more than the other depending on the population size. Evolution by genetic drift usually has a greater effect in smaller populations where chance has a greater influence. In larger populations any chance factors tend to even out across the whole population.

Example — the evolution of human blood groups

Different Native American tribes show different blood group frequencies. For example, Blackfoot Indians are mainly group A, but Navajos are mainly group O. Blood group doesn't affect survival or reproduction, so the differences aren't due to evolution by natural selection. In the past, human populations were much smaller and were often found in isolated groups. The blood group differences were due to evolution by genetic drift — by chance the allele for blood group O was passed on more often in the Navajo tribe, so over time this allele and blood group became more common.

Genetic bottlenecks

A genetic bottleneck is an event that causes a big reduction in the size of a population, e.g. when a large population suddenly becomes smaller because of a natural disaster. Evolution by genetic drift has a greater effect if there's a genetic bottleneck.

Example

The mice in a large population are either black or grey. The coat colour doesn't affect their survival or reproduction. A large flood hits the population and the only survivors are grey mice and one black mouse. Grey becomes the most common colour due to genetic drift (see Figure 4).

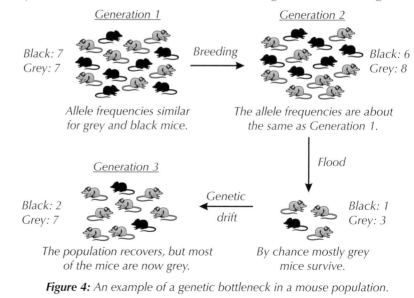

Generation 1

Black: 7
Grey: 7

Breeding

Generation 2

Black: 6
Grey: 8

Allele frequencies similar for grey and black mice.

The allele frequencies are about the same as Generation 1.

Flood

Generation 3

Black: 2
Grey: 7

Genetic drift

Black: 1
Grey: 3

The population recovers, but most of the mice are now grey.

By chance mostly grey mice survive.

Figure 4: *An example of a genetic bottleneck in a mouse population.*

Q1 Flowers of a plant species can be purple, pink or white. Each colour is coded for by a different allele. The graphs below show the frequencies of these alleles in two populations of the plant species.

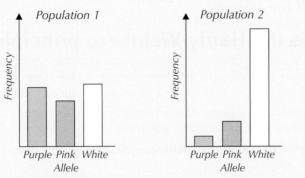

a) Describe the differences in allele frequencies between the two populations.

b) Explain how genetic drift could have led to the allele frequencies shown in Population 2.

c) Which is likely to be the smaller population, 1 or 2? Give a reason for your answer.

Q2 The frequency of an allele involved in fur colouring was calculated for two populations of woodland mammal found in the north and south of a large forest. The results are shown in the table below. In 1999 a fire destroyed thousands of square miles of trees in the north of the forest.

a) The allele frequency for the southern population peaked in 2000. Suggest an explanation for this.

b) The allele is involved in the production of dark fur. Use this information to explain how natural selection might have accounted for the results for the northern population.

Year	Allele frequency	
	North	South
1994	0.31	0.17
1996	0.33	0.17
1998	0.33	0.19
2000	0.48	0.32
2002	0.52	0.24

Tip: Take your time looking at any data you're given — make sure you really understand what the table in Q2 is showing you before you attempt to answer the questions.

Tip: To help you answer Q2 b), think about how the fire might change the forest environment.

Q1 Explain what is meant by the following terms:

a) gene pool,

b) allele frequency.

Q2 How are allele frequency and evolution related?

Q3 Explain why variation is needed for evolution to take place.

Q4 How does a stable environment affect selection?

Q5 What is a genetic bottleneck and how does it influence evolution?

3. The Hardy-Weinberg Principle

Learning Objective:

- Be able to use the Hardy–Weinberg principle to calculate allele frequencies in populations.

Specification Reference 5.1.2

A little bit of maths now... but I promise it's not too bad. Basically, you can work out allele and genotype frequencies for a whole population — which is more useful than it sounds.

What is the Hardy-Weinberg principle?

The Hardy-Weinberg principle is a mathematical model which predicts that the frequencies of alleles in a population won't change from one generation to the next. But this prediction is only true under certain conditions:

- It has to be a large population where there's no immigration, emigration, mutations or natural selection (see page 138).
- There needs to be random mating — all possible genotypes can breed with all others.

The Hardy-Weinberg equations (see below) are based on this principle. They can be used to estimate the frequency of particular alleles and genotypes within populations. If frequencies do change between generations in a large population then immigration, emigration, natural selection or mutations have happened.

The Hardy-Weinberg equations

There are two Hardy-Weinberg equations — one is used for working out allele frequency and the other one is usually used when you're dealing with genotype frequencies.

Allele frequency

The total frequency of all possible alleles for a characteristic in a certain population is 1.0. So the frequencies of the individual alleles (the dominant one and the recessive one) must add up to 1.0. Here's that idea in an equation:

Tip: If the frequencies for two alleles add up to <u>more than one</u>, they're not alleles for the same gene (characteristic). If they come to <u>less than one</u>, there are more than two alleles for that gene.

$$p + q = 1$$

Where...

p = the frequency of the dominant allele

q = the frequency of the recessive allele

Genotype frequency

The total frequency of all possible genotypes for one characteristic in a certain population is 1.0. So the frequencies of the individual genotypes must add up to 1.0. But remember there are three genotypes — homozygous recessive, homozygous dominant and heterozygous. Here's the second equation:

Tip: Remember, homozygous dominant means two copies of the dominant allele (e.g. BB), homozygous recessive means two copies of the recessive allele (e.g. bb) and heterozygous means one copy of each allele (e.g. Bb). See pages 116-117.

$$p^2 + 2pq + q^2 = 1$$

Where...

p^2 = frequency of homozygous dominant genotype

$2pq$ = frequency of heterozygous genotype

q^2 = frequency of homozygous recessive genotype

Uses of the Hardy-Weinberg principle

The best way to understand how to use the principle and the equations is to follow through some examples — like the ones on the next page...

Predicting allele frequency

You can figure out the frequency of one allele if you know the frequency of the other:

Example

- A species of plant has either red or white flowers. Allele R (red) is dominant and allele r (white) is recessive. If the frequency of R is 0.4 in Population X, what is the frequency of r?
- You know the frequency of one allele and just need to find the frequency of the other using $p + q = 1$ (where p = dominant allele, R, and q = recessive allele, r). So:

$$p + q = 1$$
$$R + r = 1$$
$$0.4 + r = 1$$
$$r = 1 - 0.4 = 0.6$$

So the frequency of the r allele in Population X is 0.6.

You can also figure out allele frequencies if you're given information about genotype (or phenotype) frequencies:

Example

- There are two alleles for flower colour (R and r), so there are three possible genotypes — RR, Rr and rr. If the frequency of genotype RR is 0.56 in Population Y, what is the allele frequency of r?
- You know that RR is the homozygous dominant genotype, so RR = p^2. You also know that the allele frequency for R = p, so:

$$p^2 = 0.56$$
$$p = \sqrt{0.56} = 0.75, \text{ so } R = 0.75$$

You also know that $p + q = 1$, where p = the dominant allele, R, and q = the recessive allele, r. So:

$$p + q = 1$$
$$R + r = 1$$
$$0.75 + r = 1$$
$$r = 1 - 0.75 = 0.25$$

So the frequency of the r allele (white) in Population Y is 0.25.

Tip: Remember, genotype is the alleles an organism has (e.g. Rr) and phenotype is the characteristics the alleles produce (e.g. red flowers). See p. 116 for more.

Exam Tip
You'll be allowed to take a calculator into the exam to help you with calculations like these.

Predicting genotype frequency

Here you're after genotype, so it's p^2, q^2 or $2pq$ you need to find:

Example

- If there are two alleles for flower colour (R and r), there are three possible genotypes — RR, Rr and rr. In Population Z, the frequency of genotype RR is 0.34 and the frequency of genotype Rr is 0.27. Find the frequency of rr in Population Z.
- $p^2 + 2pq + q^2 = 1$, where p^2 = homozygous dominant genotype, RR, $2pq$ = heterozygous genotype, Rr, and q^2 = homozygous recessive genotype, rr. So:

$$p^2 + 2pq + q^2 = 1$$
$$RR + Rr + rr = 1$$
$$0.34 + 0.27 + rr = 1$$
$$rr = 1 - 0.34 - 0.27 = 0.39$$

So the frequency of the rr genotype in Population Z is 0.39.

Tip: The more examples you practise, the more confident you'll be at working out allele and genotype frequencies when it comes to your exam.

Predicting the percentage of a population that has a certain genotype

You're looking at genotype again, so it's ultimately something to do with p^2, q^2 or $2pq$. But you might have to use a combination of equations to get there:

┌─ **Example** ─────────────────────────────────────

- The frequency of cystic fibrosis (genotype ff) in the UK is currently approximately 1 birth in 2000. Use this information to estimate the percentage of people in the UK that are cystic fibrosis carriers (Ff).
- To do this you need to find the frequency of the heterozygous genotype Ff, i.e. $2pq$, using both equations. (You can't just use the big one as you only know one of the three genotypes — q^2.)

First calculate q:

Frequency of cystic fibrosis (homozygous recessive, ff) is 1 in 2000

$$ff = q^2 = \frac{1}{2000} = 0.0005. \text{ So } q = \sqrt{0.0005} = 0.022$$

Next calculate p:

Use $p + q = 1$, rearranged: $p = 1 - q = 1 - 0.022 = 0.978$

Then calculate $2pq$:

$$2pq = 2 \times p \times q = 2 \times 0.978 \times 0.022 = 0.043$$

The frequency of genotype Ff is 0.043, so the percentage of the UK population that are carriers is $0.043 \times 100 = 4.3\%$.

Exam Tip

It's easier than it might seem to decide which equation to use.
If you're given one allele frequency and asked to find the other it's the simple equation.
If you know two out of the three genotype frequencies, you can find the other frequency using the big equation. For anything else you'll probably need to use a combination of equations.

Tip: There's more on carriers on p. 117.

Practice Questions — Application

Q1 In a human population, the allele frequency for the recessive albino allele is measured over generations as shown in the table below.

a) Calculate the frequency of the pigmented (non-albino) allele in generation 1.

b) Calculate the frequency of the heterozygous genotype in generation 1.

c) Does the Hardy-Weinberg principle apply to this population? Explain your answer.

Generation	Allele frequency
1	0.10
4	0.07
7	0.03

Q2 ADA deficiency is an inherited metabolic disorder caused by a recessive allele. The recessive allele frequency in a population is 0.16. What is the frequency of the homozygous dominant genotype in the same population?

Q3 Seed texture in pea plants is controlled by two alleles, the dominant round allele and the recessive wrinkled allele. 31% of a population have wrinkled seeds. What percentage of the population have a heterozygous genotype?

Practice Questions — Fact Recall

Q1 Describe the Hardy-Weinberg principle and the conditions under which it is true.

Q2 Write down the two Hardy-Weinberg equations and describe what each component represents.

Figure 1: *G H Hardy (top) and Wilhelm Weinberg (bottom) came up with the ideas behind the Hardy-Weinberg principle.*

4. Artificial Selection

Selection for particular characteristics happens naturally in populations as a result of environmental factors — but it can also happen artificially when humans get involved...

What is artificial selection?
Artificial selection is when humans select individuals in a population to breed together to get desirable traits. There are two examples you need to learn:

1. Modern dairy cattle
Modern dairy cows have been produced through artificial selection.
One of the characteristics that has been selected for is a high milk yield.
Here's how it's done:

- Farmers select a female with a very high milk yield and a male whose mother had a very high milk yield and breed these two together.
- Then they select the offspring with the highest milk yields and breed them together.
- This is continued over several generations until a very high milk-yielding cow is produced.

Other characteristics selected for in dairy cows include:

- a high milk quality (rich and creamy),
- a long lactation period (so the cow produces milk for longer),
- large udders (to make milking easier),
- resistance to mastitis (inflammation of the udders) and other diseases,
- a calm temperament.

Artificial selection has been taking place for hundreds of years but it's been made much easier by modern techniques, e.g. artificial insemination and IVF give farmers more control over which cows reproduce. Cloning (see page 152) allows farmers to produce genetically identical copies of their best cows, so they can be certain of the offspring's characteristics.

2. Bread wheat
Bread wheat (*Triticum aestivum*) is the plant from which flour is produced for bread-making. It produces a high yield of wheat because of artificial selection by humans:

- Wheat plants with a high wheat yield (e.g. large ears) are bred together.
- The offspring with the highest yields are then bred together.
- This is continued over several generations to produce a plant that has a very high yield.

Large ears × Large ears → **Breed** → Very large ears

Other characteristics selected for in bread wheat include:

- a higher tolerance of the cold than other wheat varieties,
- short stalks (so they don't collapse under the weight of the ears),
- uniform stalk heights (to make harvesting easier).

Techniques such as plant cloning (see page 155) can be useful in the artificial selection of crop plants.

Learning Objectives:
- Be able to describe how artificial selection has been used to produce the modern dairy cow and to produce bread wheat (*Triticum aestivum*).
- Be able to compare and contrast natural selection and artificial selection.

Specification Reference 5.1.2

Tip: Artificial selection is also called selective breeding, which you might remember from AS level.

Figure 1: *A vet preparing to artificially inseminate a cow with bull semen (sperm).*

Figure 2: *The large ears of Triticum aestivum.*

Comparing natural selection with artificial selection

You need to be able to describe the similarities and differences between natural and artificial selection:

Exam Tip
Make sure you learn the similarities as well as the differences between natural and artificial selection — it's easy to forget the things they have in common.

Similarities:

- Both change the allele frequencies in the next generation — the alleles that code for the beneficial/desirable characteristic will become more common in the next generation.

- Both may make use of random mutations when they occur — if a random mutation produces an allele that gives a beneficial/desirable phenotype, it will be selected for in the next generation.

Differences:

- In natural selection, the organisms that reproduce are selected by the environment but in artificial selection this is carried out by humans.

- Artificial selection aims for a predetermined result, e.g. a farmer aims for a higher yield of milk, but in natural selection the result is unpredictable.

- Natural selection makes the species better adapted to the environment, but artificial selection makes the species more useful for humans.

Practice Questions — Fact Recall

Q1 a) Describe how large udders may have been selected for in modern dairy cows.

  b) Apart from large udders, give one other characteristic that has been artificially selected for in dairy cows.

Q2 What is the Latin name for bread wheat?

Q3 Give two characteristics that have been selected for in bread wheat.

Q4 Give two similarities between natural selection and artificial selection.

5. Speciation

The next few pages cover what a species is and how a new one is formed...

What is speciation?

A **species** is defined as a group of similar organisms that can reproduce to give fertile offspring. Speciation is the development of a new species. It occurs when populations of the same species become **reproductively isolated** — changes in allele frequencies cause changes in phenotype that mean they can no longer breed together to produce fertile offspring.

Geographical isolation and speciation

Populations can become reproductively isolated through a combination of geographical isolation and natural selection. Geographical isolation happens when a physical barrier, e.g. a flood or an earthquake, divides a population of a species, causing some individuals to become separated from the main population. Populations that are geographically isolated will experience slightly different conditions. For example, there might be a different climate on each side of the physical barrier. Because the environment is different for each population, different characteristics will become more common due to natural selection (because there are different selection pressures):

- Because different characteristics will be advantageous on each side, the allele frequencies will change in each population, e.g. if one allele is more advantageous on one side of the barrier, the frequency of that allele on that side will increase.

- Mutations will take place independently in each population, also changing the allele frequencies.

- The changes in allele frequencies will lead to changes in phenotype frequencies, e.g. the advantageous characteristics (phenotypes) will become more common on that side.

Eventually, individuals from different populations will have changed so much that they won't be able to breed with one another to produce fertile offspring — they'll have become reproductively isolated. The two groups will have become separate species — see Figure 1.

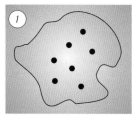

Population of individuals
• = individual organism

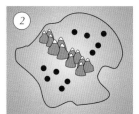

Physical barriers stop interbreeding between populations.

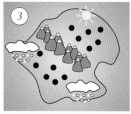

Populations adapt to new environments.

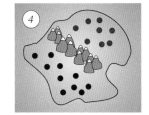

Allele and phenotype frequency change leading to the development of new species.

__Figure 1:__ Diagram showing how geographical isolation could lead to reproductive isolation and so speciation.

Learning Objectives:

- Be able to explain the role of isolating mechanisms in the evolution of new species, with reference to ecological (geographic), seasonal (temporal) and reproductive mechanisms.

- Be able to explain the significance of the various concepts of the species, with reference to the biological species concept and the phylogenetic (cladistic/evolutionary) species concept.

Specification Reference 5.1.2

Tip: Geographical isolation is also known as ecological isolation.

Exam Tip
It's important to use the correct terminology in the exam, so make sure you understand and can use terms such as 'allele frequency', 'geographical isolation' and 'speciation'.

__Figure 2:__ Four species of 'Darwin's finches'. These are often seen as a classic example of speciation.

Tip: Don't confuse geographical isolation with reproductive isolation. Populations that are geographically isolated are physically separated, but may still be able to reproduce if brought back together. Geographical isolation can lead to reproductive isolation if natural selection significantly changes the allele frequencies in the two separated populations.

How does reproductive isolation occur?

Reproductive isolation occurs because the changes in the alleles and phenotypes of the two populations prevent them from successfully breeding together. These changes include:

- Seasonal changes — individuals from the same population develop different flowering or mating seasons, or become sexually active at different times of the year.
- Mechanical changes — changes in genitalia prevent successful mating.
- Behavioural changes — a group of individuals develop courtship rituals that aren't attractive to the main population.

A population doesn't have to become geographically isolated to become reproductively isolated. Random mutations could occur within a population, resulting in the changes mentioned above, preventing members of that population breeding with other members of the species.

Practice Question — Application

Q1 African elephants have been traditionally classified as one species, *Loxodonta africana*. However, recent research suggests that there are actually two separate species of African elephant, one living in a savannah (grassland) habitat and one living in forested areas.
The two populations are thought to have separated from each other several million years ago when a drier climate caused some elephants to move out of the forests and onto the savannah.

Using your knowledge of speciation, describe how the two separate species of African elephant may have evolved.

Figure 3: *DNA evidence suggests that African forest elephants (top) are a different species to the savannah elephant (bottom).*

Classifying species

As you saw on the previous page, a species is traditionally defined as a group of similar organisms that can reproduce to give fertile offspring. This way of defining a species is called the **biological species concept**.

Scientists can have problems when using this concept though, e.g. it can be difficult to decide which species an organism belongs to or if it's a new, distinct species. This is because you can't always see organisms' reproductive behaviour (you can't always tell if different organisms can reproduce to give fertile offspring). For example:

- They might be extinct, so you can't study their reproductive behaviour.
- They might reproduce asexually — they never reproduce together even if they belong to the same species, e.g. bacteria.
- There might be practical and ethical issues involved — you can't see if some organisms reproduce successfully in the wild (due to geography) and you can't study them in a lab (because it's unethical), e.g. humans and chimps are classed as separate species but no one's ever tried mating them.

Because of these problems, scientists sometimes use the **phylogenetic species concept** to classify organisms. Phylogenetics is the study of the evolutionary history of groups of organisms (you might remember it from AS). All organisms have evolved from shared common ancestors (relatives). The more closely related two species are, the more recent their last common ancestor will be. Phylogenetics tells us what's related to what and how closely related they are.

Tip: Using the phylogenetic species concept to classify species means you don't need to be able to study an organism's reproductive behaviour in order to classify it.

Scientists can use phylogenetics to decide which species an organism belongs to or if it's a new species — if it's closely related to members of another species then it's probably the same species, but if it's quite different to any known species it's probably a new species.

There are also problems with classifying organisms using this concept, e.g. there's no cut-off to say how different two organisms have to be to be different species. For example, chimpanzees and humans are different species but about 94% of our DNA is exactly the same.

Tip: The phylogenetic concept is also called the cladistic or evolutionary species concept.

Practice Questions — Fact Recall

Q1 Explain what is meant by the following terms:
   a) speciation,
   b) reproductive isolation,
   c) geographical isolation.
Q2 Give three types of change that can lead to a population becoming reproductively isolated.
Q3 Name two concepts used to define a species.

Section Summary

Make sure you know...

- How to describe the differences between continuous and discontinuous variation.
- That characteristics which show continuous variation are usually polygenic (influenced by many genes), while characteristics that display discontinuous variation are usually monogenic (influenced by one gene).
- That both genotype and the environment contribute to phenotypic variation.
- Why variation is essential for natural selection — because organisms vary, some individuals will be better adapted to selection pressures than others. These organisms are more likely to survive, reproduce and pass on their beneficial alleles than others. This will increase the frequency of the beneficial allele in the population over many generations.
- That in a stable environment, selection will favour alleles for characteristics towards the middle of the range (stabilising selection).
- That in a changing environment, selection will favour alleles for characteristics of an extreme type (directional selection).
- That in evolution by genetic drift, alleles become more common in a population by chance.
- That genetic drift has a bigger effect in small populations than in large populations.
- That the Hardy-Weinberg principle predicts that allele frequencies in a population won't change between one generation and the next, provided that certain conditions are met.
- How to use the Hardy-Weinberg equations ($p + q = 1$ and $p^2 + 2pq + q^2 = 1$) to calculate allele and genotype frequencies.
- How artificial selection has been used to produce the modern dairy cow and bread wheat (*Triticum aestivum*).
- The similarities and differences between artificial and natural selection.
- That speciation is the development of a new species and it happens when populations of the same species become reproductively isolated (unable to interbreed to produce fertile offspring).
- The different ways in which reproductive isolation can occur.
- How species are classified using the biological and phylogenetic species concepts.

Exam-style Questions

1   The Amish population of North America has an unusually high incidence of genetic disorders. One such disorder is a rare form of dwarfism called Ellis van Creveld syndrome. The disorder can lead to health problems and death in childhood.

(a)   Ellis van Creveld syndrome is a monogenic disorder that shows discontinuous variation.

   (i)   Explain what is meant when a phenotypic trait is described as 'monogenic'.

(1 mark)

   (ii)   Explain what is meant by the term 'discontinuous variation'.

(2 marks)

(b)   Ellis van Creveld syndrome is caused by a recessive allele (e).
In some Amish communities, the frequency of Ellis van Creveld syndrome (genotype ee) may be as high as 5 births in every 1000.
The Hardy-Weinberg equations are:

$$p + q = 1$$
$$p^2 + 2pq + q^2 = 1$$

Use the Hardy-Weinberg equations to calculate the percentage of these communities that are **carriers** of Ellis van Creveld syndrome (genotype Ee). Show your working. Give your answer to **two decimal places**.

(3 marks)

(c)   The frequency of the Ellis van Creveld allele is much higher in some Amish communities than in the general population.

   What process is likely to have led to the high frequency of this allele?
   Give a reason for your answer.

(2 marks)

2   A scientist is studying two populations of a fish species. The populations are found in two separate lakes that were once part of a single, larger lake. The scientist is looking for evidence that the two populations are now separate species.

(a) (i)   How does the **biological species concept** define a species?

(1 mark)

   (ii)   Give **one** problem with using the biological species concept to decide which species an organism belongs to.

(1 mark)

(b) (i)   The scientist believes that the geographical isolation of the two populations has led to **speciation**. Describe how this could have happened.

   In your answer, you should make clear the link between geographical isolation, changing allele frequencies and speciation.

(8 marks)

   (ii)   Speciation does not always require geographical isolation.
   Explain how speciation may take place without geographical isolation.

(2 marks)

3   Fig. 3.1 shows the average yield per crop plant in a population of *Triticum aestivum* (bread wheat).

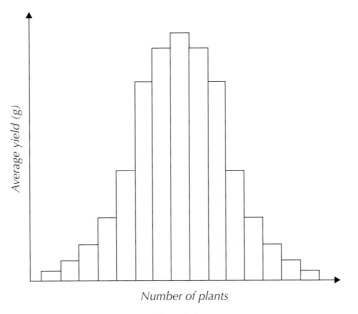

Fig. 3.1

(a) (i)   Name and describe the type of variation shown in Fig. 3.1.

(3 marks)

(ii)   Is wheat yield likely to be controlled by genotype, the environment or a combination of the two? Explain your answer.

(1 mark)

(b)   High yielding *Triticum aestivum* has been produced through artificial selection.

(i)   What is artificial selection?

(1 mark)

(ii)   Describe how *Triticum aestivum* could have been bred to have a high wheat yield through artificial selection.

(3 marks)

(c)   Goatgrass is a grass plant with a relatively high tolerance of the cold.
It is native to parts of Russia and Eastern Europe and grows through the winter.

Genes from goatgrass have been used to improve the cold tolerance of *Triticum aestivum*.

(i)   Goatgrass evolved a high cold tolerance through the process of natural selection. Explain how.

(5 marks)

(ii)   Give **three** differences between the natural selection of goatgrass and the artificial selection of *Triticum aestivum*.

(3 marks)

Learning Objectives:

- Be able to outline the differences between reproductive and non-reproductive cloning.

- Be able to describe how artificial clones of animals can be produced.

- Be able to discuss the advantages and disadvantages of cloning animals.

Specification Reference 5.2.1

Tip: Because the clones are genetically identical they should all respond in exactly the same way to a drug.

1. Animal Cloning

A clone is an organism that is genetically identical to another organism. Scientists have been able to clone animals for quite a while now, but the process has advantages and disadvantages. Read on to find out more...

What is cloning?

Cloning is the process of producing genetically identical cells or organisms from the cells of an existing organism. Cloning can occur naturally in some plants and animals, but it can also be carried out artificially. You need to know about the two types of artificial cloning used for animals:

1. Reproductive cloning

Reproductive cloning is used to make a complete organism that's genetically identical to another organism. Reproductive cloning can be used by scientists to produce animals for use in research.

> **Example**
>
> Scientists can test new drugs on cloned animals. It's really useful to use cloned animals in drug trials because the clones are all genetically identical. This means that the variables that come from genetic differences are removed, so the results are more reliable.

Reproductive cloning can also be used to save endangered animals from extinction by cloning new individuals.

> **Example**
>
> The European mouflon is a species of wild sheep which is currently endangered. Scientists have successfully cloned a European mouflon and it's hoped that this could help save the species.

It can also be used by farmers to increase the number of animals with desirable characteristics to breed from, e.g. a prize-winning cow with high milk production could be cloned.

Loads of different animals have been cloned, including sheep, cattle, pigs and horses.

Figure 1: *Two wild mouflon in Austria.*

2. Non-reproductive cloning

Non-reproductive cloning is used to make **embryonic stem cells** that are genetically identical to another organism. It's also called therapeutic cloning.

The embryonic stem cells are harvested from young embryos. They have the potential to become any cell type in an organism, so scientists think they could be used to replace damaged tissues in a range of diseases, including heart disease, spinal cord injuries and degenerative brain disorders like Parkinson's disease. If replacement tissue is made from cloned embryonic stem cells that are genetically identical to the patient's own cells then the tissue won't be rejected by their immune system.

Tip: These treatments aren't available yet, although some of them are at the clinical trial stage of testing.

Nuclear transfer

Reproductive and non-reproductive cloning are both carried out using a technique called nuclear transfer. Figure 2 shows how it's done with sheep (but the principles are the same for any animal):

1. A body cell is taken from sheep A. The nucleus is extracted and kept.
2. An egg cell is taken from sheep B. Its nucleus is removed to form an **enucleated egg cell**.
3. The nucleus from sheep A is inserted into the enucleated egg cell — the egg cell from sheep B now contains the genetic information from sheep A.
4. The egg cell is stimulated to divide and an embryo is formed.
5. In reproductive cloning the embryo is implanted into a surrogate mother. A lamb is produced that's a genetically identical copy of sheep A.
6. In non-reproductive cloning stem cells are harvested from the embryo. The stem cells are genetically identical to the cells in sheep A.

Tip: You can stimulate a fertilised egg to divide by giving it a small electric shock.

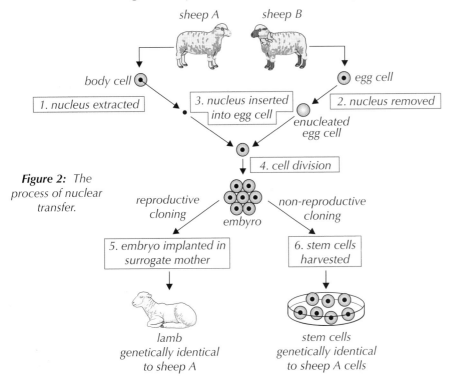

Figure 2: The process of nuclear transfer.

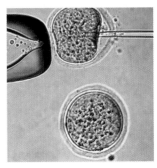

Figure 3: Nuclear transfer — here the nucleus of an adult mouse cell is being injected into an empty mouse egg (top, centre).

Tip: Producing a clone can involve up to three different sheep (the nucleus donor, the egg donor and the surrogate mother), but the clone will only have genetic information from the nucleus donor.

The pros and cons of animal cloning

You need to be able to discuss the advantages and disadvantages of cloning:

Advantages

The main advantage of animal cloning is that desirable genetic characteristics are always passed on to clones — this doesn't always happen with sexual reproduction because of processes such as independent assortment and crossing-over, which generate genetic variation during meiosis. So if a farmer had a cow that produced a lot of milk, the only way he could guarantee that his calves would also produce a lot of milk would be to clone the cow.

Another advantage of cloning is that infertile animals can be reproduced, so if a farmer's prize winning cow was infertile for any reason, he could still reproduce it. Animals can also be cloned at any time — farmers wouldn't have to wait until a breeding season to produce new animals.

Tip: See pages 114-115 for more on independent assortment and crossing over during meiosis.

Exam Tip
If you're asked to write about the advantages and disadvantages of animal cloning in the exam, make sure you write a balanced account of both — or you could lose marks.

Figure 4: *Dolly the sheep.*

Tip: Reproductive cloning of humans is currently illegal in the UK. Non-reproductive human cloning (for therapeutic purposes) is allowed under licence. There's more on how society uses science to make decisions on p. 6.

Tip: All of the problems with animal cloning could also apply to human cloning (e.g. health problems and an early death) — this is another reason why some people think human cloning shouldn't be allowed.

Disadvantages

A big disadvantage of animal cloning is that it's not just the desirable traits that are always passed on — undesirable genetic characteristics are also always passed on to clones. So if a farmer's prize winning cow happened to have a weak immune system, all of the clones would also have weak immune systems. Reproductive cloning is also very difficult, time-consuming and expensive and some evidence suggests that clones may not live as long as natural offspring.

─ Example ──────────────────────
Dolly the sheep was a clone generated by nuclear transfer. It took 277 nuclear transfer attempts before Dolly was finally born, which shows just how difficult it is to successfully clone an animal. The average life expectancy of sheep the same breed as Dolly is 11-12 years but Dolly had to be put down at the age of six after developing a lung disease and arthritis.

Human cloning

There are lots of ethical issues surrounding the use of human cloning. For example:

- The use of human embryos as a source of stem cells is controversial. The embryos are usually destroyed after the embryonic stem cells have been harvested — some people believe that doing this is destroying a human life.

- Some people think a cloned human would have a lower quality of life, e.g. they might suffer social exclusion or have difficulty developing their own personal identity.

- Some people think that cloning humans would be wrong because it undermines natural sexual reproduction, and traditional family structures.

Practice Questions — Application

Q1 A scientist wants to clone some mice for use in a drug trial. He wants to test the effects of the drug on whole organisms. Should he use reproductive or non-reproductive cloning? Explain your answer.

Q2 The diagram below shows the early stages of a process used to clone a dog:

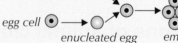

a) What is this process called?

b) What would happen next to the embryo if this were:

i) reproductive cloning?

ii) non-reproductive cloning?

Practice Questions — Fact Recall

Q1 What is: a) reproductive cloning? b) non-reproductive cloning?

Q2 Give three advantages and three disadvantages of animal cloning.

Q3 Give three reasons why someone might be against human cloning.

2. Cloning Plants

It's not only animals that can be cloned — plants can be cloned as well.
Some plants produce clones naturally, but they can also be cloned artificially.

artificial

Tissue culture

Plants can be cloned from existing plants using a technique called tissue culture. Here's how it's done:

1. Cells are taken from the original plant that's going to be cloned. Cells from the stem and root tips are used because they're stem cells — like in humans, plant stem cells can develop into any type of cell.

2. The cells are sterilised to kill any microorganisms — bacteria and fungi compete for nutrients with the plant cells, which decreases their growth rate.

3. The cells are placed on a culture medium containing organic nutrients (like glucose and amino acids) and a high concentration of plant hormones (such as auxins, see p. 218). This is carried out under aseptic conditions (see p. 164).
   The cells divide to produce a mass of undifferentiated cells. The mass can be subdivided to produced lots of plants very quickly (see below).

4. When the cells have divided and grown into a small plant they're taken out of the medium and planted in soil — they'll develop into plants that are genetically identical to the original plant.

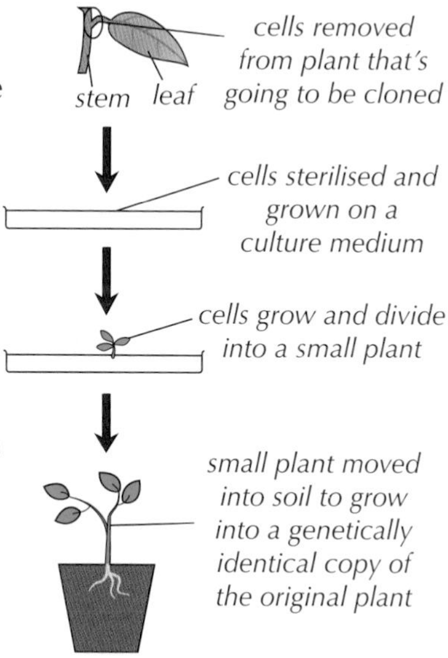

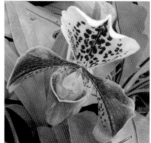

cells removed from plant that's going to be cloned

stem   leaf

cells sterilised and grown on a culture medium

cells grow and divide into a small plant

small plant moved into soil to grow into a genetically identical copy of the original plant

Figure 1: *The process of using tissue culture to clone a plant.*

Learning Objectives:

- Be able to describe the production of artificial clones of plants from tissue culture.
- Be able to describe the production of natural clones in plants using the example of vegetative propagation in elm trees.
- Be able to discuss the advantages and disadvantages of plant cloning in agriculture.

Specification Reference 5.2.1

Tip: Plant hormones are included to help promote plant growth.

Uses of tissue culture

Tissue culture is used to clone plants that don't readily reproduce or are endangered or rare.

Example

A number of British orchid species are now endangered in the UK. It's very difficult to reproduce orchids using seeds because it can take a long time for the plants to produce flowers, they have a very specialised mechanism of pollination and the seeds usually need a specific fungus present in order to germinate. But many have been successfully reproduced using tissue culture.

It's also used to grow whole plants from genetically engineered plant cells.

Figure 2: *A lady's slipper orchid — one of the species of orchid which is critically endangered in the UK.*

Tip: See pages 173-175 for lots more on genetic engineering.

Micropropagation

Micropropagation is when tissue culture is used to produce lots of cloned plants very quickly. Cells are taken from developing cloned plants and subcultured (grown on another fresh culture medium) — repeating this process creates large numbers of clones (see Figure 3).

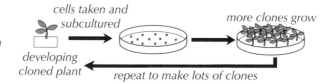

Figure 3: *Micropropagation of cloned plants.*

cells taken and subcultured

developing cloned plant

more clones grow

repeat to make lots of clones

Figure 4: *Micropropagation.*

Figure 5: An elm tree.

Vegetative propagation

Vegetative propagation is the natural production of plant clones from non-reproductive tissues, e.g. roots, leaves and stems. Plants grow structures on roots, leaves or stems that can grow into an identical new plant.

EXAMPLE: Elm trees

You need to know how elm trees produce clones from structures called **suckers**. A sucker is a shoot that grows from the shallow roots of an elm tree. Suckers grow from sucker buds (undeveloped shoots) that are scattered around the tree's root system. The buds are normally dormant. During times of stress (e.g. drought, damage or disease) or when a tree is dying, the buds are activated and suckers begin to form. Suckers can pop up many metres away from the parent tree, which can help to avoid the stress that triggered their growth. They eventually form completely separate trees — clones of the tree that the suckers grew from (see Figure 6).

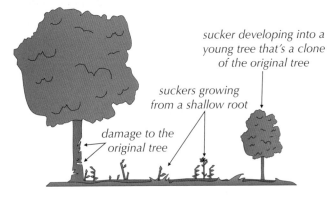

sucker developing into a young tree that's a clone of the original tree

suckers growing from a shallow root

damage to the original tree

Figure 6: Reproduction of an elm tree by vegetative propagation.

The pros and cons of cloning plants

Cloned plants are widely used in agriculture, e.g. several varieties of apples and grapes are clones. But there are advantages and disadvantages to this.

Advantages

The main advantages of cloning plants are:

- Desirable genetic characteristics (e.g. high fruit production) are always passed on to clones. This doesn't always happen when plants reproduce sexually (see page 114 for more).

- Plants can be reproduced in any season because tissue culture (see previous page) is carried out indoors.

- Sterile plants can be reproduced.

- Plants that take a long time to produce seeds can be reproduced quickly.

Disadvantages

Disadvantages of cloning plants include:

- Undesirable genetic characteristics (e.g. producing fruit with lots of seeds) are always passed on to clones.

- Cloned plant populations have no genetic variability, so a single disease could kill them all (since if one plant in the cloned population is susceptible to a particular disease, they all will be).

- Production costs are very high due to high energy use and the training of skilled workers.

Practice Questions — Application

Q1 A florist has discovered a wild flower that has an unusual pattern on its petals. She wants to reproduce the flower so she can sell it.

a) Name and briefly describe a method which could be used to produce a large number of clones of the plant very quickly.

b) Explain why producing clones of the plant might be better than reproducing the flower sexually.

Q2 Strawberry plants can reproduce by vegetative propagation in a similar way to elm trees. When they are growing well they extend structures called runners from their stems (see Figure 7). These runners each have a miniature strawberry plant on the end, which eventually break away from the mother plant to form a clone.

a) Give three differences between vegetative propagation in strawberry plants and vegetative propagation in elm trees.

b) Gardeners can use the runners to reproduce their strawberry plants. Give two disadvantages of reproducing strawberry plants in this way, rather than from seeds.

Practice Questions — Fact Recall

Q1 Describe how tissue culture can be used to clone a plant.

Q2 Give two situations where cloning a plant using tissue culture might be useful.

Q3 What is micropropagation?

Q4 a) What is vegetative propagation?

b) Describe how elm trees reproduce using vegetative propagation.

Figure 7: *Runners being extended from the stems of a strawberry plant.*

3. Biotechnology and Enzymes

Learning Objectives:

- Be able to state that biotechnology is the industrial use of living organisms (or parts of living organisms) to produce food, drugs or other products.

- Be able to explain why microorganisms are often used in biotechnological processes.

- Be able to describe how enzymes can be immobilised.

- Be able to explain why immobilised enzymes are used in large-scale production.

Specification Reference 5.2.2

The biotechnology industry is pretty big these days — it's used to produce loads of useful products. This topic looks at what biotechnology is and how enzymes can be used in biotechnological processes.

What is biotechnology?

Biotechnology is the industrial use of living organisms (or parts of living organisms, see below) to produce food, drugs and other products.

— Examples —————————————————————————————
- Bread and wine are made using yeast.
- Cheese and yoghurt are made by adding bacteria to milk.
- Bacteria are used in the processing of coffee and cocoa beans.

The living organisms used are mostly microorganisms (bacteria and fungi). Here are a few reasons why:

- Their ideal growth conditions can be easily created.
- They grow rapidly under the right conditions, so products can be made quickly.
- They can grow on a range of inexpensive materials.
- They can be grown at any time of the year.

Tip: You covered the uses of microorganisms in the food industry in more detail at AS level.

Enzymes in biotechnology

Enzymes are parts of living organisms used in biotechnology to make a variety of products.

— Examples —————————————————————————————
- Rennet (a mix of enzymes) is extracted from calf stomachs and used to make cheese.
- Lactase (the enzyme that breaks down lactose) is prepared from *Aspergillus* fungi and is used in the production of lactose-free products.
- Enzymes are also commonly used in the production of textiles and detergents.

Figure 1: *Rennet being added to milk to make cheese.*

Tip: You came across enzymes at AS. They're proteins that catalyse reactions in living organisms.

Enzymes used in industry can be contained within the cells of organisms — these are called **intracellular enzymes**. Enzymes are also used that aren't contained within cells — these are called **isolated enzymes**. Some are secreted naturally by microorganisms (called **extracellular enzymes**), but others have to be extracted. Naturally secreted enzymes are cheaper to use because it can be expensive to extract enzymes from cells. The different types of enzymes are illustrated in Figure 2.

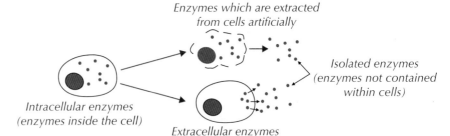

Figure 2: *The different types of enzyme used in the biotechnology industry.*

Immobilising isolated enzymes

Isolated enzymes used in industry can become mixed in with the products of a reaction. The products then need to be separated from this mixture, which can be complicated and costly. This is avoided in large-scale production by using **immobilised enzymes** — enzymes that are attached to an insoluble material so they can't become mixed with the products. There are three main ways that enzymes are immobilised:

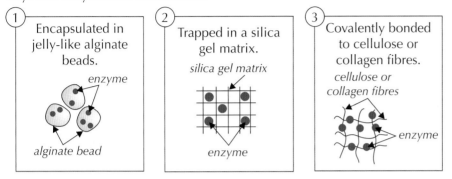

In industry, the substrate solution for a reaction is run through a column of immobilised enzymes (see Figure 3). The active sites of the enzymes are still available to catalyse the reaction but the solution flowing out of the column will only contain the desired product.

Here are some of the advantages of using immobilised enzymes in industry:

- Columns of immobilised enzymes can be washed and reused — this reduces the cost of running a reaction on an industrial scale because you don't have to keep buying new enzymes.

- The product isn't mixed with the enzymes — no money or time is spent separating them out.

- Immobilised enzymes are more stable than free enzymes — they're less likely to denature (become inactive) in high temperatures or extremes of pH.

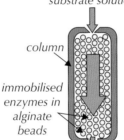

Figure 3: A column of immobilised enzymes.

Exam Tip
Make sure you know how and why enzymes are immobilised — it could come up in the exam.

Tip: There aren't that many disadvantages to using immobilised enzymes — unless of course you want the enzyme to be left in the mixture at the end.

Practice Questions — Application

Q1 A scientist wants to remove all of the protein from a sample. He decides to use a protease enzyme, but since the enzyme is a protein itself it can't be left in the sample at the end. Suggest how the scientist could overcome this problem.

Q2 A biotech company needs an isolated enzyme. They have a choice of two — one is secreted and the other is intracellular. Which enzyme would be best to use and why?

Practice Questions — Fact Recall

Q1 What is biotechnology?

Q2 Give three reasons why biotechnology mostly uses microorganisms.

Q3 Describe three ways in which enzymes can be immobilised.

Q4 Explain three advantages of immobilising enzymes in industry.

Learning Objectives:

- Be able to describe, with the aid of diagrams, and explain the standard growth curve of a microorganism in a closed culture.

- Be able to describe the differences between primary and secondary metabolites.

- Be able to explain the importance of manipulating the growing conditions in a fermentation vessel in order to maximise the yield of product required.

- Be able to compare and contrast the processes of continuous culture and batch culture.

    Specification Reference 5.2.2

Tip: If a culture isn't isolated from the external environment it's called an <u>open culture</u>.

Exam Tip
Make sure you learn what each of the four phases are called, what the growth curve looks like during each phase and why the curve has the shape it does.

Tip: Metabolic reactions are reactions that occur in living cells.

4. Biotechnology — Culturing Microorganisms

If you want to use microorganisms for a particular industrial process, you have to grow them first. This topic tells you how...

Closed cultures

A culture is a population of one type of microorganism that's been grown under controlled conditions. A **closed culture** is when growth takes place in a vessel that's isolated from the external environment — extra nutrients aren't added and waste products aren't removed from the vessel during growth.

Growth curves

In a closed culture a population of microorganisms follows a **standard growth curve**. This growth curve has four phases (see Figure 1).

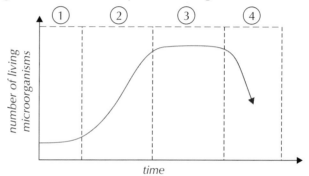

Figure 1: *The standard growth curve of a population of microorganisms in a closed culture.*

Here's what's happening in each of the four phases:

1. **Lag phase** — the population size increases very slowly because the microorganisms have to make enzymes and other molecules before they can reproduce. This means the reproduction rate is low.

2. **Exponential phase** — the population size increases quickly because the culture conditions are at their most favourable for reproduction (lots of food and little competition). The number of microorganisms doubles at regular intervals.

3. **Stationary phase** — the population size stays level because the death rate of the microorganisms equals their reproductive rate. Microorganisms die because there's not enough food and poisonous waste products build up.

4. **Decline phase** — the population size falls because the death rate is greater than the reproductive rate. This is because food is very scarce and waste products are at toxic levels.

Primary and secondary metabolites

A **metabolite** is a substance that is formed during a metabolic reaction. When growing conditions are favourable (e.g. during the exponential phase) microorganisms produce primary metabolites — small molecules that are essential for the growth of the microorganisms. When growing conditions are less favourable (e.g. during the stationary phase) some microorganisms produce secondary metabolites — molecules that aren't essential for growth but are useful in other ways.

Secondary metabolites help microorganisms survive, e.g. the antibiotic penicillin is a secondary metabolite made by *Penicillium* (a fungus). It kills bacteria that inhibit its growth. Some secondary metabolites are desirable to biotechnology industries, e.g. *Penicillium* is cultured on an industrial scale to produce lots of penicillin — it's used to treat bacterial infections in humans and animals.

You can determine whether a particular metabolite is a primary metabolite or a secondary metabolite by looking at which phase of the growth curve the metabolite is produced in. If a metabolite is mostly produced in the lag and exponential phases, it is probably essential for growth and so will be a primary metabolite. If a metabolite is mostly produced after the main growth phases (i.e. in the stationary or decline phases), it can't be essential for growth and so must be a secondary metabolite.

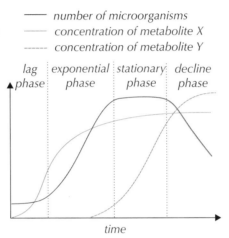

Figure 2: *A culture of the* Penicillium *fungus — this fungus produces penicillin.*

--- Example ---

The graph shows how the concentrations of two metabolites (X and Y) change during the growth of a culture.

The concentration of metabolite X mostly increases during the lag and exponential phases of growth, so X must be a primary metabolite.

The concentration of metabolite Y mostly increases after the main phase of growth, so Y must be a secondary metabolite.

— number of microorganisms
···· concentration of metabolite X
---- concentration of metabolite Y

lag phase | exponential phase | stationary phase | decline phase

time

Exam Tip
In the exam, the four different phases won't be marked onto the graph for you. If you're asked whether something is a primary or secondary metabolite, marking the four phases on for yourself can really help you see what's what.

Tip: If the concentration of a substance starts high and decreases during the lag and exponential phases, it could be being used for growth or to make a metabolite.

Fermentation vessels

Cultures of microorganisms are grown in large containers called fermentation vessels. Figure 3 shows what a typical fermentation vessel looks like:

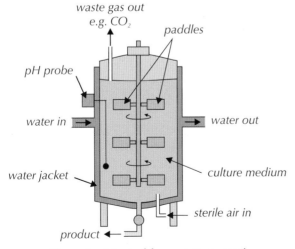

waste gas out
e.g. CO_2
paddles
pH probe
water in
water out
water jacket
culture medium
sterile air in
product

Figure 3: *A typical fermentation vessel.*

The conditions inside the fermentation vessels are kept at the optimum for growth — this maximises the yield of desirable products from the microorganisms. The factors that need to be controlled are on the next page.

Figure 4: *A vessel for the fermentation of yeast.*

pH

The pH is monitored by a pH probe and kept at the optimum level. This increases the product yield because enzymes can work efficiently, so the rate of reaction is kept as high as possible.

Temperature

The temperature is kept at the optimum level by a water jacket that surrounds the vessel. This increases the product yield because enzymes can work efficiently, so the rate of reaction is kept as high as possible.

Oxygen supply

The volume of oxygen is kept at the optimum level for respiration by pumping in sterile air when needed. This increases the product yield because microorganisms can always respire to provide the energy for growth.

Nutrient concentration

Microorganisms are kept in contact with fresh medium by paddles that circulate the medium around the vessel. This increases the product yield because microorganisms can always access the nutrients needed for growth.

Contamination

Vessels are sterilised between uses with superheated steam to kill any unwanted organisms and make sure the next culture is not contaminated. This increases the product yield because the microorganisms aren't competing with other organisms.

Batch and continuous cultures

There are two main culture methods — batch and continuous:

- **Batch culture** is where microorganisms are grown in individual batches in a fermentation vessel — when one culture ends it's removed and then a different batch of microorganisms is grown in the vessel.
- **Continuous culture** is where microorganisms are continually grown in a fermentation vessel without stopping.

Here are some of the differences between batch and continuous cultures:

Batch culture

- A fixed volume of growth medium (nutrients) is added to the fermentation vessel at the start of the culture and no more is added. The culture is a closed system.
- Each culture goes through the lag, exponential and stationary growth phases.
- The product is harvested once, during the stationary phase.
- The product yield is relatively low — stopping the reaction and sterilising the vessel between fermentations means there's a period when no product is being harvested.
- If contamination occurs it only affects one batch. It's not very expensive to discard the contaminated batch and start a new one.
- It's used when you want to produce secondary metabolites.

Continuous culture

- Growth medium flows through the vessel at a steady rate so there's a constant supply of fresh nutrients. The culture is an open system.

Figure 5: A scientist making adjustments to the conditions inside a fermentation vessel.

- The culture goes through the lag phase but is then kept at the exponential growth phase.
- The product is continuously taken out of the fermentation vessel at a steady rate.
- The product yield is relatively high — microorganisms are constantly growing at an exponential rate.
- If the culture is contaminated the whole lot has to be discarded — this is very expensive when the cultures are done on an industrial scale.
- It's usually used when you want primary metabolites or the microorganisms themselves as the desired product.

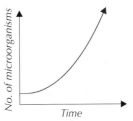

Tip: The growth curve for continuous cultures looks like this:

There's no stationary or decline phase because it's an open culture — nutrients are constantly being added and waste is constantly being removed. So the microorganisms don't run out of food and waste can't build up to toxic levels.

Practice Questions — Application

Q1 The graph below shows how the concentration of a metabolite changes during the growth of a culture of microorganisms.

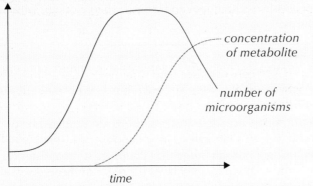

concentration of metabolite

number of microorganisms

time

a) Is this metabolite a primary metabolite or a secondary metabolite? Explain your answer.

b) Would you use a batch or a continuous culture if you wanted to produce this metabolite on an industrial scale? Explain why.

Q2 A biotech company is developing an industrial process to culture a type of genetically engineered *E. coli*. Tests have shown that cultures of the genetically engineered *E. coli* are easily contaminated with normal *E. coli*. Suggest whether the company should use a batch culture or a continuous culture. Explain your answer.

Practice Questions — Fact Recall

Q1 What is a culture?

Q2 Explain what is meant by 'a closed culture'.

Q3 a) Name the four phases on the growth curve of a population of microorganisms in a closed culture.

b) Describe and explain what is happening during each phase.

Q4 State three things that are controlled in a fermentation vessel.

Q5 a) What is a batch culture?

b) What is a continuous culture?

Q6 Give three differences between batch and continuous cultures.

Figure 6: *An E. coli fermentation unit.*

Learning Objective:

- Be able to explain the importance of asepsis in the manipulation of microorganisms.

Specification Reference 5.2.2

5. Asepsis in Biotechnology

In the biotechnology industry it's really important to keep everything sterile. If your culture or your product gets contaminated, you'll have to start all over again and that could be very expensive.

What is asepsis?

Asepsis is the practice of preventing contamination of cultures by unwanted microorganisms. It's important when culturing microorganisms because contamination can affect the growth of the microorganism that you're interested in. Contaminated cultures in laboratory experiments give inaccurate results. Contamination on an industrial scale can be very costly because entire cultures may have to be thrown away.

Tip: Aseptic conditions are also important in plant tissue culture (see p. 155), to prevent the growth of unwanted microorganisms.

Aseptic techniques

A number of aseptic techniques can be used when working with microorganisms:

┌─ **Examples** ──────────────────────────

- Work surfaces are regularly disinfected to minimise contamination.

- Gloves are worn and long hair is tied back to prevent it from falling into anything.

Tip: Ethanol is usually used to disinfect work surfaces in a lab.

- The instruments used to transfer cultures are sterilised before and after each use, e.g. in a laboratory, inoculation loops (small wire loops) are heated using a Bunsen burner to kill any microorganisms on them. On an industrial scale, autoclaves (large steam-heated vessels) are used to sterilise equipment.

- In laboratories, the necks of culture containers are briefly flamed before they're opened or closed — this causes air to move out of the container, preventing unwanted microorganisms from falling in.

- Lids are held over open containers after they're removed, instead of putting them on a work surface. This prevents unwanted microorganisms from falling onto the culture.

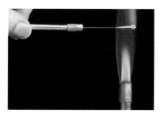

Figure 1: *An inoculation loop being sterilised in a Bunsen burner.*

Pasteurisation

Pasteurisation is the process of sterilising food — usually liquid foods such as beer, milk and juices. The food is heated to a temperature which is high enough to kill microorganisms, but not high enough to change the overall chemistry of the food (i.e. not high enough to cook it). The food is heated for a fixed length of time before being cooled again straightaway.

Many foods are pasteurised before being processed using biotechnology. For example, milk is pasteurised before a bacterial culture is added to it to make cheese. There are two main advantages of this:

Figure 2: *A milk processing plant where milk is pasteurised.*

1. It kills unwanted microorganisms — these microorganisms may be harmful to human health or they may compete with microorganisms that are being added to the food and reduce the yield of the product you want.

2. It denatures any enzymes — these enzymes may catalyse unwanted reactions that could spoil the food or change its flavour.

Q1 A group of students followed instructions to make some yoghurt. They took some milk straight from a cow and added the appropriate bacterial culture to it. But the experiment was largely unsuccessful — their yield of yoghurt was low and the yoghurt they did make tasted bad, despite them following the recipe.

a) Suggest why their yield of yoghurt was low.

b) Suggest why the yoghurt tasted bad.

c) How could they improve their results next time?

Practice Questions — Fact Recall

Q1 What is asepsis?

Q2 Give three examples of aseptic techniques that could be used in a laboratory.

Q3 What is pasteurisation?

Q4 Give two advantages of pasteurising food stuffs before adding microbes to them.

Section Summary

Make sure you know...

- That cloning is the process of producing genetically identical cells or organisms from the cells of an existing organism.
- The differences between reproductive cloning and non-reproductive cloning.
- How reproductive and non-reproductive cloning of animals is achieved using nuclear transfer.
- The advantages and disadvantages of cloning animals.
- How plants can be artificially cloned using tissue culture.
- What micropropagation is and how it can be used to produce a large number of clones very quickly.
- That vegetative propagation is the natural production of plant clones from non-reproductive tissues.
- How elm trees reproduce by vegetative propagation (using suckers).
- The advantages and disadvantages of cloning plants in agriculture.
- That biotechnology is the industrial use of living organisms, or parts of living organisms, to produce food, drugs and other products.
- The reasons why the organisms used in biotechnology are mostly microorganisms.
- That enzymes can be immobilised by encapsulating them in jelly-like alginate beads, trapping them in a silica gel matrix or covalently bonding them to cellulose or collagen fibres.
- The advantages of immobilising enzymes in industry.
- That in a closed culture, a population of microorganisms is grown in isolated conditions.
- What the standard growth curve for a population of microorganisms in a closed culture looks like, and what's happening during the lag, exponential, stationary and decline phases.
- What metabolites are and the difference between primary metabolites and secondary metabolites.
- How and why pH, temperature, oxygen supply, nutrient concentration and contamination are controlled in a fermentation vessel.
- The differences between batch culture and continuous culture, and when you would use each one.
- Why asepsis is important in biotechnology and how it's achieved.

Exam-style Questions

1   A group of scientists are manufacturing insulin for use in the treatment of diabetes.

(a)   The researchers genetically modify bacteria to produce the human insulin protein
and grow the cells in the fermentation vessel shown in Fig. 1.1.

(i) Identify **three** features of the
fermentation vessel in Fig. 1.1
which help to increase the yield
of protein produced. For each
feature explain how it helps to
increase the yield.

(3 marks)

(ii) Explain why it's important that
the air entering the fermentation
vessel is sterile.

(2 marks)

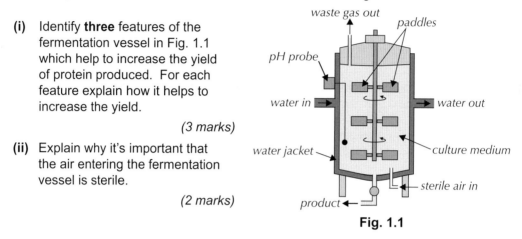

Fig. 1.1

(b)   The growth curve of the bacterial population is shown in Fig. 1.2.

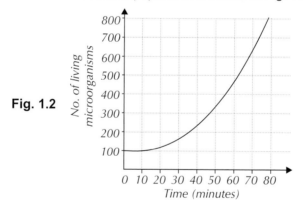

Fig. 1.2

(i) Using Fig. 1.2, determine how long it takes for the initial bacterial population to
double in size.

(1 mark)

(ii) Explain why it takes less time for the bacterial population to then double
in size again.

(2 marks)

(iii) Sketch out the growth curve you would expect to see if the bacteria had been grown
in a **closed culture**.

(1 mark)

(iv) Explain the differences between the growth curve of a bacterial population in a
closed culture and the growth curve in Fig. 1.2.

(6 marks)

(c)   The scientists believe that, in the future, diabetes could be cured using therapeutic cloning. This would involve taking a body cell from the patient and generating embryonic stem cells from it using the process of nuclear transfer.

   (i)   Is this an example of reproductive or non-reproductive cloning? Explain your answer.

(1 mark)

   (ii) Describe how embryonic stem cells could be produced from a human body cell using nuclear transfer.

   In your answer, you should make clear the sequence of the steps in the process.

(7 marks)

2   A company produces out of season plants for a garden centre using tissue culture. The plants it produces are clones.

(a) (i)   When performing tissue culture, explain why the cells that are removed from the original plant are usually taken from the stem and root tips.

(2 marks)

   (ii) In addition to being able to produce plants out of season, give **two** further advantages of cloning plants.

(2 marks)

(b)   When inspecting clones grown from the same culture, a scientist working for the company notices that one of the clones has a bacterial infection. Suggest why this could be major problem.

(2 marks)

(c)   An antibiotic against the bacteria causing the infection is produced by a fungus. The fungus can be cultured using batch culture or continuous culture.

   (i)   Explain why fungi are commonly used in the biotechnology industry.

(4 marks)

   (ii) Tick the correct boxes to show which of the statements below are a feature of batch culture and which are a feature of continuous culture. The first one has been done for you.

	Batch	Continuous
The culture is a closed system.	✓	
The culture is kept in the exponential phase of growth.		
Product is harvested in the stationary phase of growth.		
The product yield is relatively high.		
Used if secondary metabolites are required.		

(4 marks)

Tip: The techniques described over the next few pages will turn up again in the rest of the section, so make sure you're familiar with them now.

Tip: We've only shown very small pieces of DNA to make the diagrams easier to follow, but real genes are much longer. (Real primers are longer too but not as big as genes.)

1. Common Gene Technologies

Gene technologies can be used to do things like copy, cut out and separate fragments of DNA. This allows us to study and alter genes. You might not get much opportunity to use the techniques involved, but you do need to know the theory behind a few of the more common ones...

What are gene technologies?

Gene technologies are basically all the techniques used to study genes and their function — you need to learn some of these techniques for the exam. They include:

- The polymerase chain reaction (PCR) (see below).
- Cutting out DNA fragments using restriction enzymes (see next page).
- Gel electrophoresis (see p. 170).
- Finding specific sequences of DNA using DNA probes (see p. 171).

As well as helping us to study genes, these techniques have other uses, such as in genetic engineering (see p. 173), gene cloning (see p. 175) and gene therapy (see p. 182).

The polymerase chain reaction

The polymerase chain reaction (PCR) can be used to make millions of copies of a fragment of DNA in just a few hours. The fragment could contain a gene or just a bit of DNA that you're interested in. PCR has several stages and is repeated over and over to make lots of copies. Here's how it works:

Step 1

A reaction mixture is set up that contains the DNA sample, free nucleotides, **primers** and **DNA polymerase**. Primers are short pieces of DNA that are complementary to the bases at the start of the fragment you want. DNA polymerase is an enzyme that creates new DNA strands.

Step 2

The DNA mixture is heated to 95 °C to break the hydrogen bonds between the two strands of DNA. The mixture is then cooled to 50-65 °C so that the primers can bind (anneal) to the strands.

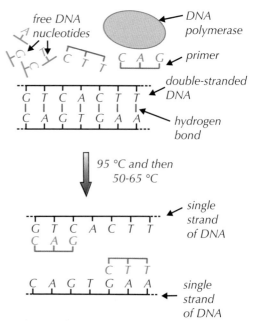

Step 3

The reaction mixture is heated to 72 °C, so DNA polymerase can work. The DNA polymerase lines up free DNA nucleotides alongside each template strand. Complementary base pairing means new complementary strands are formed.

Step 4

Two new copies of the fragment of DNA are formed and one cycle of PCR is complete. When the cycle starts again — the mixture is heated to 95 °C and this time all four strands (two original and two new) are used as templates.

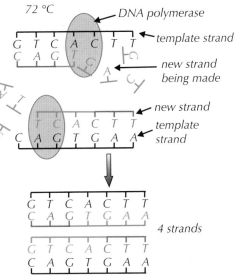

Figure 1: *Scientist using a programmable PCR machine.*

As shown below, each PCR cycle doubles the amount of DNA, e.g. 1st cycle = 2 × 2 = 4 DNA fragments, 2nd cycle = 4 × 2 = 8 DNA fragments and so on.

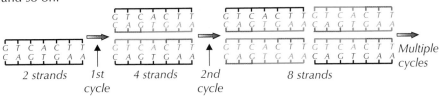

Tip: PCR produces lots of identical copies of DNA, so it can be used to clone genes — this is called *in vitro* cloning (see page 175).

Using restriction enzymes

You can isolate (cut out) a DNA fragment from an organism's DNA using enzymes called restriction enzymes. Here's how they work:

Some sections of DNA have **palindromic sequences** of nucleotides. These sequences consist of antiparallel base pairs (base pairs that read the same in opposite directions) — see Figure 2.

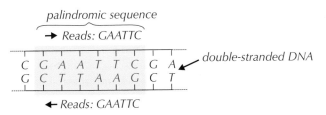

Figure 2: *A palindromic DNA sequence.*

Restriction enzymes recognise specific palindromic sequences (known as **recognition sequences**) and cut (digest) the DNA at these places. Different restriction enzymes cut at different specific recognition sequences, because the shape of the recognition sequence is complementary to an enzyme's active site.

Tip: Restriction enzymes are also known as restriction endonucleases.

Tip: Remember, the active site is where an enzyme's substrate binds. In this case, the recognition sequence is the substrate molecule.

┌─ Examples ─────────────────────
- The restriction enzyme *Eco*RI cuts at GAATTC.
- The restriction enzyme *Hind*III cuts at AAGCTT.

If recognition sequences are present at either side of the DNA fragment you want, you can use restriction enzymes to separate it from the rest of the DNA — see Figure 3. The DNA sample is incubated with the specific restriction enzyme, which cuts the DNA fragment via a hydrolysis reaction. Sometimes the cut leaves **sticky ends** — small tails of unpaired bases at each end of the fragment. Sticky ends can be used to bind (anneal) the DNA fragment to another piece of DNA that has sticky ends with complementary sequences (there's more about this on pages 173-174).

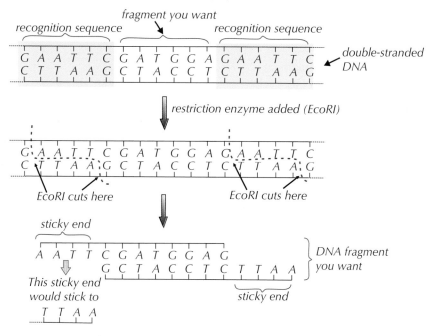

Tip: You won't always find the same restriction enzyme site either side of the fragment you want. E.g. you might get an *EcoRI* site on one side and a *Hind*III on the other, so you'd have to incubate the DNA sample with both enzymes to cut the piece you're after.

Figure 3: Using a restriction enzyme to cut DNA.

Gel electrophoresis

Tip: The size (length) of DNA fragments is measured in bases, e.g. ATCC = 4 bases or base pairs (bp) or nucleotides, 1000 bases is one kilobase (1 kb).

Gel electrophoresis is a technique used to separate DNA fragments by size (length). First, a fluorescent tag is added to all the DNA fragments so they can be viewed under UV light. The DNA mixture is placed into a well in a slab of gel and covered in a buffer solution that conducts electricity — see Figure 5. An electrical current is then passed through the gel — DNA fragments are negatively charged, so they move towards the positive electrode at the far end of the gel. Smaller (shorter) DNA fragments move faster and travel further through the gel, so the DNA fragments separate according to size (see Figure 6, next page). The DNA fragments are viewed as bands under UV light.

Figure 4: A scientist loading a DNA sample into a gel.

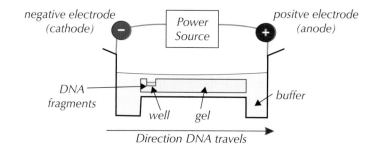

Figure 5: A side view of the equipment used in gel electrophoresis.

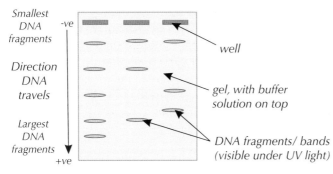

Figure 6: Top view of gel during electrophoresis.

Figure 7: An electrophoresis gel under a UV light. The bands of DNA are glowing pink.

Tip: Gel electrophoresis forms the basis of genetic fingerprinting — a process that can be used to determine how closely related (genetically similar) two or more organisms are.

DNA probes

DNA probes (also called gene probes) can be used to identify DNA fragments that contain specific sequences of bases, e.g. they can be used to locate genes on chromosomes or see if a person's DNA contains a mutated gene (e.g. a gene that causes a genetic disorder). DNA probes are short single strands of DNA — see Figure 8. They have a specific base sequence that's complementary to the target sequence — the specific sequence you're looking for. This means a DNA probe will **hybridise** (bind) to the target sequence if it's present in a sample of DNA.

A DNA probe also has a label attached, so that it can be detected. The two most common labels are a radioactive label (detected using X-ray film) or a fluorescent label (detected using UV light).

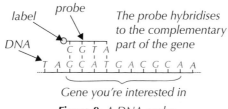

Figure 8: A DNA probe.

Figure 10 and the text below explain how fluorescently labelled probes are used:

Step 1

A sample of DNA is digested into fragments using restriction enzymes and separated using electrophoresis.

Step 2

The separated DNA fragments are then transferred to a nylon membrane and incubated with a fluorescently labelled DNA probe. If the target sequence is present, the DNA probe will hybridise (bind) to it.

Step 3

The membrane is then exposed to UV light and if the target sequence is present there will be a fluorescent band. E.g. the DNA fragment X contains the target sequence.

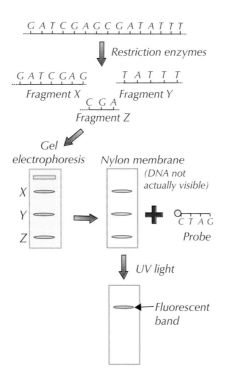

Figure 10: Using a DNA probe.

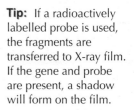

Figure 9: Human chromosomes (red) with DNA probes (yellow) hybridised to complementary base sequences.

Tip: If a radioactively labelled probe is used, the fragments are transferred to X-ray film. If the gene and probe are present, a shadow will form on the film.

Q1 The following DNA fragment is being copied using PCR.
The arrows mark the start of each DNA strand.

Start ⤵

```
G  C  A  T  A  C  C  G  T  A  A  T  G  G
C  G  T  A  T  G  G  C  A  T  T  A  C  C
```
⤴ Start

Tip: Restriction enzymes are used a lot in gene technology to cut DNA fragments, so make sure you can answer Q2 — they'll pop up again, I promise.

a) The scientist carrying out the PCR uses primers that are four bases long. Give the sequences of the primers he will need to use to copy the DNA fragment.

b) The scientist carries out six cycles of PCR. How many single strands of DNA will he have once the six cycles are complete?

Q2 Using information from the table below, describe and explain how restriction enzymes could be used to cut this DNA sequence:

CAGGATCCTCCTTACATAGTGAATTCATGC

Restriction enzyme	Recognition sequence
BamHI	GGATCC
HindIII	AAGCTT
EcoRI	GAATTC

Q1 What does PCR stand for?

Q2 Explain what is meant by the term 'palindromic sequence'.

Q3 What are sticky ends? Why are they useful?

Q4 Name the technique used to separate DNA fragments by size.

Q5 Where would the longest DNA fragments be found in a gel — at the top (near the cathode) or at the bottom (near the anode)?

Q6 a) Why does a DNA probe hybridise to its target DNA sequence?

b) What can DNA probes be used for?

2. Genetic Engineering and Gene Cloning

Genetic engineering uses gene technologies to alter organisms' DNA. The same technologies can be used to clone genes.

What is genetic engineering?

Genetic engineering is the manipulation of an organism's DNA. Organisms that have had their DNA altered by genetic engineering are called **transformed organisms**. These organisms have **recombinant DNA** — DNA formed by joining together DNA from different sources.

Genetic engineering involves extracting a gene from one organism and then inserting it into another organism (often one that's a different species). Genes can also be manufactured (e.g. by PCR) instead of extracted from an organism. The organism with the inserted gene will then produce the protein coded for by that gene.

An organism that has been genetically engineered to include a gene from a different species is sometimes called a **transgenic organism**. There's more on transgenic organisms on pages 178-179.

Genetic engineering — the process

You need to know how to use genetic engineering to transform microorganisms, e.g. bacteria. There are four parts to the process:

Part 1 — Obtaining DNA containing the desired gene

The first step is to get hold of a DNA fragment that contains the desired gene (i.e. the gene you're interested in). The fragment can be isolated from another organism using restriction enzymes (see pages 169-170).

Part 2 — Making recombinant DNA

The next step is to insert the DNA fragment into **vector DNA** — a vector is something that's used to transfer DNA into a cell. Vectors can be **plasmids** (small, circular molecules of DNA in bacteria) or **bacteriophages** (viruses that infect bacteria). The vector DNA is isolated, then restriction enzymes and **DNA ligase** (an enzyme) are used to stick the DNA fragment and vector DNA together. Here's how it works:

Step 1
The vector DNA is isolated.

Step 2
The vector DNA is cut open using the same restriction enzyme that was used to isolate the DNA fragment containing the desired gene. This means that the sticky ends of the vector DNA are complementary to the sticky ends of the DNA fragment containing the gene.

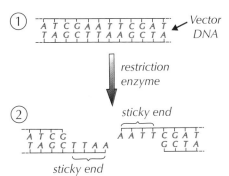

Learning Objectives:
- Be able to explain that genetic engineering involves the extraction of genes from one organism, or the manufacture of genes, in order to place them in another organism (often of a different species) such that the receiving organism expresses the gene product.
- Be able to define the term 'recombinant DNA'.
- Be able to explain how isolated DNA fragments can be placed in plasmids, with reference to the role of ligase.
- Be able to state other vectors into which fragments of DNA may be incorporated.
- Be able to explain how plasmids may be taken up by bacterial cells in order to produce a transgenic microorganism that can express a desired gene product.
- Be able to outline how genetic markers in plasmids can be used to identify the bacteria that have taken up a recombinant plasmid.
- Be able to describe the advantage to microorganisms of the capacity to take up plasmid DNA from the environment.

Specification Reference 5.2.3

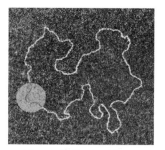

Figure 1: *Recombinant plasmid DNA. The DNA fragment containing the desired gene is highlighted red.*

Step 3

The vector DNA and DNA fragment are mixed together with DNA ligase. DNA ligase joins the sugar-phosphate backbones (see p. 95) of the two bits of DNA. This process is called ligation.

Step 4

The new combination of bases in the DNA (vector DNA + DNA fragment) is called recombinant DNA.

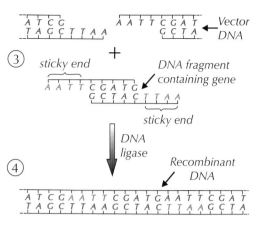

Part 3 — Transforming cells

The vector with the recombinant DNA is used to transfer the gene into the bacterial cells (called **host cells**). If a plasmid vector is used, the host cells have to be persuaded to take in the plasmid vector and its DNA.

┌─ **Examples** ─────────────────────────────

Heat-shock

Host bacterial cells are placed into ice-cold calcium chloride solution to make their cell walls more permeable. The plasmids are added and the mixture is heat-shocked (heated to around 42 °C for 1-2 minutes), which encourages the cells to take in the plasmids.

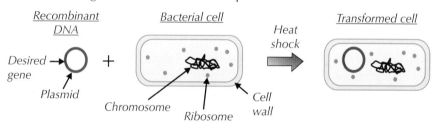

Electroporation

The bacteria are given a very short but powerful electric shock, which makes the cells temporarily permeable to DNA.

With a bacteriophage vector, the bacteriophage will infect the host bacterium by injecting its DNA into it — see Figure 2. The phage DNA (with the desired gene in it) then integrates into the bacterial DNA.

Cells that take up the vectors containing the desired gene are genetically engineered, so are called transformed.

Part 4 — Identifying transformed cells

Not all host cells will have taken up the vector and its DNA. **Marker genes** can be used to identify the transformed cells (see Figure 3 on the next page):

Step 1

Marker genes can be inserted into vectors at the same time as the desired gene. This means any transformed host cells will contain the desired gene and the marker gene. (Scientists may also use vector DNA that already contains a marker gene in it, then they don't have to add it in.)

Figure 2: *This isn't an alien spaceship — it's actually a bacteriophage (orange) injecting its viral DNA into an E. coli bacterium (blue).*

Tip: Marker genes are also called genetic markers.

Step 2

The host cells are grown on agar plates and each cell divides and replicates its DNA, creating a colony of cloned cells. Transformed cells will produce colonies where all the cells contain the desired gene and the marker gene.

The marker gene can code for antibiotic resistance — if the host cells are grown on agar plates containing the specific antibiotic, only transformed cells that have the marker gene will survive and grow. Marker genes can also code for fluorescence — when the agar plate is placed under a UV light only transformed cells will fluoresce.

The transformed cells will be able to produce the desired gene product.

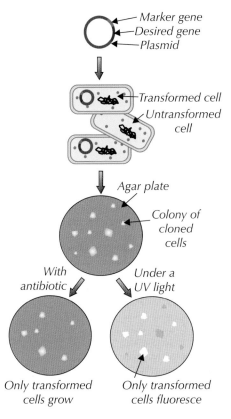

Figure 3: Genetic engineering part 4 — identifying transformed cells.

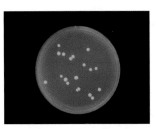

Figure 4: Fluorescing transformed bacteria colonies containing the commonly used marker gene for GFP (green florescent protein).

The benefits of taking up plasmids

Some microorganisms can naturally take up plasmids from their surroundings. This is beneficial for the microorganisms because the plasmids often contain useful genes. This means the microorganisms gain useful characteristics, so they're more likely to have an advantage over other microorganisms, which increases their chance of survival. Plasmids can contain many useful things:

- Genes that code for resistance to antibiotics, e.g. genes for enzymes that break down antibiotics.

- Genes that help microorganisms invade hosts, e.g. genes for enzymes that break down host tissues.

- Genes that mean microorganisms can use different nutrients, e.g. genes for enzymes that break down sugars not normally used.

Gene cloning

Gene cloning is all about making lots of identical copies of a gene. Genes can be cloned ***in vivo*** (within a living organism) using the genetic engineering technique described on the previous few pages. Once the transformed cells have been identified, they're allowed to multiply — in doing so, they produce lots and lots of copies of the desired gene. Genes can also be cloned ***in vitro*** (outside of a living organism) using PCR (see pages 168-169). The advantages and disadvantages of each technique are covered on the next page.

Tip: *In vitro* is Latin for within glass. *In vivo* is Latin for within the living. (It's because they're Latin that they're written in italics.)

In vivo cloning: the advantages

- *In vivo* cloning can be a cheaper method than PCR, because the materials needed to transform and grow bacteria are relatively inexpensive.

- Large fragments of DNA can be cloned using *in vivo* cloning, e.g. between 20 to 45 kilobases of DNA can be inserted into some plasmids and bacteriophages. This makes *in vivo* cloning really useful if you don't know the exact location or sequence of the gene you want to clone — you can clone a large chunk of DNA that should contain the gene.

- *In vivo* cloning can be less technically difficult than PCR because the conditions for PCR have to be optimised (e.g. it has to be exactly the right temperature for the primers to anneal).

- You usually get fewer mutations (see p. 106) occurring in the clones using *in vivo* cloning than you do using PCR.

In vivo cloning: the disadvantages

In vivo cloning also has disadvantages — the DNA fragment has to be isolated from other cell components, it can be quite a slow process (because some types of bacteria grow quite slowly) and it uses lots of laboratory space and equipment (e.g. incubators).

In vitro cloning (PCR): the advantages

- This technique only replicates the DNA fragment of interest (e.g. the desired gene). This means that you don't have to isolate the DNA fragment from host DNA or cell components.

- PCR is a faster process — it can clone millions of copies of DNA in just a few hours (compared to a few weeks for *in vivo* cloning).

- PCR can be safer — you're not dealing with live cells, which is especially important if you're dealing with genes from dangerous pathogens, e.g. the smallpox virus or HIV.

- It uses less laboratory space and equipment, and can be less labour intensive — you don't have all the separate stages of *in vivo* cloning (selection, growth, harvesting the DNA) and PCR machines are programmable (so they can just be left to run by themselves).

- You can use older, lower quality DNA for PCR — DNA deteriorates (breaks down) overtime. In theory, for PCR, you need just one intact piece of DNA and you can make millions of copies from it.

In vitro cloning (PCR): the disadvantages

PCR also has disadvantages — it can only replicate a small DNA fragment (compared to *in vivo* cloning), and it can be expensive if you want to produce a lot of DNA (because of the need to buy primers, PCR chemicals, DNA polymerase etc.). PCR can also introduce more mutations than *in vivo* cloning because the types of DNA polymerase used aren't always great at proofreading the DNA they've made.

Exam Tip
If you're asked to compare two processes in an exam question, make sure you do <u>compare</u> them. Try to write an equal amount about both and make sure you're using comparative words and phrases like 'quicker' or 'slower', 'less than' or 'more than'.

Tip: When DNA polymerases proofread the DNA they've made, they identify and correct mistakes in the base sequence.

Tip: *Taq* is a DNA polymerase commonly used in PCR — it has an error rate of about 1 in 10 000 base pairs.

Practice Questions — Application

Q1 A scientist is studying the role of a protein in cancer progression. He transformed some *E. coli* cells with recombinant DNA containing the gene that codes for this protein. He then grew the cells on an agar plate containing penicillin.

a) A DNA fragment containing the desired gene was made using restriction enzymes. Describe and explain how the recombinant DNA was produced using this fragment.

b) Explain why you think the cells have been grown on an agar plate containing penicillin.

Q2 Read the passage below, then answer the questions that follow.

The LacZ gene is found in *E.coli*. It codes for an enzyme called β-galactosidase. β-galactosidase breaks down the colourless substance X-gal into a blue pigment.

LacZα and LacZΩ are mutated versions of the LacZ gene. Each one codes for a protein that forms part of the β-galactosidase enzyme. When the two proteins are produced in the same cell, they assemble to form a fully-functional β-galactosidase enzyme. Neither protein works as the enzyme by itself.

LacZα and LacZΩ can be used as marker genes to test whether *E.coli* have taken up recombinant DNA. The desired gene is inserted into the middle of a LacZα gene on bacterial plasmids (see diagram on the right). The plasmids also contain a gene for ampicillin-resistance.

Ampicillin-resistance gene

LacZα gene

Desired gene inserted into LacZα gene

Plasmid

The plasmids are taken up by *E.coli* containing a copy of the LacZΩ gene. The *E.coli* are then cultured on agar plates containing X-gal and ampicillin.

a) What is the role of the bacterial plasmids?

b) Explain why the plasmids contain an ampicillin-resistance gene.

c) *E.coli* that have taken up plasmids containing the desired gene will be white. *E.coli* containing plasmids without the desired gene will be blue. Explain why this is the case.

Practice Questions — Fact Recall

Q1 What is genetic engineering?

Q2 What is recombinant DNA?

Q3 Give an example of a vector used in genetic engineering.

Q4 What type of enzyme is used to cut DNA to give sticky ends?

Q5 Describe the role of DNA ligase in genetic engineering.

Q6 What does it mean when a cell is described as being 'transformed'?

Q7 Give two disadvantages of *in vivo* cloning over *in vitro* cloning.

3. More on Genetic Engineering

Learning Objectives:

- Be able to outline the process involved in the genetic engineering of bacteria to produce human insulin.

- Be able to outline the process involved in the genetic engineering of Golden Rice.

- Be able to outline how animals can be genetically engineered for xenotransplantation.

- Be able to discuss the ethical concerns raised by the genetic manipulation of animals (including humans), plants and microorganisms.

Specification Reference 5.2.3

You need to know about genetic engineering for your exam, but the information is important in everyday life too — you get stories about genetically engineered organisms (like food crops) popping up a lot in newspapers.

Producing human insulin

People with Type 1 diabetes need to inject insulin to regulate their blood glucose concentration (see page 36). Insulin used to be obtained from the pancreases of dead animals, such as pigs. Nowadays we use genetically engineered bacteria to manufacture human insulin. Here's how it's done:

1. The gene for human insulin is identified and isolated from human pancreatic cells. This can be done using:

   - restriction enzymes (see page 169).

   - an enzyme called **reverse transcriptase**.

   Reverse transcriptase can be used to make DNA from an RNA template — the DNA produced is called **complementary DNA** (cDNA). This is really useful because many cells only contain two copies of each gene, making it difficult to obtain a DNA fragment containing the desired gene. But cells can contain many mRNA molecules that are complementary to the gene, so mRNA is often easier to obtain. Pancreatic cells contain loads of insulin mRNA, which could be used to make cDNA using reverse transcriptase. The cDNA is then cut with restriction enzymes to produce sticky ends.

2. A plasmid is cut open using the same restriction enzymes that were used in the isolation of the insulin gene.

3. The insulin gene is inserted into the plasmid (forming recombinant DNA).

4. The plasmid is taken up by bacteria and any transformed bacteria are identified using marker genes. The transformed bacteria are then grown in a fermenter — human insulin is produced as the bacteria grow and divide.

5. The human insulin is extracted and purified so it can be used in humans.

This process is summarised in Figure 2 below:

Tip: Reverse transcriptase is often found in viruses with an RNA genome. It converts the virus's RNA to DNA.

Tip: The techniques here are covered in more detail on pages 173-175.

Figure 1: *When insulin was still obtained from animals the first stage was grinding the pancreases.*

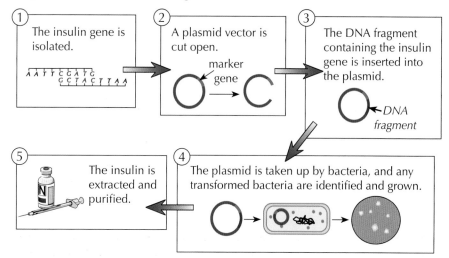

Figure 2: *The production of human insulin using genetically engineered bacteria.*

Advantages of using human insulin

There are many advantages of using genetically engineered human insulin over animal insulin:

- It's identical to the insulin in our bodies, so it's more effective than animal insulin and there's less risk of an allergic reaction.
- It's cheaper and faster to produce than animal insulin, providing a more reliable and larger supply of insulin.
- Using genetically engineered insulin overcomes any ethical or religious issues arising from using animal insulin.

Tip: Genetically engineered organisms are also known as transformed organisms. You might also hear them referred to as GM (genetically modified) organisms.

Producing Golden Rice

Golden Rice is a type of genetically engineered rice. The rice is genetically engineered to contain a gene from a maize plant and a gene from a soil bacterium, which together enable the rice to produce beta-carotene. The beta-carotene is used by our bodies to produce vitamin A. Golden Rice is being developed to reduce vitamin A deficiency in areas where there's a shortage of dietary vitamin A, e.g. south Asia, parts of Africa. Here's how it's produced:

Exam Tip
You need to know how Golden Rice and human insulin are produced using genetic engineering. But in the exam they could ask you a question about the genetic engineering of an organism or product you've not come across before — so make sure you learn the general method (p. 173-175) as well as these specific examples.

Step 1

The *psy* gene (from maize) and the *crtl* gene (from the soil bacterium) are isolated using restriction enzymes — see Figure 3. A plasmid is removed from the *Agrobacterium tumefaciens* bacterium and cut open with the same restriction enzymes. The *psy* and *crtl* genes and a marker gene are inserted into the plasmid.

Step 2

The recombinant plasmid is put back into the bacterium.

Step 3

Rice plant cells are incubated with the transformed *A. tumefaciens* bacteria, which infect the rice plant cells. *A. tumefaciens* inserts the genes into the plant cells' DNA, creating transformed rice plant cells.

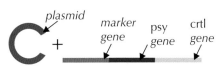

Cut with the same restriction enzymes to give complementary sticky ends

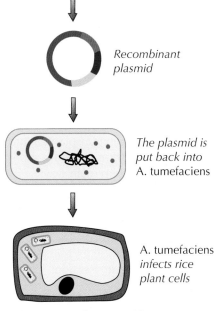

Recombinant plasmid

The plasmid is put back into A. tumefaciens

A. tumefaciens infects rice plant cells

Figure 3: *Producing Golden Rice by genetic engineering.*

Figure 4: *Genetically engineered (transformed) Golden Rice (right) compared to normal white rice (left).*

Step 4

The rice plant cells are then grown on a selective medium — only transformed rice plants will be able to grow because they contain the marker gene that's needed to grow on this medium.

Xenotransplantation

Organ failure (e.g. kidney or liver failure) may be treated with an organ transplant. However, there's a shortage of donor organs available for transplant in the UK, which means many people die whilst waiting for a suitable donor organ. Xenotransplantation is the transfer of cells, tissues or organs from one species to another. It's hoped that xenotransplantation can be used to provide animal donor organs for humans.

With any form of transplantation there's a chance of rejection — the immune system of the recipient recognises proteins on the surface of the transplanted cells as foreign and starts an immune response against them. Rejection is an even greater problem with xenotransplantation because the genetic differences between organisms of different species are even greater than between organisms of the same species — see Figure 5.

Tip:
Xenotransplantation hasn't been successfully carried out in humans yet, but there's lots of research being done on it.

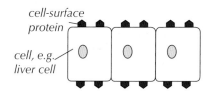

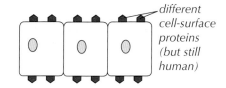

Cells in an original, failing organ
— body recognises the cells as self so the immune system doesn't attack.

Cells in a human transplant organ
— the body may recognise the cells as foreign and so attack.

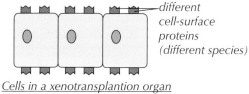

Cells in a xenotransplantion organ
— the body is even more likely to recognise the cells as foreign because the cell-surface proteins are so different.

Figure 5: Cell-surface proteins and organ rejection after transplantation.

Tip: Scientists often use organs from pigs in their research into xerotransplantation. This is because their organs are a similar size to human organs, they're relatively quick and easy to breed, and they're less likely to cause new diseases in humans than many other animals.

Scientists are trying to genetically engineer animals so that their organs aren't rejected when transplanted into humans. This involves altering the animal's DNA, so that cell-surface proteins on the animal's organs are altered. It can be done in two main ways:

1. Inserting human genes

Human genes for human cell-surface proteins are injected into a newly fertilised animal embryo. The genes integrate into the animal's DNA. The animal then produces human cell-surface proteins, which reduces the risk of transplant rejection.

2. Removing or deactivating animal genes

The genes for animal cell-surface proteins are 'knocked out' — they're removed or inactivated in the nucleus of an animal cell. The nucleus is then transferred into an unfertilised animal egg cell (this is called nuclear transfer). The egg cell is then stimulated to divide into an embryo and the animal created doesn't produce animal cell-surface proteins, which reduces the risk of transplant rejection.

Tip: The nuclear transfer technique described here is also used when cloning animals (see page 153).

The issues surrounding genetic engineering

Genetic engineering can be used for loads of things other than producing insulin, reducing vitamin A deficiency and producing organs suitable for transplant from animals. For example, it can be used to produce pest- or herbicide-resistant crops and drugs (and could even be used to genetically engineer humans). All these applications have ethical issues and concerns surrounding them though:

- Some people are worried that using antibiotic-resistance genes as marker genes may increase the number of antibiotic-resistant, pathogenic (disease-causing) microorganisms in our environment.

- Environmentalists are worried that GM crops (like Golden Rice) may encourage farmers to carry out monoculture (where only one type of crop is planted). Monoculture decreases biodiversity and could leave the whole crop vulnerable to disease, because all the plants are genetically identical.

- Some people are worried that genetically engineering animals for xenotransplantation may cause them suffering.

- Some people are concerned about the possibility of 'superweeds' — weeds that are resistant to herbicides because they've bred with genetically engineered herbicide-resistant crops.

- Some people are concerned that large biotechnology companies may use GM crops to exploit farmers in poor countries — e.g. by selling them crops that they can't really afford.

- Some people worry humans will be genetically engineered (e.g. to be more intelligent), creating a genetic underclass. This is currently illegal though.

Figure 6: *Scientists are attempting to genetically engineer plants like this one to produce oils that could be used instead of fossil fuels.*

Tip: There's more on society using science to make decisions on p.6.

Tip: Biodiversity describes the variety of living organisms in an area. Monoculture reduces biodiversity by reducing the number of plant species in an area. This in turn reduces the number of other species, e.g. insects, that the area can support.

Exam Tip
If you're asked to discuss the issues surrounding genetic engineering in the exam, make sure you think about both sides of the debate. That means writing about the arguments both for and against genetic engineering.

Practice Questions — Fact Recall

Q1 Give two ways in which the human insulin gene can be isolated for use in genetic engineering.

Q2 Give one advantage of using human insulin made from genetically engineered microorganisms over animal insulin.

Q3 State two organisms whose genes were used to genetically engineer Golden Rice to produce beta-carotene.

Q4 Why has Golden Rice been developed?

Q5 What is the role of genetic engineering in xenotransplantation?

Q6 Describe one possible benefit of xenotransplantation.

Q7 Give one concern people may have about using genetically engineered plants.

Q8 Why are some people opposed to genetic engineering in humans?

- Be able to explain the term 'gene therapy'.
- Be able to explain the differences between somatic cell gene therapy and germ line cell gene therapy.
- Be able to discuss the ethical concerns raised by the genetic manipulation of animals (including humans).

Specification Reference 5.2.3

Tip: If you can't remember the difference between dominant and recessive alleles, check out page 117.

Tip: Cancers are also caused by mutations. It's possible that some cancers could be treated using gene therapy in the future.

4. Gene Therapy

There is a chance that in the future we'll be able to treat genetic disorders at the source — by using gene therapy to alter the mutations that have caused them.

How does gene therapy work?

Genetic disorders are inherited disorders caused by abnormal genes or chromosomes, e.g. cystic fibrosis. Gene therapy could be used to cure these disorders — it isn't being used yet but some treatments are undergoing clinical trials.

Gene therapy involves altering alleles inside cells to cure genetic disorders. How you do this depends on whether the disorder is caused by a mutated dominant allele or two mutated recessive alleles.

- If it's caused by two mutated recessive alleles you can add a working dominant allele to make up for them — you 'supplement' the faulty ones.
- If it's caused by a mutated dominant allele you can 'silence' the dominant allele (e.g. by sticking a bit of DNA in the middle of the allele so it doesn't work any more).

You get the 'new' allele (DNA) inside the cell by using vectors (see pages 173-174). A range of different vectors can be used, e.g. altered viruses, plasmids or liposomes (spheres made of lipid).

Types of gene therapy

There are two types of gene therapy:

1. Somatic therapy

This involves altering the alleles in body cells, particularly the cells that are most affected by the disorder.

> **Example**
>
> Cystic fibrosis (CF) is a genetic disorder that's very damaging to the respiratory system, so somatic therapy for CF targets the epithelial cells lining the lungs.

Somatic therapy doesn't affect the individual's sex cells (sperm or eggs) though, so any offspring could still inherit the disease.

2. Germ line therapy

This involves altering the alleles in the sex cells. This means that every cell of any offspring produced from these cells will be affected by the gene therapy and they won't suffer from the disease. Germ line therapy in humans is currently illegal though.

Advantages of gene therapy

There are several advantages to gene therapy:

- Gene therapy could prolong the lives of people with life threatening genetic disorders.
- Gene therapy could give people with genetic disorders a better quality of life if it helps to ease symptoms.
- Germ line therapy would allow the carriers of genetic disorders to conceive a baby without that disorder.
- Germ line therapy could decrease the number of people that suffer from genetic disorders and cancer, which is beneficial for individuals and society as a whole (as fewer people will require treatment).

Disadvantages of gene therapy

Gene therapy isn't without its downsides:

- The body could identify vectors as foreign bodies and start an immune response against them.
- An allele could be inserted into the wrong place in the DNA, possibly causing more problems, e.g. cancer.
- An inserted allele could get overexpressed, producing too much of the missing protein, and so causing other problems.
- Disorders caused by multiple genes (e.g. lots of cancers) would be difficult to treat with this technique.
- The effects of the treatment may be short-lived in somatic therapy.
- The patient might have to undergo multiple treatments with somatic therapy.
- It might be difficult to get the allele into specific body cells.

Tip: Gene expression is when genes are transcribed and translated into proteins (see pages 98-100). If a gene is overexpressed, this means that too much of the protein it codes for gets made.

Ethical issues surrounding gene therapy

There are also many ethical issues associated with gene therapy. For example, some people are worried that the technology could be used in ways other than for medical treatment, such as for treating the cosmetic effects of aging. Other people worry that there's the potential to do more harm than good by using the technology (e.g. risk of overexpression of genes — see the disadvantages above). There's also the concern that gene therapy is expensive — some people believe that health service resources could be better spent on other treatments that have passed clinical trials.

Practice Questions — Application

Haemophilia B is caused by a mutation in the gene for the blood clotting factor IX (FIX). Sufferers usually have FIX levels less than 1% of normal values, causing frequent bleeding and often early death. Increasing levels to greater than 1% can greatly improve patient health. Treatment usually involves FIX injections multiple times a week, which is expensive and inconvenient. A trial has investigated the use of somatic gene therapy to treat haemophilia B. Six patients were injected with a virus carrying the normal FIX gene. Some results are shown on the right.

Q1 Explain the role of the virus.

Q2 Calculate the average maximum FIX level after gene therapy.

Q3 Was the trial a success? Give evidence to support your answer.

Q4 Describe the possible advantages and disadvantages of this treatment.

Tip: See page 5 for more about evidence and drawing conclusions.

Patient	Maximum FIX level (% of normal) after therapy
1	2
2	2
3	3
4	4
5	8
6	12

Practice Questions — Fact Recall

Q1 Define the term 'gene therapy'.

Q2 Describe the difference between somatic gene therapy and germ line gene therapy.

Learning Objectives:

- Be able to outline the steps involved in sequencing the genome of an organism.
- Be able to outline how gene sequencing allows for genome-wide comparisons between individuals and between species.

Specification Reference 5.2.3

5. Sequencing Genes and Genomes

Gene sequencing means finding out the order of bases in a gene. Genome sequencing means finding out the order of bases in all of an organism's DNA.

DNA sequencing

DNA can be sequenced by the **chain termination method** — a method used to determine the order of bases in a section of DNA (gene). Here's how it works:

Step 1

A mixture of the following is added to four separate tubes:

- A single-stranded DNA template — the DNA to be sequenced.
- DNA polymerase — the enzyme that joins DNA nucleotides together.
- Lots of DNA primer — short pieces of DNA (see p. 168).
- Free nucleotides — lots of free A, T, C and G nucleotides.
- A fluorescently-labelled modified nucleotide — like a regular nucleotide, but once it's added to a DNA strand, no more bases are added after it. A different modified nucleotide is added to each tube (these are called A*, T*, C*, G*).

Tip: PCR is covered in more detail on pages 168-169.

Step 2

The tubes undergo PCR, which produces many strands of DNA. The strands are different lengths because each one terminates at a different point depending on where the modified nucleotide was added. For example, look at Figure 1 below — in tube A (with the modified adenine nucleotide A*) sometimes A* is added to the DNA at point 4 instead of A, stopping the addition of any more bases (the strand is terminated). Sometimes A is added at point 4, then A* is added at point 5. Sometimes A is added at point 4, A again at point 5, G at point 6 and A* is added at point 7. So strands of three different lengths (4 bases, 5 bases and 7 bases) all ending in A* are produced.

Tip: It's just random chance whether the nucleotide (e.g. A) or the modified nucleotide (e.g. A*) gets added at a particular point.

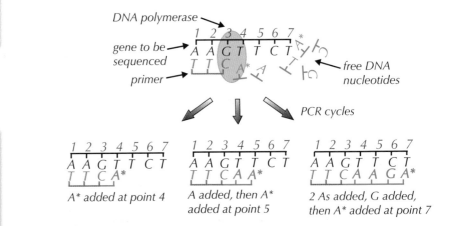

Tip: In this example, A* can't be added at, e.g., point 3 because A doesn't pair with G in complementary base pairing.

A added at point 4*   *A added, then A* added at point 5*   *2 As added, G added, then A* added at point 7*

Figure 1: *DNA sequencing example showing what happens in Tube A, which contains A*.*

Step 3

The DNA fragments in each tube are separated by electrophoresis and visualised under UV light (because of the fluorescent label). The complementary base sequence can be read from the gel (see Figure 2). The smallest nucleotide (e.g. one base) is at the bottom of the gel. Each band after this represents one more base added. So by reading the bands from the bottom of the gel upwards, you can build up the DNA sequence one base at a time.

Tip: Remember, the smallest (shortest) DNA fragments travel the furthest through the gel — towards the positive electrode.

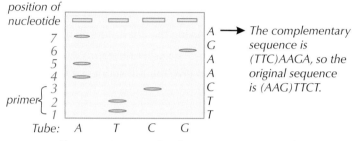

The complementary sequence is (TTC)AAGA, so the original sequence is (AAG)TTCT.

Figure 2: *An example of a DNA sequencing gel.*

Modern Sequencing

Nowadays sequencing is done in one tube in an automated DNA sequencer, and a machine reads the sequence. So instead of running a gel and determining the sequence from that, you get a computer read-out — see Figure 3.

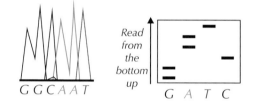

Figure 3: *An automated DNA sequence computer read-out (left) and a DNA sequencing gel (right).*

Figure 4: *An actual DNA sequencing gel.*

Genome sequencing

The chain-termination method can only be used for DNA fragments up to about 750 bp long. So if you want to sequence the entire genome (all the DNA) of an organism, you need to chop it up into smaller pieces first. The smaller pieces are sequenced and then put back in order to give the sequence of the whole genome. Here's how it's done:

Step 1

A genome is cut into smaller fragments (about 100 000 bp) using restriction enzymes — see Figure 5a.

Step 2

The fragments are inserted into **bacterial artificial chromosomes** (**BACs**) — these are man-made plasmids. Each fragment is inserted into a different BAC.

Step 3

The BACs are then inserted into bacteria — each bacterium contains a BAC with a different DNA fragment.

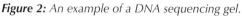

Figure 5a: *Genome sequencing — the first three stages.*

Tip: Genomes vary massively in size — the human genome is about 3 billion bases long, the zebra fish genome is about 1 billion bp, and the HIV genome is only around 9700 bp long. The size of the genome equates roughly to the number of genes. So humans have about 21 000 genes, zebra fish have about 16 000 genes and HIV has 9 genes.

Step 4

The bacteria divide, creating colonies of cloned (identical) cells that all contain a specific DNA fragment — see Figure 5b. Together the different colonies make a complete **genomic DNA library**.

Step 5

DNA is extracted from each colony and cut up using restriction enzymes, producing overlapping pieces of DNA.

Step 6

Each piece of DNA is sequenced, using the chain-termination method.

Step 7

The pieces are put back in order to give the full sequence from that BAC (using powerful computer systems).

Step 8

Finally the DNA fragments from all the BACs are put back in order, by computers, to complete the entire genome.

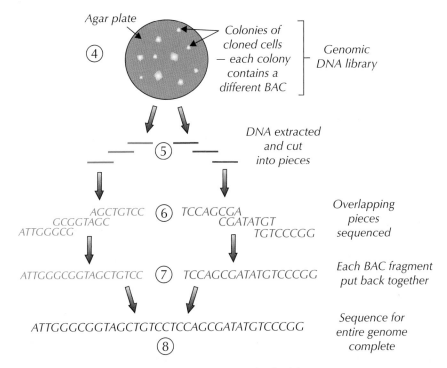

Figure 5b: Genome sequencing — the final five stages.

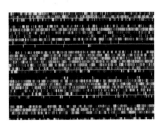

Figure 6: Computer screen display of part of the human genome sequence. The four different bases are represented by bands of different colours.

Comparing genomes

Gene sequences and whole genome sequences can be compared between organisms of different species and between organisms of the same species. There are many reasons why we'd want to do this:

1. Comparisons between different species

Comparing the genomes of different species can help us to understand the evolutionary relationships between different species. All organisms evolved from shared common ancestors (relatives). Closely related species evolved away from each other more recently and so share more DNA. So DNA can tell us how closely related different species are.

Example

Humans, chimpanzees and mice all evolved from a common ancestor. Humans and mice diverged a long time ago, but humans and chimps diverged quite recently. This is shown on the phylogenetic tree below.

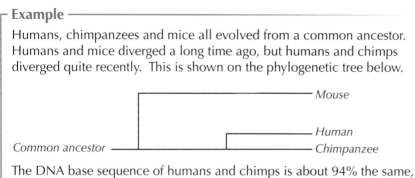

The DNA base sequence of humans and chimps is about 94% the same, but human and mouse DNA is only about 85% the same.

Tip: Phylogenetic trees are just diagrams that show the evolutionary relationships between different species. Species with branches that are close together, are closely related (e.g. humans and chimpanzees). A branch split shows when the species diverged from the common ancestor.

Comparing the genomes across species can also help us to understand the way in which genes interact during development and how they're controlled.

Example

For example, genome sequencing has shown that the homeobox sequence (see page 104) is the same in animals, plants and fungi. By studying how genes with the homeobox sequence work in the *Drosophila* fruit fly scientists can begin to piece together how they work in humans too.

Medical research also often involves comparing genomes across species.

Example

Human genes that are associated with disease, like cancer or heart disease, can be found in the genomes of other mammals, such as mice and rats. This means mice or rats could be used as animal models for research into these diseases.

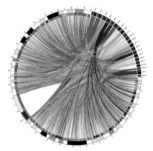

Figure 7: *A circular genome map used to visually compare the sequence of one human chromosome with the entire mouse genome. The coloured lines connect genes that have evolved from common ancestor genes.*

2. Comparisons within the same species

Comparing genomes of the same species can help us to trace early human migration. When different groups of early humans separated and moved to different parts of the world, their genomes changed in slightly different ways. By comparing the genomes of people from different parts of the world, it's possible to build up a picture of early human migration.

Compering genomes of the same species is also used in the study of the genetics of human diseases. Some gene mutations have been linked to a greater risk of disease (e.g. mutations in the BRCA1 gene are linked to breast cancer). Comparisons between the genomes of sufferers and non-sufferers can be used to detect particular mutations that could be responsible for the increased risk of disease.

Researchers may also compare genomes within a species when they're developing medical treatments for particular genotypes. The same medicine can be more effective in some patients than in others, which can be due to their different genomes. In the future, it may be possible to sequence a patient's genome so they can receive the most effective medicine for them.

Practice Questions — Application

Scientists have found a large femur (thigh) bone from an unknown animal species in a swamp. They decide to sequence the bone's DNA, so they can establish what species the bone came from.

The DNA sequencing gel obtained from the DNA of the bone and three reference samples are shown below. Use the gels to answer the questions that follow.

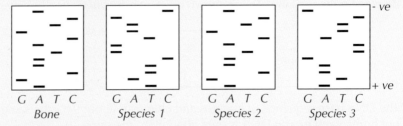

G A T C
Bone

G A T C
Species 1

G A T C
Species 2

G A T C
Species 3

- ve

+ ve

Q1 Give the original DNA sequence of the reference sample from Species 1.

Q2 Which species did the bone come from? Explain your answer.

Section Summary

Make sure you know...

- That millions of identical copies of a DNA fragment can be made using the polymerase chain reaction (PCR).
- That fragments of DNA can be isolated using restriction enzymes. These enzymes recognise and cut DNA at different, specific palindromic sequences (called recognition sequences).
- That when some restriction enzymes cut DNA they leave sticky ends (small tails of unpaired bases) that can be used to bind together DNA fragments with complementary sticky ends.
- That DNA fragments can be run on an electrophoresis gel to separate them according to size (length).
- That DNA probes are short strands of DNA that can be used to locate certain sequences of DNA. The base sequence of a DNA probe is complementary to its target sequence, so will hybridise (bind) to it.
- That genetic engineering can be used to produce transformed organisms and that this involves creating recombinant DNA (DNA made by joining together DNA from different sources), producing transformed cells (cells that have taken up the recombinant DNA), and then identifying and growing the transformed cells.
- The benefits to microorganisms of taking up plasmids from their environment.
- That in vivo cloning is when copies of a gene are made inside a living organism, but that in vitro cloning is when copies of a gene are made outside of a living organism using PCR.
- The relative advantages and disadvantages of both in vivo and in vitro cloning.
- How bacteria are genetically engineered to produce human insulin and the advantages of using this insulin over insulin from other sources.
- How Golden Rice was created and how animals are genetically engineered for xenotransplantation.
- The ethical concerns surrounding the genetic modification of animals, plants and microorganisms.
- That many human diseases, such as genetic disorders, can be caused by mutated genes.
- That gene therapy involves altering defective alleles inside body cells (somatic gene therapy) or sex cells (germ line gene therapy), to attempt to treat or cure genetic disorders and cancer.
- The ethical concerns raised by gene therapy and the genetic manipulation of humans.
- That DNA sequencing is used to determine the order of bases in a section of DNA (e.g. a fragment of a gene) and that the chain termination method is one way this can be carried out.
- That whole genomes can be sequenced using BACs and the chain termination method.
- That the results of whole genome sequencing can be used to compare genomes between and within species, and be able to describe some of the reasons why this is done.

Exam-style Questions

1   An agricultural company is creating a transformed wheat plant containing a gene for herbicide resistance. After announcing some early positive results, the company was approached by anti-genetic engineering activists. The company spoke with some of the activists to hear their concerns but continued production of the plant.

(a)   Suggest **two** ethical concerns that the anti-genetic engineering company may have had with the agricultural company's work.

(2 marks)

Scientists at the company used a **DNA probe** to first locate the resistance gene.

(b) (i)   What is a DNA probe?

(2 marks)

(ii)   Describe how a DNA probe could have been used to locate the gene.

In your answer, you should make clear the sequence of the steps involved in locating the gene.

(7 marks)

(c)   The scientists introduced the gene into some host bacteria. The host bacteria were grown on standard agar plates to produce colonies, which were then transferred to a second set of plates. The first and second sets of plates are shown in Fig. 1.1.

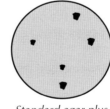

First plate

Second plates

Key:

A — *host cells containing no marker gene*

B — *host cells containing marker gene but no target gene*

1-7 — possible transformed cells

Standard agar

Standard agar plus 250 mg/ml penicillin

Fig. 1.1

(i)   Explain why the colonies of bacteria were transferred to the second set of plates.

(3 marks)

(ii)   Explain why the bacteria in **colony A** were added to the plates.

(2 marks)

(iii)   Suggest **one** colony for use in further experiments on the transformed wheat plant. Explain your choice.

(1 mark)

2   A study was carried out to investigate the effectiveness of gene therapy in patients with X-linked severe combined immunodeficiency disease (SCID). SCID is an inherited disorder that affects the immune system. It is caused by a mutation in the IL2RG gene.

Ten patients were treated with a virus vector carrying a correct version of the IL2RG gene. After gene transfer, the patient's immune system was monitored for at least three years and noted as functional (good) or not. Their health was also monitored for the same time. Fig. 2.1 shows the results.

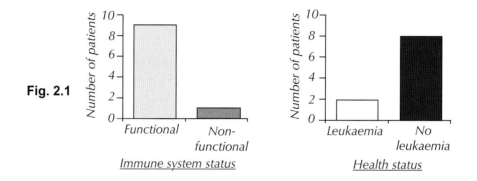

Fig. 2.1

(a)   Besides viruses, give **one** other example of a type of vector.

(1 mark)

(b) (i)   Describe the results shown in Fig. 2.1.

(2 marks)

(ii)   Suggest **two** ways the study could be improved.

(2 marks)

(c)   Outline **one** ethical concern that may be raised by studies using gene therapy.

(1 mark)

3   Scientists are cloning the gene *BtrA* so they can study the effects of the protein it codes for in a species of fish. They start by using PCR to obtain fragments of DNA containing the gene.

(a)   Describe **one** other method they could use to obtain a DNA fragment.

(2 marks)

The scientists next incubate the PCR fragments with a restriction enzyme to produce sticky ends, then use *in vivo* cloning techniques to introduce the gene into a bacterial cell along with a fluorescent marker gene.

(b)   Explain the importance of producing sticky ends for gene cloning.

(2 marks)

(c)   Describe the *in vivo* cloning techniques used after the production of the sticky ends on the DNA fragments.

(6 marks)

(d)   Suggest **one** reason why the scientists used **in vivo** instead of *in vitro* cloning techniques.

(1 mark)

1. Ecosystems and Energy Flow

You need to know what an ecosystem is and how energy flows through it. You also need to learn a whole load of ecology-based definitions — so it's probably time to stop reading this introduction and get started...

What is an ecosystem?

An **ecosystem** is all the organisms living in a certain area and all the non-living conditions (factors) found there. It's a dynamic system — this means it's changing all the time. An ecosystem includes both **biotic** and **abiotic factors**:

- Biotic factors are the living features of an ecosystem, for example, the presence of predators or food.

- Abiotic factors are the non-living features of an ecosystem, such as the temperature and soil.

> **Example**
> In a freshwater ecosystem such as a lake, the biotic factors would include the fish and the abiotic factors would include the temperature of the water.

The place where an organism lives within an ecosystem is known as its **habitat** — for example, a rocky shore on the lake.

Energy transfer through ecosystems

The main route by which energy enters an ecosystem is photosynthesis (e.g. by plants, see p. 60). (Some energy enters sea ecosystems when bacteria use chemicals from deep sea vents as an energy source). During photosynthesis plants convert sunlight energy into a form that can be used by other organisms. Organisms that produce organic molecules using sunlight energy are called **producers** — so plants are producers.

Energy is transferred through the living organisms of an ecosystem when organisms eat other organisms. An organism that eats other organisms is called a **consumer**. Producers are eaten by organisms called **primary consumers**. Primary consumers are then eaten by **secondary consumers** and secondary consumers are eaten by **tertiary consumers**. Primary consumers are mainly herbivores (plant-eaters). Secondary and tertiary consumers eat other animals, so they're known as carnivores (or carnivorous organisms).

Food chains and **food webs** show how energy is transferred through an ecosystem. Food chains show simple lines of energy transfer, and food webs show lots of food chains in an ecosystem and how they overlap — there's an example of each on the next page. A **trophic level** is a stage in a food chain that's occupied by a particular group of organisms, e.g. producers are the first trophic level in a food chain.

Learning Objectives:

- Be able to define the term 'ecosystem'.

- Know that ecosystems are dynamic systems.

- Be able to define the terms 'biotic factor' and 'abiotic factor' using named examples.

- Be able to define the terms 'producer', 'consumer', 'trophic level' and 'decomposer'.

- Be able to describe how energy is transferred through ecosystems.

- Be able to discuss the efficiency of energy transfers between trophic levels.

- Be able to outline how energy transfers between trophic levels can be measured.

- Be able to explain how human activities can manipulate the flow of energy through ecosystems.

Specification Reference 5.3.1

Tip: Remember, the <u>primary</u> consumer is the <u>first</u> consumer in a food chain, the <u>secondary</u> consumer is the <u>second</u> consumer in the food chain, and the <u>tertiary</u> consumer is the <u>third</u> consumer.

Example

The example below shows a food chain (red box) and a food web (blue box).

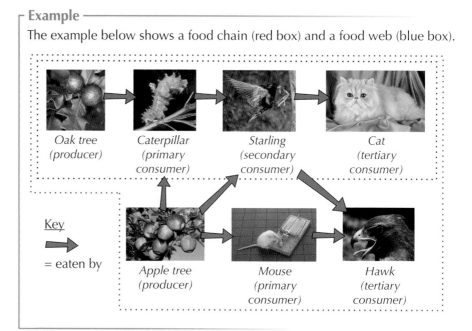

Oak tree
(producer)

Caterpillar
(primary
consumer)

Starling
(secondary
consumer)

Cat
(tertiary
consumer)

Key

⟶

= eaten by

Apple tree
(producer)

Mouse
(primary
consumer)

Hawk
(tertiary
consumer)

Tip: The arrows in a food chain show you the direction of energy flow.

Energy locked up in the things that can't be eaten (e.g. bones, faeces) gets recycled back into the ecosystem by **decomposers** — organisms that break down dead or undigested organic material, e.g. bacteria and fungi.

Calculating energy transfer

Not all the energy (e.g. from sunlight or food) that's available to the organisms in a trophic level is transferred to the next trophic level — around 90% of the total available energy is lost in various ways. Some of the available energy (60%) is never taken in by the organisms in the first place. Reasons for this include:

Tip: When light energy from the sun is 'lost', this doesn't mean it disappears — it's just converted into different forms of energy.

- Plants can't use all the light energy that reaches their leaves, e.g. some is the wrong wavelength, some is reflected, and some passes straight through the leaves.

- Some sunlight can't be used because it hits parts of the plant that can't photosynthesise, e.g. the bark of a tree.

Tip: The photosynthetic pigments in plants only absorb the blue and red wavelengths of light in sunlight, see p.70.

- Some parts of food, e.g. roots or bones, aren't eaten by organisms so the energy isn't taken in.

- Some parts of food are indigestible so pass through organisms and come out as waste, e.g. faeces.

The rest of the available energy (40%) is taken in (absorbed) — this is called the **gross productivity**. But not all of this is available to the next trophic level either. 30% of the total energy available (75% of the gross productivity) is lost to the environment when organisms use energy produced from respiration for movement or body heat. This is called **respiratory loss**.

Figure 1: Respiratory loss from a rabbit.

This means that only 10% of the total energy available (25% of the gross productivity) becomes biomass (e.g. it's stored or used for growth) — this is called the **net productivity**. Net productivity is the amount of energy that's available to the next trophic level.

Energy transfer in a food chain is summarised in Figure 2 on the next page.

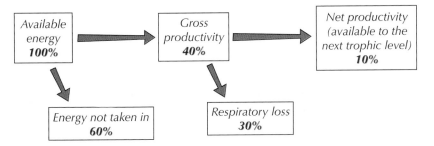

Figure 2: Diagram showing energy transfer in a typical food chain.

Tip: The net productivity of the first organism in a food chain (e.g. a plant) is called the net <u>primary</u> productivity. Factors that affect the rate of photosynthesis (e.g. light intensity, temperature, etc. — see page 70) will affect the net primary productivity of food chains.

Net productivity can be worked out with a simple calculation. Here's how it's calculated:

net productivity = gross productivity – respiratory loss

Example

Rabbits feed on grass which contains 20 000 kJm^{-2}yr^{-1} of energy. However, they don't take in 12 000 kJm^{-2}yr^{-1} of the energy available to them. You can use this information to work out the rabbits' gross productivity.

gross productivity = energy available – energy not taken in

= 20 000 – 12 000

= 8000 kJm^{-2}yr^{-1}

Tip: The unit kJm^{-2}yr^{-1} just means kilojoules per square metre per year.

The rabbits lose 6000 kJm^{-2}yr^{-1} using energy from respiration. You can use this to calculate the net productivity of the rabbits:

net productivity = gross productivity – respiratory loss

= 8000 – 6000

= 2000 kJm^{-2}yr^{-1}

So 2000 kJm^{-2}yr^{-1} is available to the next trophic level.

Tip: In this example, the rabbits take in 8000 kJm^{-2}yr^{-1} of energy.

Efficiency of energy transfer

To find out how efficient the transfer of energy is between two trophic levels you need to work out the percentage efficiency of energy transfer. If you know the amount of energy available to a trophic level (net productivity of the previous trophic level) and the net productivity of that trophic level, you can work it out using this equation:

$$\% \text{ efficiency of energy transfer} = \frac{\text{net productivity of trophic level}}{\text{net productivity of previous trophic level}} \times 100$$

Example

Following on from the example above, the rabbits receive 20 000 kJm^{-2}yr^{-1} from the grass, and their net productivity is 2000 kJm^{-2}yr^{-1}.

So the percentage efficiency of energy transfer is:

$$(2000 \div 20\,000) \times 100 = 10\%$$

Tip: This just shows that 10% of the energy available in the grass is passed on to the rabbit.

The efficiency of energy transfer is not the same throughout a food chain — as you move up a food chain, energy transfer generally becomes more efficient. Different amounts of energy are lost at different stages for different reasons, as shown in the table below:

Stage of food chain	Efficiency of energy transfer	Reason
Sun to producer	Low, around 2-3%	Not all the light energy that plants receive can be absorbed (see page 192) and some energy that is absorbed is then lost during photosynthesis.
Producer to consumer	5-10%	Energy transfer is less efficient from producer to consumer (i.e. to herbivores) than from consumer to consumer (i.e. to carnivores). This is because plants contain a greater proportion of indigestible material (e.g. cellulose within plant cell walls) than animals (which contain a large proportion of relatively digestible meat).
Consumer to consumer	High, around 15-20%	

Even though the efficiency of energy transfer tends to increase as you move up the food chain, energy is still lost at each trophic level — so the more stages there are in a food chain, the more energy is lost overall.

Measuring the efficiency of energy transfer

To calculate the efficiency of energy transfer between trophic levels, you need to know the net productivity of each trophic level. This means measuring the amount of energy in each trophic level. To measure the energy of the organisms in one trophic level, first you calculate the amount of energy or biomass in a sample of the organisms. There are a couple of ways to do this:

- **Using a calorimeter** — A calorimeter is a piece of equipment used for measuring the amount of heat energy released when something is burnt. You can use a calorimeter to directly measure the amount of energy (in joules) in a sample of organic material. This involves burning a known mass of the sample with oxygen, in a sealed chamber surrounded by water. As the sample burns it releases energy, which heats up the temperature of the water. The temperature increase of the water is recorded and this measurement is used to calculate how much energy the sample contained.

- **Measuring an organism's dry mass (biomass)** — You can indirectly measure the amount of energy in an organism by measuring its dry mass (its biomass). To do this, you need to dry the organism out — this is done by heating it up to 80 °C until all the water in it has evaporated. You then weigh the organism. Biomass is created using energy, so it's an indicator of how much energy an organism contains — the more biomass an organism has, the more energy it contains.

Then you multiply the results from the sample to get an estimate of the energy in one trophic level. There are some examples of this on the next page.

- A field of grass measures 10 000 m². To find the amount of energy in the whole field you could find the amount of energy in a 1 m² sample of grass, then multiply this figure by 10 000.

- Twenty rabbits live in the field of grass. To find the amount of energy in the rabbit population, you could find the amount of energy in one rabbit, then multiply this figure by 20.

Controlling energy flow through ecosystems

Farmers try to reduce the amount of energy lost from food chains in order to increase productivity. They use farming methods that make the transfer of energy between trophic levels more efficient:

Herbicides

Herbicides kill weeds that compete with agricultural crops for energy. Reducing competition means crops receive more energy, so they grow faster and become larger, increasing productivity.

Fungicides

Fungicides kill fungal infections that damage agricultural crops. The crops use more energy for growth and less for fighting infection, so they grow faster and become larger, increasing productivity.

Insecticides

Insecticides kill insect pests that eat and damage crops. Killing insect pests means less biomass is lost from crops, so they grow to be larger, which means productivity is greater.

Natural predators

Natural predators introduced to the ecosystem eat the pest species, e.g. ladybirds eat greenfly. This means the crops lose less energy and biomass, increasing productivity.

Fertilisers

Fertilisers are chemicals that provide crops with minerals needed for growth, e.g. nitrates. Crops use up minerals in the soil as they grow, so their growth is limited when there aren't enough minerals. Adding fertiliser replaces the lost minerals, so more energy from the ecosystem can be used to grow, increasing the efficiency of energy conversion.

Rearing livestock intensively

Rearing livestock intensively involves controlling the conditions they live in and when they're slaughtered, so more of their energy is used for growth and less is used for other activities — the efficiency of energy conversion is increased so more biomass is produced and productivity is increased.

Tip: All these methods try to increase (or prevent the loss) of an organism's biomass, which increases the amount of energy available to the next trophic level.

Examples

- Animals may be kept in warm, indoor pens where their movement is restricted. Less energy is wasted keeping warm and moving around.

- Animals may be given feed that's higher in energy than their natural food. This increases the energy input, so more energy is available for growth.

- Animals may be slaughtered before they reach adulthood. Young animals use a greater amount of their energy for growth, so this means more energy is transferred to their biomass.

Tip: Restricting an animal's movement means they respire less, which lowers their respiratory loss.

Figure 3: Battery farmed hens are an example of intensively reared livestock.

The benefits of these methods are that more food can be produced in a shorter space of time, often at lower cost. However, enhancing productivity by intensive rearing raises ethical issues. For example, some people think the conditions intensively reared animals are kept in cause the animals pain, distress or restricts their natural behaviour, so it shouldn't be done.

Practice Questions — Application

Q1 In a food chain mussels have a gross productivity of 22 861 $kJm^{-2}yr^{-1}$ and a respiratory loss of 17 000 $kJm^{-2}yr^{-1}$.
a) Calculate the net productivity of the mussels.

The mussels provide food for crayfish which have a net productivity of 627 $kJm^{-2}yr^{-1}$.
b) Calculate the efficiency of energy transfer between the mussels and the crayfish.

Q2 The diagram below shows the net productivity in a food chain. Use the diagram to answer the following questions.

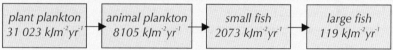

| plant plankton 31 023 $kJm^{-2}yr^{-1}$ | animal plankton 8105 $kJm^{-2}yr^{-1}$ | small fish 2073 $kJm^{-2}yr^{-1}$ | large fish 119 $kJm^{-2}yr^{-1}$ |

a) The gross productivity of the small fish is 8072 $kJm^{-2}yr^{-1}$. Calculate the respiratory loss of the small fish.

b) The respiratory loss of the large fish is 450 $kJm^{-2}yr^{-1}$. Calculate the gross productivity of the large fish.

c) Give one reason why the gross productivity of the large fish is less than the net productivity of the small fish.

d) Calculate the percentage efficiency of energy transfer between each stage of the food chain.

Practice Questions — Fact Recall

Q1 What is the main route by which energy enters an ecosystem?

Q2 Define the term: a) producer,   b) consumer.

Q3 What name is given to the amount of energy taken in by an organism?

Q4 Is energy transfer more efficient to herbivores or to carnivores? Explain your answer.

Q5 Give one method that can be used to measure the amount of energy in a sample of organic material.

Q6 Give two examples of farming methods that increase the transfer of energy through an ecosystem. Explain how each of the methods work.

2. The Nitrogen Cycle

Nitrogen in an ecosystem is cycled between different organisms and the environment, in a process cleverly named... the nitrogen cycle.

What is the nitrogen cycle?

Plants and animals need nitrogen to make proteins and nucleic acids for growth. The atmosphere's made up of about 78% nitrogen, but plants and animals can't use it in that form — they need bacteria to convert it into nitrogen compounds first. The nitrogen cycle shows how nitrogen is converted into a usable form and then passed on between different living organisms and the non-living environment. The nitrogen cycle includes food chains (nitrogen is passed on when organisms are eaten), and four different processes that involve bacteria — nitrogen fixation, ammonification, nitrification and denitrification:

Learning Objectives:

- Be able to describe how microorganisms recycle nitrogen within ecosystems, and be able to identify *Nitrosomonas*, *Nitrobacter* and *Rhizobium* by name.
- Be able to describe the role of decomposers in the decomposition of organic material.

Specification Reference 5.3.1

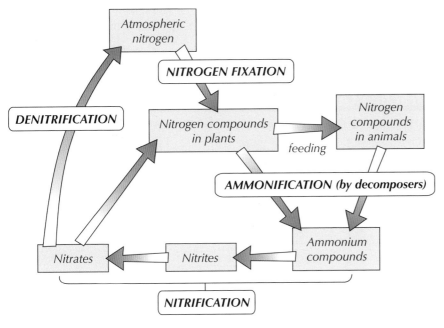

Figure 1: *The four main processes in the nitrogen cycle.*

Tip: The nitrogen cycle shows that nitrogen in an ecosystem is recycled and can be reused by organisms.

Nitrogen fixation

Nitrogen fixation is when nitrogen gas in the atmosphere is converted to ammonia by bacteria called *Rhizobium*. The ammonia can then be used by plants.

Rhizobium are found inside root nodules (growths on the roots — see Figure 1) of leguminous plants (e.g. peas, beans and clover). They form a **mutualistic relationship** with the plants — they provide the plant with nitrogen compounds and the plant provides them with carbohydrates.

Figure 2: *Pink nodules of* Rhizobium *on plant roots.*

Ammonification

Ammonification is when nitrogen compounds from dead organisms are turned into ammonium compounds by decomposers. Animal waste (urine and faeces) also contains nitrogen compounds. These are also turned into ammonium compounds by decomposers.

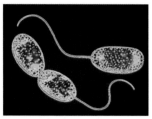

Figure 3: Nitrobacter *bacteria.*

Figure 4: Pseudomonas aeruginosa *are a type of denitrifying bacteria.*

Nitrification

Nitrification is when ammonium compounds in the soil are changed into nitrogen compounds that can then be used by plants. First nitrifying bacteria called *Nitrosomonas* change ammonium compounds into nitrites. Then other nitrifying bacteria called *Nitrobacter* change nitrites into nitrates.

Denitrification

Denitrification is when nitrates in the soil are converted into nitrogen gas by denitrifying bacteria — they use nitrates in the soil to carry out respiration and produce nitrogen gas. This happens under anaerobic conditions (where there's no oxygen), e.g. in waterlogged soils.

Other ways for nitrogen to enter an ecosystem

Not all of the usable nitrogen in an ecosystem has come from nitrogen fixation by bacteria. Other ways that nitrogen gets into an ecosystem is by lightning (which also fixes atmospheric nitrogen) or by artificial fertilisers (they're produced from atmospheric nitrogen on an industrial scale in the Haber process).

Exam Tip
You need to know the microorganisms involved at each stage in the nitrogen cycle, so make sure you get them straight in your head now.

Practice Questions — Fact Recall

Q1 Give one reason why plants and animals need nitrogen.

Q2 Copy and complete the table below about processes in the nitrogen cycle.

Name of process	Bacteria responsible
Nitrogen fixation	
Ammonification	
Nitrification	
Denitrification	

Q3 Describe the process of ammonification.

Q4 Name the process by which nitrates in the soil are converted into nitrogen gas by bacteria.

3. Succession

The types of organisms found in an environment change over time — and the environment itself changes too. This is due to a process called succession.

What is succession?

Succession is the process by which an ecosystem (see page 191) changes over time. Succession happens in a series of stages. At each stage, the species in an area slowly change the environmental conditions (for example, by making the soil more fertile), making those conditions more suitable for other species. This means that the **biotic conditions** change as the **abiotic conditions** change, causing one community of organisms to be succeeded (replaced) by another. There are two main types of succession — primary succession (see below) and secondary succession (see page 201).

Primary succession

Primary succession happens on land that's been newly formed or exposed, e.g. where a volcano has erupted to form a new rock surface, or where sea level has dropped exposing a new area of land. There's no soil or organic material to start with, e.g. just bare rock.

Pioneer stage of succession

Primary succession starts when species colonise a new land surface. Seeds and spores are blown in by the wind and begin to grow. The first species to colonise the area are called **pioneer species**. The abiotic conditions are hostile (harsh) and only pioneer species can grow because they're specialised to cope with the harsh conditions.

Examples

Hostile abiotic conditions

- There is limited water available because there's no soil to retain water.
- There are few minerals or nutrients because there's no soil.
- There may be high light intensity, exposure to wind and rain, and fluctuating temperatures because the area is directly exposed to the Sun and the elements.

Pioneer species

- Marram grass can grow on sand dunes near the sea because it has deep roots to get water and can tolerate the salty environment (see Figure 1).
- Lichens are organisms usually made up of a fungus and an alga. They're able to survive in rocky conditions because the fungus secretes acids which erode the rock, releasing minerals.
- Shrubs of the *Calligonum* genus are pioneer species that can grow in areas that experience periodic drought.

Figure 1: *Marram grass is able to grow in hostile conditions on sand dunes.*

The pioneer species change the abiotic conditions — they die and microorganisms decompose the dead organic material (humus). This forms a basic soil. This makes conditions less hostile, e.g. the basic soil helps to retain water, which means new organisms can move in and grow. The new organisms then die and are decomposed, adding more organic material, making the soil deeper and richer in minerals such as nitrates. Nitrogen-fixing bacteria turn nitrogen from the atmosphere into ammonia, which can then be used by plants (see page 197). This means larger plants like shrubs can start to grow in the deeper soil, which retains even more water and contains more nutrients.

Learning Objective:

- Be able to describe one example of primary succession resulting in a climax community.

Specification Reference 5.3.1

Tip: Remember, biotic conditions (factors) are the living features of an ecosystem, e.g. the plant and animal communities. Abiotic conditions (factors) are the non-living features, such as light, CO_2 and water availability.

Tip: The pioneer species help to stabilise an environment — they make it possible for other species to grow there.

Later stages of succession

At each stage, different plants and animals that are better adapted for the improved conditions move in, out-compete the plants and animals that are already there, and become the dominant species in the ecosystem. The dominant species are the ones which cause the most change to the abiotic environment, making it more suitable for other species.

As succession goes on, the ecosystem becomes more complex. New species move in alongside existing species, which means the species diversity increases. Plants create more habitats for animals, the abiotic conditions become less hostile and the amount of biomass increases.

Eventually these changes result in a **climax community** — the ecosystem is supporting the largest and most complex community of plants and animals it can. It won't change much more — it's in a steady state.

Figure 2: *Lichens (orange and white) have adaptations that allow them to live on bare rock.*

Example — primary succession

1. Bare rock lacks soil, is exposed to strong winds and has periods of drought. Lichens (the pioneer species) are able to survive because they can grow in cracks to avoid the wind, break down rock to release minerals and are adapted to survive periods of drought.

bare rock ⟵   *lichen*

2. The lichens die and are decomposed helping to form a thin soil, which thickens as more organic material is formed. This means other species such as mosses can grow.

thin soil ⟵   *moss*

3. Larger plants that need more water can move in as the soil deepens, e.g. grasses and small flowering plants. The soil continues to deepen as the larger plants die and are decomposed.

small flowering plants   *grass*

4. Shrubs, ferns and small trees begin to grow, out-competing the grasses and smaller plants to become the dominant species. Diversity increases.

shrubs   *small trees (rowan and alder)*   *ferns*

5. Finally, the soil is deep and rich enough in nutrients to support large trees. These become the dominant species, and the climax community is formed.

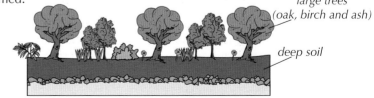
large trees (oak, birch and ash)   *deep soil*

Secondary succession

Secondary succession happens on land that's been cleared of all the plants, but where the soil remains, e.g. after a forest fire or where a forest has been cut down by humans. The established community of species is usually destroyed, but without too much disturbance to the soil. It can occur during any stage (including the climax community) after the pioneer stage.

The process of secondary succession is similar to primary succession, but because there's already a soil layer, secondary succession starts at a later stage — and the pioneer species are larger plants, e.g. shrubs.

Figure 3: Secondary succession following a forest fire.

Climatic climax communities

Which species make up the climax community depends on what the climate's like in an ecosystem. The climax community for a particular climate is called its **climatic climax**.

─ Examples ─

- In a temperate climate, e.g. the UK, there's plenty of available water, mild temperatures and not much change between the seasons. The climatic climax will contain large trees because they can grow in these conditions once deep soils have developed (see Figure 4).

- In a polar climate there's not much available water, temperatures are low and there are massive changes between the seasons. Large trees won't ever be able to grow in these conditions, so the climatic climax contains only herbs or shrubs, but it's still the climax community (see Figure 5).

Figure 4: The climax community in many parts of Britain is deciduous woodland.

Practice Questions — Application

A team analysed data on ecological changes in part of a national park. Their results are shown in the graph below.

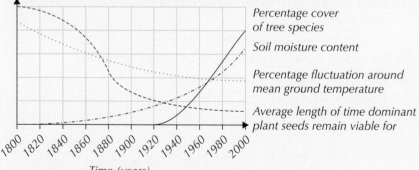

Percentage cover of tree species

Soil moisture content

Percentage fluctuation around mean ground temperature

Average length of time dominant plant seeds remain viable for

Time (years)

Q1 What type of succession is shown on the graph? Explain your answer.

Q2 Describe the characteristics of the dominant plant community between 1800 and 1860.

Q3 Describe and suggest an explanation for the change shown in the average length of time dominant plant seeds remain viable for.

Q4 During what time period would you expect to see a high percentage of plants whose seeds require high light intensity for germination? Explain your answer.

Q5 Describe and suggest an explanation for the change in the soil moisture content shown on the graph.

Figure 5: The climax community in most of Greenland is arctic tundra.

Tip: 'Remains viable for' means how long the plant seeds are capable of germinating (sprouting).

Preventing and deflecting succession

Human activities can prevent succession, stopping the normal climax community from developing. When succession is stopped artificially like this, the climax community is called a **plagioclimax**.

> **Example**
>
> The management of a nature reserve in Dorset prevents the growth of large trees on areas of the land. This keeps the land as heathland and is done to protect some of the small reptiles that inhabit the area — if large trees were allowed to grow, other species of animals would move into the area which would out-compete the reptiles. The nature reserve is a plagioclimax.

Figure 6: Succession is prevented at a nature reserve in Dorset, creating a plagioclimax.

Deflected succession is when succession is prevented by human activity, but the plagioclimax that develops is one that's different to any of the natural stages of the ecosystem — the path of succession has been deflected from its natural course.

> **Example**
>
> A regularly mown grassy field won't develop woody plants, even if the climate of the ecosystem could support them. The growing points of the woody plants are cut off by the lawnmower, so larger plants can't establish themselves — only the grasses can survive being mowed, so the climax community is a grassy field. A grassy field isn't a natural stage — there should also be things like small flowering plants, so succession has been deflected.

Tip: Grazing and burning have the same effect as mowing.

Exam Tip
You need to be able to use the correct ecological terms (like primary succession and climax community) in your exam.

Practice Questions — Fact Recall

Q1 What is succession?

Q2 Which type of succession happens in areas with no soil?

Q3 What name is given to the first species to colonise an area in primary succession?

Q4 What is a climax community?

Q5 Suggest an event that could cause secondary succession.

Q6 What is a climatic climax community?

Q7 What is a plagioclimax?

4. Variation in Population Size

The size of a population changes all the time for lots of different reasons. But to understand why a population grows and shrinks, first you need to know exactly what a population is...

Populations

A **population** is all the organisms of one species in a habitat.

┌─ Examples ─
- All the foxes in a wood form a population.
- All the people in a town form a population.

Population size is the total number of organisms of one species in a habitat. This number changes over time because of the effect of various factors.

Abiotic factors and population size

The population size of any species varies because of abiotic factors, e.g. the amount of light, water or space available, the temperature of their surroundings or the chemical composition of their surroundings. When abiotic factors are ideal for a species, organisms can grow fast and reproduce successfully.

┌─ Example ─
When the temperature of a mammal's surroundings is the ideal temperature for metabolic reactions to take place, they don't have to use up as much energy maintaining their body temperature. This means more energy can be used for growth and reproduction, so their population size will increase.

When abiotic factors aren't ideal for a species, organisms can't grow as fast or reproduce as successfully.

┌─ Example ─
When the temperature of a mammal's surroundings is significantly lower or higher than their optimum body temperature, they have to use a lot of energy to maintain the right body temperature. This means less energy will be available for growth and reproduction, so their population size will decrease.

Biotic factors and population size

Population size can also vary because of biotic factors. These factors include interspecific competition, intraspecific competition and predation.

1. Interspecific competition

Interspecific competition is when organisms of different species compete with each other for the same resources. This can mean that the resources available to both populations are reduced, e.g. if they share the same source of food, there will be less available to both of them. This means both populations will be limited by a lower amount of food. They'll have less energy for growth and reproduction, so the population sizes will be lower for both species.

Learning Objectives:
- Be able to explain, with examples, the terms 'interspecific competition' and 'intraspecific competition'.
- Be able to explain the meaning of the term 'carrying capacity'.
- Be able to describe predator-prey relationships and their possible effects on the population sizes of both the predator and the prey.
- Be able to explain the significance of limiting factors in determining the final size of a population.

Specification Reference 5.3.2

Tip: Remember — abiotic factors are the non-living features of the ecosystem.

Tip: Remember — biotic factors are the living features of the ecosystem.

Tip: Don't think it's only animals that compete with each other — plants compete with each other for things like minerals and light.

Figure 1: Interspecific competition between red (top) and grey (bottom) squirrels has caused a decline in the population of red squirrels in the UK.

Interspecific competition can also affect the distribution of species. If two species are competing but one is better adapted to its surroundings than the other, the less well adapted species is likely to be out-competed — it won't be able to exist alongside the better adapted species.

Example

Grey squirrels were introduced to the UK. They now compete with the native red squirrels for the same food sources and habitats. As they share the same source of food, there is less available to both of them. So in areas where both red and grey squirrels live, both populations are smaller than they would be if there was only one species there.

Since the introduction of the grey squirrel to the UK, the native red squirrel has disappeared from large areas. The grey squirrel has a better chance of survival because it's larger and can store more fat over winter. It can also eat a wider range of food than the red squirrel.

2. Intraspecific competition

Intraspecific competition is when organisms of the same species compete with each other for the same resources. It can cause a cyclical change in population size, where the population grows, shrinks, grows again and so on (see Figure 2). This is because the population of a species increases when resources are plentiful. As the population increases, there'll be more organisms competing for the same amount of space and food. Eventually, resources such as food and space become limiting — there isn't enough for all the organisms. The population then begins to decline. A smaller population then means that there's less competition for space and food, which is better for growth and reproduction — so the population starts to grow again. The maximum stable population size of a species that an ecosystem can support is called the **carrying capacity**.

Example

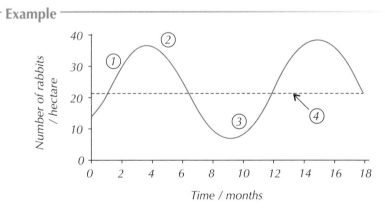

Figure 2: Intraspecific competition in a rabbit population.

1. There were lots of resources available so the population of rabbits grew.
2. The population grew so large that the resources became limiting. As there weren't enough resources, the rabbit population fell.
3. A smaller population of rabbits meant there was less competition, so the population of rabbits began to grow again.
4. The carrying capacity of the ecosystem was about 22 rabbits per hectare.

3. Predation

Predation is where an organism (the predator) kills and eats another organism (the prey), e.g. lions kill and eat (predate on) buffalo. The population sizes of predators and prey are interlinked — as the population of one changes, it causes the other population to change (see Figure 4).

As the prey population increases, there's more food for predators, so the predator population grows. As the predator population increases, more prey is eaten so the prey population then begins to fall. This means there's less food for the predators, so their population decreases, and so on.

Example

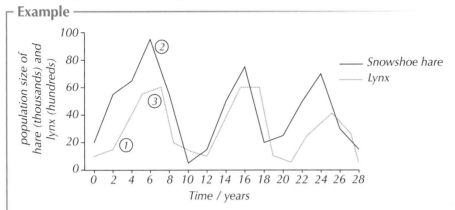

Figure 4: Populations of snowshoe hare and lynx.

Figure 3: Predation of snowshoe hares by lynxes causes the populations of both species to fluctuate over time.

1. In the graph above, the lynx population grew after the snowshoe hare population increased. This is because there was more food available for the lynx.

2. Greater numbers of lynx ate lots of snowshoe hares, so the population of hares fell.

3. Reduced snowshoe hare numbers meant there was less food for the lynx, so the population of lynx fell.

Predator-prey relationships are usually more complicated than this though because there are other factors involved, like availability of food for the prey. E.g. it's thought that the population of snowshoe hare initially begins to decline because there's too many of them for the amount of food available. This is then accelerated by predation from the lynx.

Limiting factors

Limiting factors stop the population size of a species increasing. They can be abiotic or biotic.

Example — an abiotic limiting factor

The amount of shelter in an ecosystem limits the population size of a species because there's only enough shelter for a certain number of individuals.

Example — a biotic limiting factor

Interspecific competition limits the population size of a species because the amount of resources available to a species is reduced.

Tip: Disease is another example of a biotic limiting factor of population growth — it could even make a population extinct.

Practice Questions — Application

A team investigated changes in the size of a population of owls and a population of mice over twenty years. They also monitored changes in temperature. Their results are shown on the graph below.

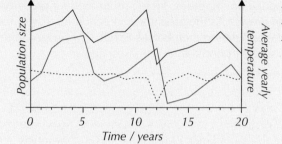

Tip: In the exam, if you're given a graph with two y-axes like the one on the right, make sure you read the key carefully so you know which line relates to which axis.

Q1 Give one factor affecting the population of owls which is biotic.

Q2 Describe how the fall in temperature between years 11 and 12 affected the mouse population size, and suggest a reason for the change in population size.

Q3 Explain how variation in the mouse population size over the twenty year period could have caused changes in the owl population size.

Tip: With 'suggest' questions, like in Q2 on the right, you probably won't have learned the exact answer — you need to use the information you're given and apply your own knowledge to answer the question.

Practice Questions — Fact Recall

Q1 What is a population?

Q2 a) What is interspecific competition?

　 b) Explain how interspecific competition may affect:

　　 i) the population sizes of two species competing.

　　 ii) the distribution of two species competing, if one species is better adapted to its surroundings.

　 c) Describe an example of interspecific competition.

Q3 a) What is intraspecific competition?

　 b) Explain why intraspecific competition causes a cyclical change in population size.

Q4 What is meant by the term 'carrying capacity'?

Q5 Explain how an increase in prey population will affect predator population.

Q6 What term is used to describe something that stops the population size of a species from growing?

5. Investigating Populations

Learning Objective:

- Be able to describe how the abundance and distribution of organisms can be measured using quadrats, point quadrats, line transects and belt transects.

Specification Reference 5.3.1

There are lots of ways of investigating populations. Whichever method you use, you need to make sure your samples are random...

Abundance and distribution

Investigating populations of organisms involves looking at the abundance and distribution of species in a particular area.

Abundance

Abundance is the number of individuals of one species in a particular area. The abundance of mobile organisms and plants can be estimated by simply counting the number of individuals in samples taken. Percentage cover can also be used to measure the abundance of plants — this is how much of the area you're investigating is covered by a species (see next page).

Distribution

Distribution is where a particular species is within the area you're investigating.

Sampling

Most of the time it would be too time-consuming to measure the number of individuals and the distribution of every species in the entire area you're investigating, so instead you take samples:

1. Choose an area to sample — a small area within the area being investigated.

2. Samples should be random to avoid bias, e.g. by randomly selecting coordinates from a grid (see below).

3. Use an appropriate technique to take a sample of the population (see next two pages).

4. Repeat the process, taking as many samples as possible in the time you have available. This gives a more reliable estimate for the whole area.

5. The number of individuals for the whole area can then be estimated by taking an average of the data collected in each sample and multiplying it by the size of the whole area. The percentage cover for the whole area can be estimated by taking the average of all the samples.

Tip: There's more on sampling and the importance of collecting data at random on p. 4.

Random number generators

If you were investigating populations in a field, you could pick random sample sites by dividing the field into a grid and using a random number generator and a random letter generator to select coordinates. This will give you coordinates at random, e.g. B7, E5, etc (see Figure 1). Then you just take your samples from these coordinates.

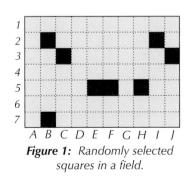

Figure 1: *Randomly selected squares in a field.*

Tip: Drawing numbers out of a hat is another way of generating random numbers.

Methods for investigating populations

There are lots of different methods for studying populations of organisms, but you need to choose the most suitable one to use — the method will depend on the type of organism and its habitat. You need to learn the ones described on the next two pages.

Frame quadrats

A frame quadrat is a square frame divided into a grid of 100 smaller squares by strings attached across the frame — see Figure 2.

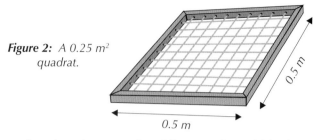

Figure 2: A 0.25 m² quadrat.

0.5 m

0.5 m

Quadrats are placed on the ground at different points within the area you're investigating. This can be done by selecting random coordinates (see previous page).
 The number of individuals of each species is recorded in each quadrat.

The percentage cover of a species can also be measured by counting how much of the quadrat is covered by the species — you count a square if it's more than half-covered (see Figure 3). Percentage cover is a quick way to investigate populations and you don't have to count all the individual plants.

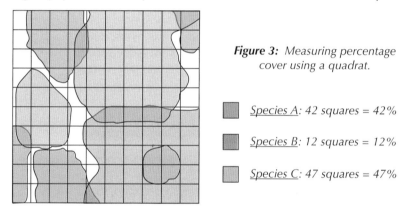

Figure 3: Measuring percentage cover using a quadrat.

Species A: 42 squares = 42%

Species B: 12 squares = 12%

Species C: 47 squares = 47%

Frame quadrats are useful for quickly investigating areas with plant species that fit within a small quadrat — most frame quadrats are 1 m by 1 m. Areas with larger plants and trees need very large quadrats. Large quadrats aren't always in a frame — they can be marked out with a tape measure.

Point quadrats

A point quadrat is a horizontal bar on two legs with a series of holes at set intervals along its length (see Figure 5). Point quadrats are placed on the ground at random points within the area you're investigating. Pins are dropped through the holes in the frame and every plant that each pin touches is recorded. If a pin touches several overlapping plants, all of them are recorded. The number of individuals of each species is recorded in each quadrat.

wood frame   pins   hole to place pin

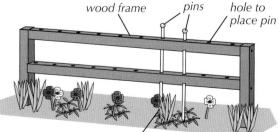

Figure 5: A point quadrat.

multiple hits

Tip: Putting your quadrat down where you happen to be standing, or even chucking it over your shoulder, doesn't count as taking a random sample. You're best off using a random number generator to select the coordinates to take your samples from.

Figure 4: Quadrats can be used to measure the abundance of plant species in a field.

Tip: Frame quadrats can also be used to measure the abundance of slow moving or sessile (immobile) animals, e.g. limpets on a rocky shore.

Tip: A problem with point quadrats is that very small or rare species may be missed.

The percentage cover of a species can also be measured by calculating the number of times a pin has touched a species as a percentage of the total number of pins dropped. Point quadrats are especially useful in areas where there's lots of dense vegetation close to the ground.

Transects

You can use lines called transects to help find out how plants are distributed across an area, e.g. how the distribution of a plant species changes from a hedge towards the middle of a field. There are three types of transect:

- **Line transects** — a tape measure is placed along the transect and the species that touch the tape measure are recorded.

- **Belt transects** — data is collected along the transect using frame quadrats placed next to each other.

- **Interrupted transects** — instead of investigating the whole transect of either a line or a belt, you can take measurements at intervals. E.g. by placing point quadrats at right angles to the direction of the transect at set intervals along its length, such as every 2 m.

Tip: Transects can be used in any ecosystem, not just fields. For example, along a beach.

Tip: Transects can also be used to investigate the distribution of slow moving or sessile animals.

Tip: Line transects are quick to carry out but a belt transect will give more data (as it covers a wider area). An interrupted belt transect is a good compromise between the two — it's quicker than a belt transect and gives more information than a line transect.

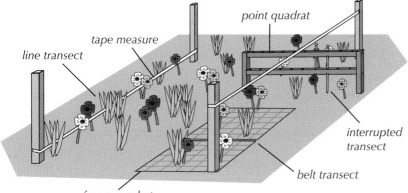

Figure 6: A line transect, a belt transect and an interrupted transect.

Practice Questions — Application

Q1 A student is investigating the abundance of daisies in a field.
   a) She decides to use a frame quadrat to measure the percentage cover of daisies in the field. Describe how she could do this.
   b) Describe how the student could take random samples using a frame quadrat.

Q2 A scientist has been investigating the effect of salt spray from a road adjacent to an inland field. Her results are shown below and on the next page.

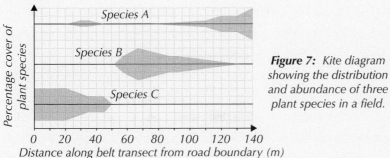

Figure 7: Kite diagram showing the distribution and abundance of three plant species in a field.

Tip: The methods described on the previous two pages aren't the only ones you can use to catch organisms, e.g. sweep nets can be used to catch flying insects.

Tip: A kite diagram shows the distribution and abundance of organisms along a transect. The thickness of the kite shape shows the abundance — the thicker the kite shape, the more organisms there are.

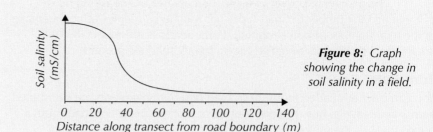

Figure 8: Graph showing the change in soil salinity in a field.

Soil salinity (mS/cm)

0   20   40   60   80   100   120   140
Distance along transect from road boundary (m)

a) Describe the data shown in the kite diagram and the graph.

b) One of the plant species is normally found in coastal areas. Which species is this likely to be, A, B or C? Explain your answer.

c) The scientist is unable to prove that salt spray from the road is responsible for the absence of species B between 0 and 20 m from the road using the data shown above. Explain why.

Practice Questions — Fact Recall

Q1 What is meant by the terms:

   a) abundance?

   b) distribution?

Q2 a) Why would an ecologist investigating the abundance of a species in an area take samples?

   b) Why is it important that these samples are taken at random?

Q3 Describe how a point quadrat would be used to investigate the abundance of a plant species in a field.

Q4 Explain the difference between a line transect and a belt transect.

6. Conservation of Ecosystems

Learning Objectives:

- Be able to explain that conservation is a dynamic process involving management and reclamation.

- Be able to discuss the economic, social and ethical reasons for conservation of biological resources.

- Be able to distinguish between the terms 'conservation' and 'preservation'.

- Be able to outline, with examples, the effects of human activities on the animal and plant populations in the Galapagos Islands.

- Be able to explain how the management of an ecosystem can provide resources in a sustainable way, with reference to timber production in a temperate country.

Specification Reference 5.3.2

Ecosystems provide us with natural resources that we use in everyday life, such as food, fuel and drugs. It's important that we protect ecosystems so that species living in the ecosystems aren't destroyed and that these resources won't run out.

What is conservation?

Conservation is the protection and management of ecosystems so that the natural resources in them can be used without them running out. E.g. using rainforests for timber without any species becoming extinct and without any habitats being destroyed. This means the natural resources will still be available for future generations.

Conservation is a dynamic process — conservation methods need to be adapted to the constant changes (caused naturally and by humans) that occur within ecosystems. It involves the management of ecosystems — controlling how resources are used and replaced.

Conservation can also involve reclamation — restoring ecosystems that have been damaged or destroyed so they can be used again, e.g. restoring forests that have been cut down so they can be used again.

Conservation is important for many reasons:

Economic reasons

Ecosystems provide resources for lots of things that humans need, e.g. rainforests contain species that provide things like drugs, clothes and food. These resources are economically important because they're traded on a local and global scale. If the ecosystems aren't conserved, the resources that we use now will be lost, so there will be less trade in the future.

Social reasons

Many ecosystems bring joy to lots of people because they're attractive to look at and people use them for activities, e.g. birdwatching and walking. The species and habitats in the ecosystems may be lost if they aren't conserved, so future generations won't be able to use and enjoy them.

Ethical reasons

Some people think we should conserve ecosystems simply because it's the 'right' thing to do — especially if an ecosystem is at risk because of human activity. Some people think we have a moral responsibility to conserve ecosystems for future generations, so they can enjoy and use them.

Ecological reasons

Conserving species and habitats can help to prevent climate change. E.g. when trees are burnt, CO_2 is released into the atmosphere, which contributes to global warming. If the trees are conserved, this doesn't happen. Conserving species and habitats also helps to prevent the disruption of food chains. Disruption of food chains can have knock-on effects on other organisms, e.g. some species of bear feed on salmon, which feed on herring — if the number of herring decreases it can affect both the salmon and the bear populations.

Tip: Cast your mind back to AS biology — the reasons for conservation are similar to the reasons for conserving biodiversity.

Preservation

Preservation is different from conservation — it's the protection of ecosystems so they're kept exactly as they are. Nothing is removed from a preserved ecosystem and they're only used for activities that don't damage them.

> **Example**
>
> Antarctica is a preserved ecosystem because it's protected from exploitation by humans — it's only used for limited tourism and scientific research, not mining or other industrial activities.

Figure 1: *Antarctica is a preserved ecosystem.*

Human impact on ecosystems

Humans often need to conserve or preserve ecosystems because our activities have badly affected them, e.g. large areas of the Amazon rainforest have been cleared without being replaced, destroying the ecosystem.

Galapagos Islands

Human activities have had a negative effect on the Galapagos Islands, a small group of islands in the Pacific Ocean about 1000 km off the coast of South America. Many species of animals and plants have evolved there that can't be found anywhere else, e.g. the Galapagos giant tortoise and the Galapagos sea lion. Here are some ways in which the animal and plant populations there have been affected by human activity:

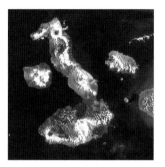

Figure 2: *Satellite picture of the western Galapagos Islands.*

- Explorers and sailors that visited the Galapagos Islands in the 19th century directly affected the populations of some animals by eating them.
  > **Example**
  >
  > A type of giant tortoise found on Floreana Island was hunted to extinction for food.

- Non-native animals introduced to the islands eat some native species. This has caused a decrease in the populations of native species.
  > **Examples**
  >
  > - Non-native dogs, cats and black rats eat young giant tortoises and Galapagos land iguanas.
  > - Pigs also destroy the nests of the iguanas and eat their eggs.
  > - Goats have eaten much of the plant life on some of the islands.

Tip: Native plants and animals are those which naturally occur on the islands.

- Non-native plants have also been introduced to the islands. These compete with native plant species, causing a decrease in their populations.
  > **Example**
  >
  > Quinine trees are taller than some native plants — they block out light to the native plants, which then struggle to survive.

Figure 3: *The existence of the Galapagos land iguanas is under threat because of non-native animals introduced to the islands.*

- Fishing has caused a decrease in the populations of some of the sea life around the Galapagos Islands.
  > **Examples**
  >
  > - The populations of sea cucumbers and hammerhead sharks have been reduced because of overfishing.
  > - Galapagos green turtle numbers have also been reduced by overfishing and they're also killed accidentally when they're caught in fishing nets. They're now an endangered species.

- A recent increase in tourism (from 41 000 tourists in 1991 to around 160 000 in 2008) has led to an increase in development on the islands.

> **Example**
>
> The airport on Baltra island has been redeveloped to receive more tourists. This causes damage to the ecosystems as more land is cleared and pollution is increased.

- The population on the islands has also increased due to the increased opportunities from tourism. This could lead to further development and so more damage to the ecosystems.

Managing ecosystems in a sustainable way

Ecosystems can be managed to provide resources in a way that's sustainable — this means enough resources are taken to meet the needs of people today, but without reducing the ability of people in the future to meet their own needs.

Temperate woodland

Temperate woodland can be managed in a sustainable way — for every tree that's cut down for timber, a new one is planted in its place. The woodland should never become depleted. Cutting down trees and planting new ones needs to be done carefully to be successful:

- Trees are cleared in strips or patches — woodland grows back more quickly in smaller areas between bits of existing woodland than it does in larger, open areas.

- The cleared strips or patches aren't too large or exposed — lots of soil erosion can occur on large areas of bare ground. If the soil is eroded, newly planted trees won't be able to grow.

- Timber is sometimes harvested by coppicing — cutting down trees in a way that lets them grow back. This means new trees don't need to be planted.

- Only native species are planted — they grow most successfully because they're adapted to the climate.

- Planted trees are attached to posts to provide support, and are grown in plastic tubes to stop them being eaten by grazing animals — this makes it more likely the trees will survive to become mature adults.

- Trees aren't planted too close together — this means the trees aren't competing with each other for space or resources, so they're more likely to survive.

Tip: Temperate woodland is found between the tropics and the polar circles (so the UK has temperate woodland).

Figure 4: *The bottom of this young tree has been attached to a post and covered with plastic to protect it while it grows.*

Practice Questions — Fact Recall

Q1 'Conservation is a dynamic process' — what does this mean?

Q2 What does reclamation mean?

Q3 Outline an economic reason for conserving an ecosystem.

Q4 Give one reason why ecosystems might be conserved for social reasons.

Q5 What is the difference between conservation and preservation?

Q6 Give two ways in which human activities have negatively affected populations of plants and/or animals on the Galapagos Islands.

Section Summary

Make sure you know:

- That an ecosystem is all the organisms living in a certain area and all the non-living conditions (factors) found there, and that it's a dynamic system — it's changing all the time.
- That biotic factors (e.g. the presence of predators and food) are all the living features of an ecosystem and that abiotic factors (e.g. temperature, soil) are all the non-living features of an ecosystem.
- That a producer is an organism that produces organic molecules using sunlight energy, a consumer is an organism that eats other organisms, a trophic level is a stage in a food chain that's occupied by a particular group of organisms, and a decomposer is an organism that breaks down dead or undigested organic material.
- That energy is transferred in an ecosystem through food chains and food webs from producers to primary consumers, then to secondary consumers and tertiary consumers by feeding.
- That you can work out the total amount of energy that can be passed from one trophic level to the next using the equation: net productivity = gross productivity – respiratory loss.
- How to work out percentage efficiency of energy transfer using the equation: (net productivity of trophic level ÷ net productivity of previous trophic level) × 100
- How the efficiency of energy transfer differs between trophic levels.
- That you can measure the amount of energy in an organism directly using a calorimeter or indirectly by measuring its dry mass (biomass).
- That farming activities such as using herbicides, fungicides, insecticides, natural predators, fertilisers and intensively rearing livestock can increase the flow of energy through an ecosystem.
- The four main processes of the nitrogen cycle and the microorganisms involved: nitrogen fixation (*Rhizobium*), ammonification, nitrification (*Nitrosomonas* and *Nitrobacter*) and denitrification.
- That succession is the process by which an ecosystem changes over time, and how this happens.
- That succession begins with a pioneer species and ends with a climax community.
- That at each stage in succession, species change the abiotic conditions, so that the environment becomes more suitable for other species, increasing species diversity.
- That the size of a population varies because of the effect of abiotic factors (such as the temperature of the surroundings) and because of the effect of biotic factors (which include interspecific competition and intraspecific competition).
- That the carrying capacity is the maximum stable population size of a species that an ecosystem can support.
- That predation affects the population sizes of both the predators and the prey — as the prey population increases, there's more food for predators, so the predator population grows. As the predator population increases, more prey is eaten so the prey population then begins to fall.
- That limiting factors (e.g. amount of shelter) stop the population size of a species increasing.
- How the abundance and distribution of organisms can be measured using frame quadrats, point quadrats, line transects and belt transects.
- That conservation is the protection and management of ecosystems.
- That conservation is a dynamic process and that it may involve reclamation — the restoration of damaged ecosystems.
- How conservation is important for economic, social, ethical and ecological reasons.
- That preservation is the protection of ecosystems so that they're kept exactly as they are.
- That human activities, such as introducing non-native species, fishing and tourism, have had negative effects on the animal and plant populations in the Galapagos Islands.
- That ecosystems (such as temperate woodland) can be managed in a sustainable way to make sure there are enough resources to meet the needs of people today and in the future.

Exam-style Questions

1   An investigation has been conducted on two species of grasshopper, species A and species B, in an area of grassy fields.

Fig. 1.1 shows changes in the population sizes of species A and B in the area under investigation.

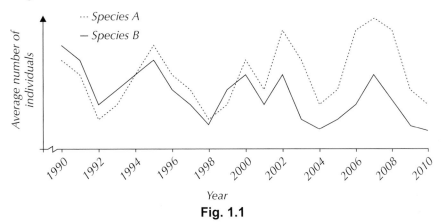

Fig. 1.1

(a) (i) Describe **and** explain the trend shown by Fig. 1.1, with reference to the type of competition it shows.

(3 marks)

   (ii) The amount of food available prevents the population size of each grasshopper species from increasing further.

What term is used to describe the amount of food available in this case?

(1 mark)

(b)   Sheep frequently graze in one of the grassy fields the scientists are investigating. Explain how this may result in deflected succession.

(2 marks)

2   A team of scientists are investigating the distribution of marsh marigolds across a field that is directly next to a stream.

(a) (i) Suggest and describe a method the scientists could use to investigate the distribution of marsh marigolds.

(2 marks)

   (ii) The team decide they want to record the percentage cover of marsh marigolds. Describe how they could measure the percentage cover **and** give **two** advantages of measuring species abundance this way.

(3 marks)

(b)   Abiotic factors were investigated at the same places as the data on marsh marigolds was recorded. Explain what is meant by the term 'abiotic factors'.

(1 mark)

3   Fig. 3.1 shows the net productivity of some organisms in a food web.
All the figures are in $kJm^{-2}yr^{-1}$.

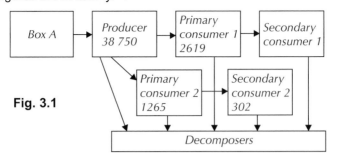

Fig. 3.1

(a)   What source of energy is represented by Box A?

(1 mark)

(b)   The respiratory loss of secondary consumer 1 is 1571 $kJm^{-2}yr^{-1}$
and its gross productivity is 2143 $kJm^{-2}yr^{-1}$. Calculate its net productivity.

(2 marks)

(c)   Give **two** reasons why the energy absorbed by secondary consumer 2
will not equal 1265 $kJm^{-2}yr^{-1}$.

(2 marks)

(d)   Calculate the difference in the percentage efficiency of energy transfer
between the producer and primary consumer 1, and the producer and primary
consumer 2.

(3 marks)

(e)   Nitrogen is passed on in a food web when organisms eat each other. Describe how
nitrogen compounds in organisms are recycled back to atmospheric nitrogen.

In your answer, you should describe the specific roles of named microorganisms.

(9 marks)

4   Many areas of woodland around the world are part of conservation projects.

(a)   Outline **one** ethical reason for the conservation of woodland.

(1 mark)

(b)   Ecosystems such as woodland can be managed in a sustainable way.
Briefly describe what this means.

(2 marks)

(c)   Complete the table below to give **three** different methods used to manage temperate
woodland in a sustainable way **and** explain how each method works.

Method	Explanation

(6 marks)

1. Plant Responses

Learning Objectives:

- Be able to explain why plants need to respond to their environment in terms of the need to avoid predation and abiotic stress.

- Be able to define the term 'tropism'.

- Be able to explain how plant responses to environmental changes are coordinated by hormones, with reference to responding to changes in light direction.

- Be able to evaluate the experimental evidence for the role of auxins in the control of apical dominance and gibberellin in the control of stem elongation.

- Be able to outline the role of hormones in leaf loss in deciduous plants.

- Be able to describe how plant hormones are used commercially.

Specification Reference 5.4.1

Plants need to respond to stimuli in order to survive. These next few pages are all about what makes plants grow the way that they do...

Responses to stimuli

Plants increase their chances of survival by responding to changes in their environment.

Examples

- They sense the direction of light and grow towards it to maximise light absorption for photosynthesis.

- They can sense gravity, so their roots and shoots grow in the right direction.

- Climbing plants have a sense of touch, so they can find things to climb and reach the sunlight.

Plants are more likely to survive if they respond to the presence of predators to avoid being eaten, e.g. some plants produce toxic substances.

Example

White clover is a plant that can produce substances that are toxic to cattle. Cattle start to eat lots of white clover when fields are overgrazed — the white clover responds by producing toxins, to avoid being eaten.

Plants are more likely to survive if they respond to **abiotic stress** — anything harmful that's non-living, like a drought. E.g. some plants respond to extreme cold by producing their own form of antifreeze.

Example

Carrots produce antifreeze proteins at low temperatures — the proteins bind to ice crystals and lower the temperature that water freezes at, stopping more ice crystals from growing.

Tropisms

A tropism is the response of a plant to a directional stimulus (a stimulus coming from a particular direction). Plants respond to stimuli by regulating their growth. A positive tropism is growth towards the stimulus, whereas a negative tropism is growth away from the stimulus.

Phototropism

Phototropism is the growth of a plant in response to light. Shoots are positively phototropic and grow towards light (see Figure 2 on the next page). Roots are negatively phototropic and grow away from light (see Figure 3 on the next page).

Figure 1: *A radish seedling showing positive phototropism.*

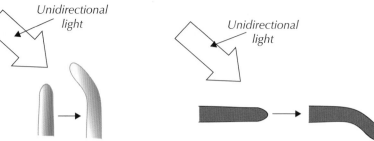

Figure 2: Phototropism in shoots.

Figure 3: Phototropism in roots.

Growth hormones

Tip: Growth hormones are also called growth substances.

Plants respond to stimuli using growth hormones — these are chemicals that speed up or slow down plant growth. Growth hormones are produced in the growing regions of the plant (e.g. shoot tips, leaves) and they move to where they're needed in the other parts of the plant.

Auxins

Tip: There are other classes of growth hormones that affect growth in different ways, e.g. growth hormones called gibberellins stimulate flowering and seed germination — see page 220.

Growth hormones called auxins are produced in the tips of shoots and diffuse backwards to stimulate the cell just behind the tips to elongate — this is where cell walls become loose and stretchy, so the cells get longer (see Figure 4). If the tip of a shoot is removed, no auxin will be available and the shoot stops growing. Auxins stimulate growth in shoots but high concentrations inhibit growth in roots.

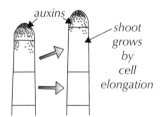

Figure 4: Effect of auxins on shoot growth.

Auxins are moved around the plant to control tropisms — they move by diffusion and active transport over short distances, and via the phloem over longer distances. This results in different parts of the plants having different amounts of auxins. The uneven distribution of auxins means there's uneven growth of the plant.

Tip: You might come across the name indoleacetic acid (IAA) — it's a type of auxin that's involved in phototropism.

Example — phototropism

Auxins move to the more shaded parts of the shoots and roots, so there's uneven growth.

Auxins move to this side — cells elongate and the shoot bends towards the light

Auxins move to this side — growth is inhibited so the root bends away from the light

Apical dominance

Auxins are produced in the tips of shoots in flowering plants — the tip of a shoot is called the apical bud. Auxins stimulate the growth of the apical bud and inhibit the growth of side shoots. This is called apical dominance — the apical bud is dominant over the side shoots (see Figure 6 on the next page).

Apical dominance prevents side shoots from growing — this saves energy and prevents side shoots from the same plant competing with the shoot tip for light. Because energy isn't being used to grow side shoots, apical dominance allows a plant in an area where there are loads of other plants to grow tall very fast, past the smaller plants, to reach the sunlight.

Figure 5: The redwood tree displays apical dominance and grows tall enough to reach the sunlight in a thick forest.

If you remove the apical bud then the plant won't produce auxins, so the side shoots will start growing by cell division and cell elongation (see Figure 7).

Auxins become less concentrated as they move away from the apical bud to the rest of the plant. If a plant grows very tall, the bottom of the plant will have a low auxin concentration so side shoots will start to grow near the bottom.

shoot tip grows but side shoots don't grow

Figure 6: Apical dominance.

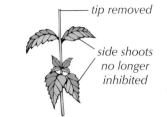

tip removed

side shoots no longer inhibited

Figure 7: Inhibition of apical dominance by removing the apical bud.

Tip: Gardeners sometimes remove a plant's apical buds. This prevents apical dominance, increasing side shoot growth and so making the plant bushier.

Investigating the role of auxins in apical dominance

HOW SCIENCE WORKS

The role of auxins in apical dominance can be investigated experimentally. Here's an example of how you do it:

— **Example** —————————————————————

Plant 30 plants of the same type (e.g. pea plants) that are a similar age, height and weight in pots. Count and record the number of side shoots growing from the main stem of each plant. For 10 plants, remove the tip of the shoot and apply a paste containing auxins to the top of the stem. Then for another 10 plants, remove the tip of the shoot and apply a paste without auxins to the top of the stem. Leave the final 10 plants as they are — these are your untouched controls. Remember, you always need to have controls (e.g. without the hormone, untouched) for comparison — so you know the effect you see is likely to be due to the hormone and not any other factor.

Let each group grow for about six days. You need to keep all the plants in the same conditions — the same light intensity, water, etc. This makes sure any variables that may affect your results are controlled, which makes your experiment more reliable. After six days, count the number of side shoots growing from the main stem of each of your plants. You might get results a bit like these:

Tip: It's really important that you keep the conditions the same for each plant — if you don't, you can't be sure what's actually causing your results. For more on controlling variables see page 3.

	plants left untreated (control group)	tips removed, paste with auxins applied	tips removed, paste without auxins applied
average number of side shoots per plant at start of experiment	4	4	4
average number of side shoots per plant at end of experiment	5	5	9

You might have to comment on the data...
The results in the table show that removing the tips of shoots caused extra side shoots to grow, but removing tips and applying auxins reduced the number of extra side shoots. The results suggest auxins inhibit the growth of side shoots — suggesting that auxins are involved in apical dominance.

An experiment was carried out to investigate the role of auxin in shoot growth. Eight shoots, equal in height and mass, had their tips removed. Sponges soaked in glucose and either auxin or water were then placed where the tip should be. Four shoots were then placed in the dark (experiment A) and the other four shoots were exposed to a light source, directed at them from the right (experiment B):

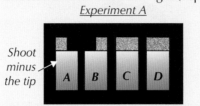
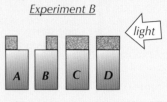

Experiment A   *Experiment B*

Shoot minus the tip   A   B   C   D   A   B   C   D

▨ *Sponge soaked in auxin and glucose*   ▨ *Sponge soaked in water and glucose*

After two days the amount of growth (in mm) and direction of growth was recorded. The results are shown in the table below.

	Growth			
	Shoot A	Shoot B	Shoot C	Shoot D
Experiment A (dark)	6 mm, right	6 mm, left	6 mm, straight	1 mm, straight
Experiment B (light)	8 mm, right	8 mm, right	8 mm, right	3 mm, straight

Q1 Why did shoot A bend to the right in experiment A?

Q2 Explain why shoot C grew straight in experiment A.

Q3 Why did shoots A, B and C grow to the right in experiment B?

Q4 What was the purpose of Sponge D in both experiments?

Q5 Suggest why the sponges in experiment A were soaked in glucose.

Gibberellins

Gibberellins are growth hormones that are produced in young leaves and in seeds. They stimulate seed germination, stem elongation, side shoot formation and flowering. Gibberellins stimulate the stems of plants to grow by stem elongation — this helps plants to grow very tall. If a dwarf variety of a plant is treated with gibberellin, it will grow to the same height as the tall variety. Unlike auxins, gibberellins don't inhibit plant growth in any way.

Auxins and gibberellins

Auxins and gibberellins sometimes work together to affect plant growth. They're often **synergistic** — this means that they work together to have a really big effect.

┌─ **Example** ─────────────────────────────
  Auxins and gibberellins work together to help plants grow very tall.

Auxins and gibberellins are sometimes **antagonistic** — this means they oppose each other's actions.

┌─ **Example** ─────────────────────────────
  Gibberellins stimulate the growth of side shoots but auxins inhibit the growth of side shoots.

Figure 8: *Gibberellins play an important role in the germination and stem elongation of corn seeds.*

Investigating the role of gibberellins in stem elongation

The role of gibberellins in stem elongation can be investigated experimentally. Here's an example of how you do it:

Example

Plant 40 plants (e.g. dwarf pea plants) that are a similar age, height and mass in pots. Leave 20 plants as they are to grow, watering them all in the same way and keeping them all in the same conditions — these are your controls. Leave the other 20 plants to grow in the same conditions, except water them with a dilute solution of gibberellin (e.g. 100 µg/ml gibberellin). Then let the plants grow for about 28 days and measure the lengths of all the stems once each week. You might get results a bit like these:

Tip: There's more on control experiments on pages 3-4.

Tip: µg/ml means microgram per millilitre (or 0.000001 g per millilitre).

time / days	average stem length / cm	
	plants watered normally	plants watered with gibberellin
0	14	14
7	15	17
14	18	27
21	19	38
28	23	46

You might have to comment on the data...

The results in the table show that stems grow more when watered with a dilute solution of gibberellin. This suggests gibberellin stimulates stem elongation.

You might have to calculate the rate of growth of the plants...

- Plants watered normally:
  Average growth in 28 days = 23 cm – 14 cm = 9 cm
  Average rate of growth over 28 days = 9 cm ÷ 28 days = 0.32 cm/day

- Plants watered with gibberellin:
  Average growth in 28 days = 46 cm – 14 cm = 32 cm
  Average rate of growth over 28 days = 32 cm ÷ 28 days = 1.14 cm/day

Leaf loss in deciduous plants

Deciduous plants are plants that lose their leaves in winter. Losing their leaves helps plants to conserve water (lost from leaves) during the cold part of the year, when it might be difficult to absorb water from the soil (the soil water may be frozen), and when there's less light for photosynthesis. Leaf loss is triggered by the shortening day length in the autumn and is controlled by hormones:

Tip: The technical term for leaf loss is abscission.

- **Auxins inhibit leaf loss** — auxins are produced by young leaves. As the leaf gets older, less auxin is produced, leading to leaf loss.

- **Ethene stimulates leaf loss** — ethene is produced by ageing leaves. As the leaves get older, more ethene is produced. A layer of cells (called the abscission layer) develops at the bottom of the leaf stalk (where the leaf joins the stem). The abscission layer separates the leaf from the rest of the plant. Ethene stimulates the cells in the abscission layer to expand, breaking the cell walls and causing the leaf to fall off.

Auxins are antagonistic (work in opposition) to ethene.

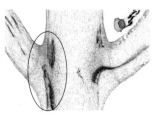

Figure 9: *Light micrograph of a developing abscission layer (dark purple, circled) between a plant's leaf stalk and stem.*

Commercial uses of plant hormones

The fruit industry uses different plant hormones to control how different fruits develop.

Ethene

Ethene stimulates enzymes that break down cell walls, break down chlorophyll and convert starch into sugars. This makes the fruit soft, ripe and ready to eat.

┌─ Example ─────────────────────────────────────

Bananas are harvested and transported before they're ripe because they're less likely to be damaged this way. They're then exposed to ethene on arrival so they all ripen at the same time on the shelves and in people's homes.

Figure 10: *Unripe bananas (top) can be exposed to ethene so that they ripen (bottom).*

Auxins and gibberellins

Auxins and gibberellins are sprayed onto unpollinated flowers, which makes the fruit develop without fertilisation.

┌─ Example ─────────────────────────────────────

Seedless grapes can be produced using auxins and gibberellins.

Auxins

Applying a low concentration of auxins in the early stages of fruit production prevents the fruit from dropping off the plant. But applying a high concentration of auxins at a later stage of fruit production triggers the fruit to drop.

┌─ Example ─────────────────────────────────────

Apples can be made to drop off the tree at exactly the right time.

Auxins are also used commercially by farmers and gardeners.

┌─ Examples ────────────────────────────────────

- Auxins are used in selective weedkillers (herbicides) — they make weeds produce long stems instead of lots of leaves. This makes the weeds grow too fast, so they can't get enough water or nutrients, so they die.

- Auxins are used as rooting hormones — they make a cutting (part of the plant, e.g. a stem cutting) grow roots. The cutting can then be planted and grown into a new plant. Many cuttings can be taken from just one original plant and treated with rooting hormones, so lots of the same plant can be grown quickly and cheaply from just one plant.

Figure 11: *Auxins enable cuttings to grow roots and grow into new plants.*

Practice Questions — Application

A student is investigating the effect of watering plants with different concentrations of gibberellin on plant height. She plants 60 plants and over the following 6 weeks she waters 20 of the plants with water, 20 of the plants with a 50 µg/ml gibberellin solution and the remaining 20 plants with a 100 µg/ml gibberellin solution. She grows all the plants under the same conditions.

Q1 The student chooses plants of the same type with similar characteristics. Explain why she does this.

Q2 Which set of plants would you expect to have the longest average stem length at the end of the 6 weeks? Explain your answer.

Q3 One of the plants has an initial stem length of 8 cm. By the end of the experiment it has grown to 26 cm.

a) Calculate the average growth rate of this plant.
Give your answer in cm/day and to 2 d.p.

b) Calculate the percentage increase in growth.

Q4 The student wants to take cuttings from her plants in order to grow new plants. What type of growth hormone should she apply to the cuttings to make the cutting grow roots?

Exam Tip
Data interpretation questions that describe an experiment may ask you about things like why controls are used, or how the reliability of the results could be improved. These questions are testing your knowledge of 'How Science Works', so make sure you brush up on this before the exam — check out pages 1-6.

Practice Questions — Fact Recall

Q1 What is meant by the term 'abiotic stress'?

Q2 What is a negative tropism?

Q3 What name is given to the growth of a plant in response to light?

Q4 What parts of a plant produce growth hormones?

Q5 Auxins travel around a plant to control tropisms.

a) How do auxins move over short distances?

b) How do auxins move over long distances?

Q6 Explain how the distribution of auxins affects the growth of:

a) shoots in response to light.

b) roots in response to gravity.

Q7 Apical dominance prevents side shoots from growing.
Explain the advantage of this in plants.

Q8 The diagram to the right shows a plant with the apical bud removed. Why does this result in the growth of side shoots?

Q9 a) If two types of growth hormone that stimulate plant growth are synergistic, would you expect the plant to grow taller than if one of the growth hormones was acting alone? Explain your answer.

b) Name two plant growth hormones that can work synergistically.

Q10 a) Why do deciduous plants lose their leaves in winter?

b) What role do auxins play in leaf loss?

c) What effect does ethene have on the abscission layer?

Tip: This might sound familiar — you learnt about the sympathetic nervous system and how it's involved in the control of heart rate back in Unit 4 (see pages 38-39).

2. Animal Responses

Just like plants, animals also respond to stimuli. You covered some of this topic in Unit 4 — I'm afraid you have to know it for Unit 5 as well.

Responding to the environment

Remember, animals increase their chances of survival by responding to changes in their external environment, e.g. by avoiding harmful environments such as places that are too hot or too cold. They also respond to changes in their internal environment to make sure that the conditions are always optimal for their metabolism (all the chemical reactions that go on inside them). Any change in the internal or external environment, e.g. a change in temperature, light intensity or pressure, is called a **stimulus**.

Receptors and effectors

Receptors detect stimuli and effectors bring about a response to a stimulus. Effectors include muscle cells and cells found in glands, e.g. the pancreas. Receptors communicate with effectors via the nervous system or the hormonal (endocrine) system, or sometimes using both. The nervous and hormonal systems coordinate the response.

Structure of the nervous system

The nervous system is split into two different systems — the central nervous system (CNS) and the peripheral nervous system. The CNS is made up of the brain and spinal cord, whereas the peripheral nervous system is made up of the neurones that connect the CNS to the rest of the body.

The peripheral nervous system also has two different systems — the somatic and autonomic nervous systems. The somatic nervous system controls conscious activities, e.g. running and playing video games. The autonomic nervous system controls unconscious activities, e.g. digestion and heart rate.

The autonomic nervous system is split into the sympathetic and parasympathetic nervous systems, which have opposite effects on the body. The sympathetic nervous system is the 'fight or flight' system that gets the body ready for action by releasing noradrenaline. The parasympathetic system is the 'rest and digest' system that calms the body down by releasing acetylcholine.

The structure of the nervous system is summarised in Figure 1.

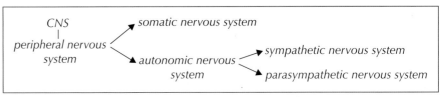

Figure 1: Organisation of the nervous system.

The 'fight or flight' response

When an organism is threatened (e.g. by a predator) it responds by preparing the body for action (e.g. for fighting or running away). This response is called the 'fight or flight' response. The nervous system and hormonal system coordinate the fight or flight response. The sympathetic nervous system is activated, which also triggers the release of adrenaline.

The sympathetic nervous system and adrenaline have the following effects:

- Heart rate is increased and the heart contracts with more force, causing blood to be pumped around the body faster.
- The muscles around the bronchioles relax, causing the airways to widen, so breathing is deeper.
- The intercostal muscles and diaphragm also contract faster and with more strength, increasing the rate and depth of breathing.
- Glycogen is converted into glucose, so more glucose is available for muscles to respire.
- Muscles in the arterioles supplying the skin and gut constrict, and muscles in the arterioles supplying the heart, lungs and skeletal muscles dilate — so blood is diverted from the skin and gut to the heart, lungs and skeletal muscles. This increases blood flow to skeletal muscles (e.g. in the legs), making them ready for action.

Tip: What happens in the 'fight or flight' response brings together topics from different areas of Biology — heart rate, breathing, glycogenolysis, muscle contraction, etc. This makes it an ideal topic for a synoptic exam question (one that tests you on both AS and A2 material). For more on synoptic questions, see the 'Exam Help' section (pages 246-251).

The brain

The brain is part of the central nervous system. You need to know the location and function of the four brain structures listed below and shown in Figure 2.

1. Cerebrum

The cerebrum is the largest part of the brain. It's divided into two halves called cerebral hemispheres. The cerebrum has a thin outer layer called the cerebral cortex, which is highly folded. The cerebrum is involved in vision, hearing, learning and thinking.

2. Hypothalamus

The hypothalamus is found just beneath the middle part of the brain. It automatically maintains body temperature at the normal level. It also produces hormones that control the pituitary gland — a gland just below the hypothalamus.

3. Medulla Oblongata

The medulla oblongata is at the base of the brain, at the top of the spinal cord. It automatically controls breathing rate and heart rate.

4. Cerebellum

The cerebellum is underneath the cerebrum and it also has a folded cortex. It's important for muscle coordination, posture and coordination of balance.

Exam Tip
Figures 2 and 3 below show cross sections through the brain. You won't always see the brain from this view though — in the exam you might be asked to locate structures when looking at the brain from a different direction, e.g. from below or from the front.

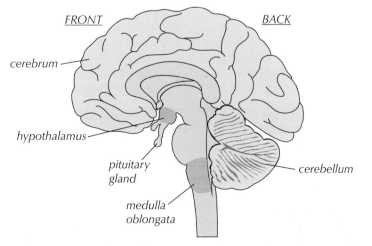

Figure 2: Structures of the brain.

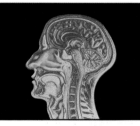

Figure 3: MRI scan showing a section through the head. The cerebrum is the highly folded structure at the top (orange). The cerebellum (blue) lies below the cerebrum at the back of the head.

Q1 The image to the right shows the human brain viewed from the front.

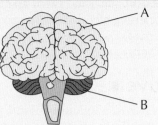

a) Name structure A.

b) Name structure B.

c) Copy and complete the table by giving one function of each of the brain structures listed below.

Name	Function
Structure A	
Medulla oblongata	
Hypothalamus	

Q2 A man is driving when a child runs out onto the road in front of him. He manages to swerve and avoid the child. Immediately afterwards he finds that his heart is beating fast and his breathing rate has increased.

a) What response is the man experiencing and what is the purpose of this response?

b) Name the branch of the autonomic nervous system responsible for the response and name the neurotransmitter released from the neurones involved.

c) The table below shows some other responses that the man's body makes. Copy and complete the table, stating if each response is increased or decreased as a result of the incident.

Response	Increased or decreased?
strength of contraction of heart muscle	
depth of breathing	
blood supply to the gut	
blood supply to the skeletal muscles	
blood glucose level	
blood supply to the skin	

Tip: Remember, neurotransmitters are chemicals released by neurones during nervous communication.

Q3 Dyspraxia is a condition which has been linked to an abnormally developed cerebellum. People with dyspraxia may have difficulty with tasks such as throwing and catching, and may often fall over. Suggest why having an abnormally developed cerebellum could cause these symptoms.

Tip: For Q3, you need to think about the role of the cerebellum and link it to the symptoms displayed by people with dyspraxia.

Q1 Why do animals need to respond to changes in their environment?

Q2 What is the central nervous system made up of?

Q3 a) What is the overall role of the autonomic nervous system?

b) Name the two divisions of the autonomic nervous system.

Q4 What is the name of the gland located just below the hypothalamus?

Q5 Where is the medulla oblongata located?

Exam Tip
The medulla oblongata always refers to the brain structure. (The inner part of some structures, e.g. the adrenal glands, is called the medulla.)

3. Muscle Contraction

Muscles are effectors that contract when they receive signals from neurones. Your body has three different types of muscle, all with different structures and functions.

Movement

The CNS (brain and spinal cord) coordinates muscular movement — it receives sensory information and decides what kind of response is needed. If the response needed is movement, the CNS sends nervous impulses along motor neurones to tell skeletal muscles to contract. Skeletal muscle (also called striated, striped or voluntary muscle) is the type of muscle you use to move, e.g. the biceps and triceps move the lower arm.

Muscles, tendons, ligaments and joints

Skeletal muscles are attached to bones by tendons. Ligaments attach bones to other bones, to hold them together. The structure of the joints between your bones determines what kind of movement is possible:

- Ball and socket joints (e.g. the shoulder) allow movement in all directions.
- Gliding joints (e.g. the wrist) allow a wide range of movement because small bones slide over each other.
- Hinge joints (e.g. the elbow) allow movement in one plane only, like up and down.

The elbow joint

The bones of your lower arm are attached to a biceps muscle and a triceps muscle by tendons. The biceps and triceps work together to move your arm — as one contracts, the other relaxes. Muscles like the biceps and triceps are called antagonistic pairs because they oppose each other's actions.

1. Bending your arm
When your biceps contracts your triceps relaxes. This pulls the bone so your arm bends at the elbow — see below.

2. Straightening your arm
When your triceps contracts your biceps relaxes. This pulls the bone so your arm straightens at the elbow — see below.

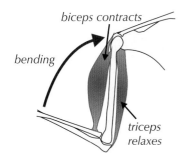

biceps contracts
bending
triceps relaxes

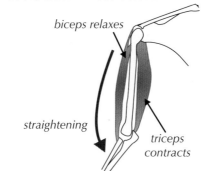

biceps relaxes
straightening
triceps contracts

Skeletal muscle

Skeletal muscle is made up of large bundles of long cells, called muscle fibres. The cell membrane of muscle fibre cells is called the sarcolemma. Bits of the sarcolemma fold inwards across the muscle fibre and stick into the sarcoplasm (a muscle cell's cytoplasm). These folds are called transverse (T) tubules and they help to spread electrical impulses throughout the sarcoplasm so they reach all parts of the muscle fibre — see Figure 2 (on the next page).

Learning Objectives:

- Be able to describe the role of the brain and nervous system in the coordination of muscular movement.
- Be able to describe how coordinated movement requires the action of skeletal muscles about joints, with reference to the movement of the elbow joint.
- Be able to explain, with the aid of diagrams and photographs, the sliding filament model of muscular contraction.
- Be able to outline the role of ATP in muscular contraction, and how the supply of ATP is maintained in muscles.
- Be able to outline the structural and functional differences between voluntary, involuntary and cardiac muscle.
- Be able to compare and contrast the action of synapses and neuromuscular junctions.

Specification Reference 5.4.2

Tip: Muscles work in pairs because they can only pull (when they contract) — they can't push.

A network of internal membranes called the sarcoplasmic reticulum runs through the sarcoplasm. The sarcoplasmic reticulum stores and releases calcium ions that are needed for muscle contraction. Muscle fibres have lots of mitochondria to provide the ATP that's needed for muscle contraction. They are multinucleate (contain many nuclei) and have lots of long, cylindrical organelles called **myofibrils**. Myofibrils are made up of proteins and are highly specialised for contraction.

Figure 1: A scanning electron microscope (SEM) of a section of muscle fibre with myofibrils (pink and yellow) bundled together.

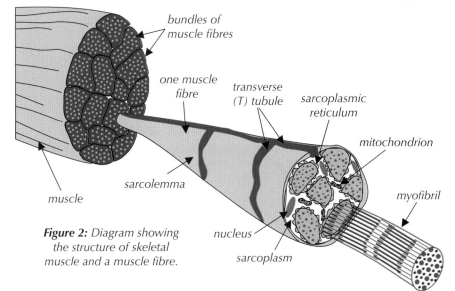

Figure 2: Diagram showing the structure of skeletal muscle and a muscle fibre.

Myofibrils

Myofibrils contain bundles of thick and thin myofilaments that move past each other to make muscles contract. The thick myofilaments are made of the protein **myosin** and the thin myofilaments are made of the protein **actin**.

If you look at a myofibril under an electron microscope, you'll see a pattern of alternating dark and light bands (see Figures 3 and 4). Dark bands contain the thick myosin filaments and some overlapping thin actin filaments — these are called A-bands. Light bands contain thin actin filaments only — these are called I-bands.

A myofibril is made up of many short units called **sarcomeres**. The ends of each sarcomere are marked with a Z-line. In the middle of each sarcomere is an M-line. The M-line is the middle of the myosin filaments. Around the M-line is the H-zone. The H-zone only contains myosin filaments.

Tip: There's more detail on the way myosin and actin work in muscle contraction on pages 230-231.

Tip: To remember which band is which, think: d**a**rk = **A**-bands and l**i**ght = **I**-bands.

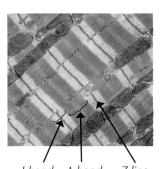

I-band   A-band   Z-line

Figure 3: A transmission electron microscope (TEM) of myofibrils showing the banding of myosin (red) and actin (yellow).

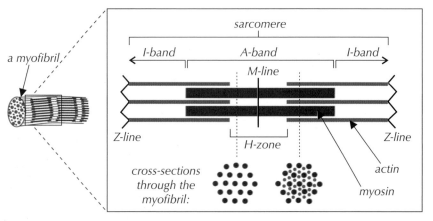

Figure 4: The structure of a sarcomere — a unit of a myofibril.

The sliding filament theory

Muscle contraction is explained by the sliding filament theory. This is where myosin and actin filaments slide over one another to make the sarcomeres contract — the myofilaments themselves don't contract. The simultaneous contraction of lots of sarcomeres means the myofibrils and muscle fibres contract. Sarcomeres return to their original length as the muscle relaxes.

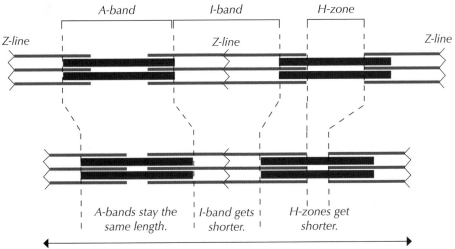

Tip: <u>A</u> bands are the only ones that stay the same length.

The Z-lines get closer together — the sarcomeres get shorter.

Figure 5: Sarcomeres during relaxation (top) and contraction (bottom).

Practice Questions — Application

Q1 Cross sections from three different sites along a sarcomere are shown below.

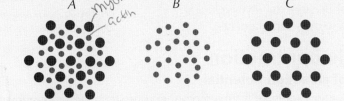

Which cross-section(s) could be from:

a) an I-band? B ✓

b) an M-line? C ✓

c) an A-band? A ✓

d) a Z-line? A B

Tip: The diagrams in Q1 might look a bit odd at first, but with a bit of logical thinking you should be able to work out the answers.
It might help if you sketch out the sarcomere structure with the bands on, so you can see what's happening.

Q2 The lengths of three different sections of a sarcomere were measured when a rabbit muscle was relaxed. These values are given in the first column of the table below. Work out which other set of values in the table (options 1-3) shows the lengths of the sections when the muscle was contracted. Explain your answer.

	Relaxed (μm)	Option 1 (μm)	Option 2 (μm)	Option 3 (μm)
A-band	1.5	1.5	1.2	1.5
I-band	0.8	0.5	0.5	1
H-zone	0.7	0.2	0.7	0.2

Myosin and actin filaments

Muscle contraction involves myosin and actin filaments sliding over one another. Here's a bit more detail about the two types of filament:

Myosin filaments

Myosin filaments have globular heads that are hinged, so they can move back and forth. Each myosin head has a binding site for actin and a binding site for ATP — see Figure 6.

Actin filaments

Actin filaments have binding sites for myosin heads, called actin-myosin binding sites. Two other proteins called **tropomyosin** and **troponin** are found between actin filaments. These proteins are attached to each other (troponin holds tropomyosin in place) and they help myofilaments move past each other (see Figure 6).

Tip: Figure 6 has been simplified — troponin and tropomyosin are actually joined in a long chain that coils round the actin filament.

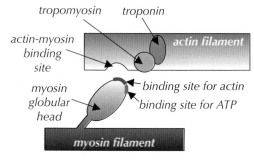

Figure 6: The structure of myosin and actin filaments.

Binding sites in resting muscles

For myosin and actin filaments to slide past each other, the myosin head needs to bind to the actin-myosin binding site on the actin filament. In a resting (unstimulated) muscle the actin-myosin binding site is blocked by tropomyosin — see Figure 7. This means myofilaments can't slide past each other because the myosin heads can't bind to the actin filaments.

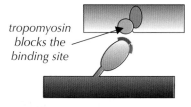

Figure 7: Actin and myosin filaments in resting muscle.

Muscle contraction

Arrival of an action potential

When an action potential from a motor neurone stimulates a muscle cell, it depolarises the sarcolemma. Depolarisation spreads down the T-tubules to the sarcoplasmic reticulum. This causes the sarcoplasmic reticulum to release stored calcium ions (Ca^{2+}) into the sarcoplasm. This influx of calcium ions into the sarcoplasm triggers muscle contraction.

Tip: Depolarisation makes the sarcolemma less negative than when it's at rest. You learnt about depolarisation in Unit 4 — look back at page 12 for a reminder.

Tip: If you can't remember your sarcolemma from your sarcoplasmic reticulum then take a look back at pages 227-228.

Calcium ions bind to troponin, causing it to change shape. This pulls the attached tropomyosin out of the actin-myosin binding site on the actin filament. This exposes the binding site, which allows the myosin head to bind. The bond formed when a myosin head binds to an actin filament is called an **actin-myosin cross bridge** — see Figure 8.

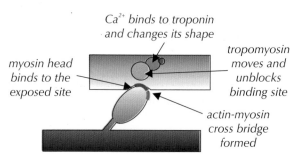

Figure 8: Formation of an actin-myosin cross bridge.

Movement of the actin filament

Calcium ions also activate the enzyme ATPase, which breaks down ATP (into ADP + Pi) to provide the energy needed for muscle contraction. The energy released from ATP moves the myosin head to the side, which pulls the actin filament along in a kind of rowing action (see Figure 9).

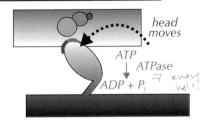

Figure 9: Movement of the myosin head.

Tip: The movement of the myosin head to the side is called a 'power stroke'.

Breaking of the cross bridge

ATP also provides the energy to break the actin-myosin cross bridge, so the myosin head detaches from the actin filament after it's moved. The myosin head then returns to it's starting position, and reattaches to a different binding site further along the actin filament — see Figure 10. A new actin-myosin cross bridge is formed and the cycle is repeated (attach, move, detach, reattach to new binding site...).

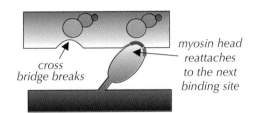

Figure 10: Myosin head forms a new actin-myosin cross bridge.

Tip: As the actin filaments are being moved along, the I-bands are getting shorter and the Z-lines are moving closer together.

Many actin-myosin cross bridges form and break very rapidly, pulling the actin filament along — which shortens the sarcomere, causing the muscle to contract. The cycle will continue as long as calcium ions are present and bound to troponin.

Return to resting state

When the muscle stops being stimulated, calcium ions leave their binding sites on the troponin molecules and are moved by active transport back into the sarcoplasmic reticulum (this needs ATP too). The troponin molecules return to their original shape, pulling the attached tropomyosin molecules with them. This means the tropomyosin molecules block the actin-myosin binding sites again — see Figure 11.

Muscles aren't contracted because no myosin heads are attached to actin filaments (so there are no actin-myosin cross bridges). The actin filaments slide back to their relaxed position, which lengthens the sarcomere.

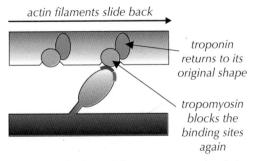

Figure 11: Blocking of the actin-myosin binding sites as the muscle returns to its resting state.

Q1 The graph below shows the calcium ion concentration in the
    sarcoplasm of a muscle fibre over time.

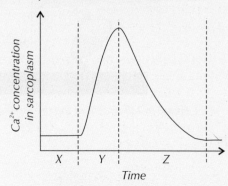

a) During what time period
   (X, Y or Z):

i)   is the muscle fibre
     the longest length?
     Explain your answer.

ii) would Ca^{2+} ions be
     bound to troponin?
     Explain your answer.

iii) would ATPase be
     activated? Explain
     your answer.

b) Describe the movement of calcium ions during time the period Z.

c) Describe the event that causes an increase in Ca^{2+} ions in the
   sarcoplasm at the beginning of time period Y.

Q2 Cardiac muscle in the heart has some similarities to skeletal muscle,
    for example, it has both actin and myosin filaments. Patients who
    suffer from heart failure may be given positive inotropic agents —
    these are substances which increase the level of calcium ions in the
    cytoplasm of muscle cells.

    Use your knowledge of muscle contraction to explain why this
    treatment may be used.

Energy for muscle contraction

So much energy is needed when muscles contract that ATP gets used up very
quickly. ATP has to be continually generated so exercise can continue —
this happens in three main ways:

1. Aerobic respiration

Most ATP is generated via oxidative phosphorylation in the cell's
mitochondria. Aerobic respiration only works when there's oxygen so it's
good for long periods of low-intensity exercise, e.g. a long walk.

2. Anaerobic respiration

ATP is made rapidly by glycolysis. The end product of glycolysis is pyruvate,
which is converted to lactate by lactate fermentation. Lactate can quickly
build up in the muscles and cause muscle fatigue. Anaerobic respiration is
good for short periods of hard exercise, e.g. a 400 m sprint.

3. ATP-phosphocreatine (PCr) system

ATP is made by phosphorylating ADP — adding a phosphate group taken
from PCr. The equation for this is shown in Figure 12. PCr is stored inside
cells and the ATP-PCr system generates ATP very quickly. PCr runs out after a
few seconds so it's used during short bursts of vigorous exercise, e.g. a tennis
serve. The ATP-PCr system is anaerobic (it doesn't need oxygen) and it's
alactic (it doesn't form any lactate).

$$ADP + PCr \rightarrow ATP + Cr \text{ (creatine)}$$

Figure 12: *Phosphorylation of ADP by PCr.*

Types of muscle

There are three types of muscle in the body — you need to know about the structural and functional differences between them.

Voluntary muscle (skeletal muscle)

Voluntary muscle contraction is controlled consciously (you have to voluntarily decide to contract it). Voluntary muscle is made up of many muscle fibres — these are multinucleate (have many nuclei) and can be many centimetres long. If you look at voluntary muscle fibres under a microscope, you can see regular cross-striations (a striped pattern) — see Figure 13.

Some muscle fibres contract very quickly — they're used for speed and strength but fatigue (get tired) quickly. Some muscle fibres contract slowly and fatigue slowly — they're used for endurance and posture.

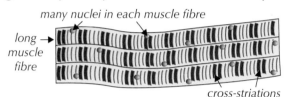

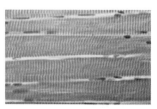

Figure 13: *The structure of voluntary muscle.*

Figure 14: *A light micrograph of a section through voluntary muscle tissue.*

Involuntary muscle (also called smooth muscle)

Involuntary muscle contraction is controlled unconsciously (it'll contract automatically without you deciding to). Involuntary muscle is also called smooth muscle because it doesn't have the striped appearance of voluntary muscle. It's found in the walls of your hollow internal organs, e.g. the gut, the blood vessels. Your gut smooth muscles contract to move food along (peristalsis) and your blood vessel smooth muscles contract to reduce the flow of blood.

Each muscle fibre is uninucleate (has one nucleus). The muscle fibres are spindle-shaped with pointed ends, and they're only about 0.2 mm long (see Figure 15). The muscle fibres contract slowly and don't fatigue.

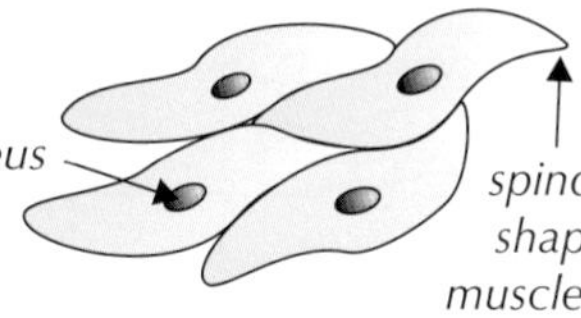

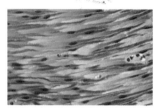

Figure 15: *The structure of involuntary muscle.*

Figure 16: *A light micrograph of a section through involuntary muscle tissue.*

Cardiac muscle (heart muscle)

Cardiac muscle contracts on its own — it's myogenic. It's found in the walls of your heart and its function is to pump blood around the body. It's made of muscle fibres connected by intercalated discs, which have low electrical resistance so nerve impulses pass easily between cells. The muscle fibres are branched to allow nerve impulses to spread quickly through the whole muscle (see Figure 17).

Each muscle fibre is uninucleate. The muscle fibres are shaped like cylinders and they're about 0.2 mm long. You can see some cross-striations under a microscope but the striped pattern isn't as strong as it is in voluntary muscle. The muscle fibres contract rhythmically and don't fatigue.

Tip: The <u>rate</u> of contraction of cardiac muscle is controlled involuntarily by the autonomic nervous system (see p. 38).

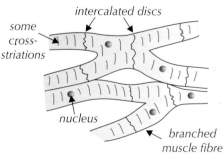

Figure 17: *The structure of cardiac muscle.*

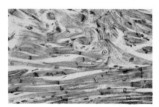

Figure 18: *A light micrograph of a section through cardiac muscle tissue.*

Neuromuscular junctions

A neuromuscular junction is a synapse between a motor neurone and a muscle cell. Neuromuscular junctions use the neurotransmitter acetylcholine (ACh), which binds to receptors called nicotinic cholinergic receptors (see Figure 19). Neuromuscular junctions work in the same way as synapses between neurones — they release neurotransmitters, which trigger depolarisation in the postsynaptic cell (see pages 16-17).

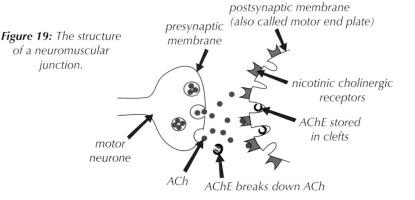

Figure 19: The structure of a neuromuscular junction.

postsynaptic membrane (also called motor end plate)

presynaptic membrane

nicotinic cholinergic receptors

AChE stored in clefts

motor neurone

ACh

AChE breaks down ACh

Figure 20: A light micrograph showing neuromuscular junctions (circled) on skeletal muscle.

There are a few differences between neuromuscular junctions and synapses where two neurones meet:

	Neuromuscular junctions	Synapses (between neurones)
Neurotransmitter	Acetylcholine	Various
Postsynaptic receptors	Nicotinic cholinergic receptors	Various
Number of postsynaptic receptors	Lots	Fewer
Postsynaptic cell	Muscle cell	Neurone
Postsynaptic membrane	Has clefts containing AChE	Smooth
Effect of neurotransmitters binding to postsynaptic receptors	Muscle cell always contracts	Action potential may or may not fire in the next neurone
Removal of neurotransmitter	Broken down by AChE	Various ways (it depends on the neurotransmitter)

Tip: AChE stands for acetylcholinesterase — it's an enzyme that breaks down acetylcholine.

Practice Questions — Application

Q1 Myasthenia gravis is an autoimmune disease in which the receptors at neuromuscular junctions are gradually destroyed. Suggest what symptoms a sufferer might have and explain your answer.

Q2 Galantamine is a drug that inhibits the enzyme AChE. Predict the effect of galantamine at a neuromuscular junction and explain your answer.

Tip: An autoimmune disease is where a person's immune system mistakes their own cells for pathogens, so it starts to attack them.

Q1 Describe the role of the brain in coordinating muscular movement.

Q2 a) Name the two muscles that are involved in bending the arm at the elbow.

   b) Explain how the two muscles you named in part a) work to bend the arm at the elbow.

Q3 Describe the structure of an A-band in a myofibril and describe its appearance under an electron microscope.

Q4 What is the sliding filament theory of muscle contraction?

Q5 Name the two proteins found between actin filaments that help myofilaments slide past each other.

Q6 Explain how calcium ions in the sarcoplasm allow the formation of actin-myosin cross bridges.

Q7 Describe the role of ATP in muscle contraction.

Q8 a) Give one advantage and one disadvantage of generating ATP via the ATP-phosphocreatine system.

   b) Give two other ways in which ATP can be generated.

Q9 Copy and complete the table below to show the structural differences between the three types of muscle fibres.

	Voluntary	Involuntary	Cardiac
Number of nuclei			
Length			
Shape of muscle fibres			
Are cross-striations visible under a light microscope?			

Tip: Remember — voluntary muscle is skeletal muscle, involuntary muscle is smooth muscle and cardiac muscle is heart muscle.

Q10 Describe the function of cardiac muscle.

Q11 What is a neuromuscular junction?

Q12 Give three differences between a neuromuscular junction and a synapse where two neurones meet.

- Be able to explain the advantages to organisms of innate behaviour.
- Be able to describe escape reflexes, taxes and kineses as examples of genetically-determined innate behaviours.
- Be able to explain the meaning of the term 'learned behaviour'.
- Be able to describe habituation, classical and operant conditioning, latent and insight learning and imprinting as examples of learned behaviours.
- Be able to discuss how the links between a range of human behaviours and the dopamine receptor DRD4 may contribute to the understanding of human behaviour.
- Be able to describe, using one example, the advantages of social behaviour in primates.

Specification Reference 5.4.3

Tip: Taxes is the plural of taxis, kineses is the plural of kinesis.

Tip: Organisms with the most effective innate behaviours are more likely to survive and pass the behaviours on to their offspring. This is an example of natural selection (see page 138).

4. Behaviour

An organism's behaviour affects its chances of surviving and reproducing. Some behaviours are automatic responses and others are learned.

Survival and reproduction

Behaviour is an organism's response to changes in its external environment. Responding in the right way to an environmental change helps organisms survive and reproduce (e.g. by finding food and a mate). An organism's behaviour is influenced by both its genes and its environment.

Innate behaviour

Innate behaviour is behaviour that organisms do instinctively. It's genetically determined — it's inherited from parents and it's not influenced by the environment. It's also stereotyped — it's always carried out in the same way and by all the individuals in a species. The advantage of innate behaviour is that organisms respond in the right way to the stimulus straight away because no learning is needed, e.g. newborn babies instinctively suckle from their mothers. Innate behaviours include escape reflexes, taxes and kineses:

Escape reflex — the organism moves away from potential danger.

> **Example**
>
> Cockroaches run away when your foot's about to squash them.

Tactic response (taxis) — directional movement in response to a stimulus. The direction of the stimulus affects the response.

> **Example**
>
> Woodlice move away from a light source. This helps keep them concealed under stones where they're safe from predators, so it helps them survive.

Kinetic response (kinesis) — non-directional (random) movement in response to a stimulus. The intensity of the stimulus affects the response.

> **Example**
>
> Woodlice show a kinetic response to low humidity. This helps them move from drier air to more humid air, and then stay put. This reduces their water loss so improves their survival chances.

Taxes and kineses allow simple organisms to move away from unpleasant stimuli and into more favourable environments.

Practice Question — Application

Q1 Read the descriptions of behaviour below and state whether each is an example of an escape reflex, a tactic response or a kinetic response.

   A Woodlice move around a lot more when they're in an open space compared to when they're in contact with other woodlice.

   B Blackworms quickly start swimming in a corkscrew motion when the back end of their body is touched.

   C *E. coli* swim towards regions where there is a high concentration of glucose.

Learned behaviour

Learned behaviour is behaviour that's influenced by the environment and is modified as a result of experience. It's not stereotyped — learned behaviour varies in different individuals in the same species. It allows animals to respond to changing conditions, e.g. they learn to avoid harmful food.

Habituation

Habituation is a reduced response to an unimportant stimulus after repeated exposure over time. An unimportant stimulus is a change that isn't threatening or rewarding. An animal quickly learns to reduce or stop its response to the unimportant stimulus, so it doesn't waste time and energy responding to unimportant things. Animals remain alert to unfamiliar stimuli though.

─ Example ──────────────────────────

If you live near a busy road, at first the noise of the traffic might keep you awake at night. Over time you'll learn to stop responding to the noise of the traffic and sleep through it. But an unfamiliar noise, like a big crash on the road, will probably still wake you up.

Classical conditioning

Classical conditioning is learning to respond naturally to a stimulus that doesn't normally cause that response. Before conditioning, a natural stimulus (called the unconditioned stimulus) can cause a natural response (called the unconditioned response).

─ Example ──────────────────────────

In dogs, the presence of food causes salivation:

<u>Before conditioning</u>:

A natural stimulus, food   *triggers*   a natural response, salivation
(unconditioned stimulus)   ⟶   (unconditioned response)

If a neutral stimulus coincides with an unconditioned stimulus enough times, eventually the neutral stimulus on its own (now called the conditioned stimulus) will cause the same response as the unconditioned stimulus — this is called a conditioned response.

Tip: A neutral stimulus is a stimulus that doesn't produce a specific response.

─ Example ──────────────────────────

If a bell is rung immediately before dogs are given food, after a time the dogs will learn to salivate in response to the bell only:

<u>During conditioning</u>:

Food (unconditioned stimulus)   *triggers*   salivation
is repeatedly presented with   ⟶   (unconditioned response)
the bell (neutral stimulus)

<u>After conditioning</u>:

Bell by itself   *triggers*   salivation
(conditioned stimulus)   ⟶   (conditioned response)

***Figure 1:** Ivan Pavlov made the discovery that dogs could learn to salivate upon hearing a bell back in the early 1900s.*

Operant conditioning

Operant conditioning is learning to associate a particular response with a reward or a punishment. When put in the same situation lots of times, an animal will work out which response gets a reward (e.g. pressing the right lever gets food) or a punishment (e.g. pressing the left lever gives a shock).

Tip: Operant conditioning can also be called 'instrumental learning'.

Figure 2: *Animal trainers often use rewards to shape animals' behaviour.*

Figure 3: *A rat can learn its way around a maze by latent learning.*

Tip: Insight learning is thought to be one of the highest forms of learning.

Tip: When you 'imprint' something, you leave a lasting impression — the moving object a young animal sees in the critical period leaves a lasting impression in the animal's mind.

The response must be rewarded (or punished) straight away — this reinforces the animal's behaviour so it's more likely to respond in the same way to get the reward again (or less likely to do it to be punished again).

Example

A rat was put in a cage with a choice of levers. Pressing one of the levers rewarded the rat with food straight away. The rat was repeatedly put in the same cage, so learned which lever to press to get the reward.

Lots of mistakes are made at first, but animals quickly learn to make fewer mistakes by using trial and error.

Latent learning

Latent learning is hidden learning — an animal doesn't immediately show it's learned something. It involves learning through repeatedly doing the same task. The animal only shows it's learned something when it's given a reward or a punishment.

Example

Three groups of rats were repeatedly put in the same maze:

- The first group of rats were reinforced with a reward each time they reached the end of the maze — they quickly learned their way around the maze.

- The second group of rats were not reinforced (they didn't receive a reward) — they continued to plod about the maze and took ages to reach the end.

- The third group of rats were only rewarded from the 11th time they did the maze — after this they very quickly reached the end, with hardly any errors. The rats had been learning the maze all along without reinforcement, but they didn't show their learning until there was a reward.

Insight learning

Insight is learning to solve a problem by working out a solution using previous experience. Solving problems by insight is quicker than by trial and error because actions are planned and worked out.

Example

Chimpanzees were put in a play area with sticks, clubs and boxes. Bunches of bananas were hung just out of reach. The chimps used their previous experience of playing with the objects to work out a solution — they piled up the boxes to reach the bananas, and used the sticks and clubs to knock them down.

Imprinting

Imprinting is a combination of a learned behaviour and an innate behaviour — e.g. an animal learns to recognise its parents, and instinctively follows them. Imprinting occurs in several species, mainly birds, which are able to move very soon after they're born. A newly-born animal has an innate instinct to follow the first moving object it sees — usually this would be its mother or father, who would provide warmth, shelter and food (helping it to survive). But the animal has no innate instinct of what its parents look like — they have to learn this. Imprinting only happens during a certain period of time soon after the animal is born. This period of time is called the **critical period**.

Example

Ducklings usually imprint on their parent ducks. But if ducklings are reared from birth (during the critical period) by a human, then the human is the first moving object the ducklings see — so the ducklings imprint on the human (they follow them).

Once learned, imprinting is fixed and irreversible. Animals use imprinting later in life to identify mates from the same species.

Figure 4: *The zoologist Konrad Lorenz being followed by ducklings he had reared since birth.*

Practice Questions — Application

Q1 Cockroaches naturally scamper when they sense a sudden movement of air. However, if they are repeatedly blown with air and no harm comes to them, they will respond less and less to the stimulus until eventually their movement isn't affected at all by being blown with air.

   a) What type of learning is described in this example?

   b) Why is this behaviour beneficial to the cockroach?

Q2 A dog owner says the word 'sit' to her dog. If the dog sits, it gets a treat, but if it doesn't sit, it doesn't get a treat. Over time, the dog learns to sit down straight away when its owner says 'sit'.

   a) What type of learning is described in this example?

   b) Suggest how the dog's response would be different if it is given a tap on the nose when it sits down on the command 'sit'. Explain your answer.

> **Tip:** Dogs generally don't like being tapped on the nose.

Q3 Some rabbits live in a complex network of underground tunnels and chambers called warrens. Rabbits learn the layout of their warren but this may only become obvious to someone observing the rabbits if the observer witness the rabbits being chased by a predator.

What type of learning is described in this example and how does it occur in the rabbits?

Q4 Siberian cranes are a type of bird that are bred in captivity to help protect their declining numbers. To help them survive their release into the wild, they are hatched under the wings of a hang glider. When they are mature enough, they learn to fly and migrate by following the hang glider.

   a) What type of learning is described in this example?

   b) Some Siberian cranes are hatched in a cage and then moved to a nest under the wings of a hang glider after a few weeks.

     i) Explain why these birds may not learn to follow the hang glider.

     ii) Suggest why birds reared in this way may be less likely to reproduce than birds reared naturally by their parents.

> **Tip:** To answer Q4 b) ii), think about the most obvious thing an individual animal needs so it can reproduce.

Q5 Some elephants in captivity have learnt to move objects in their enclosure. When they're offered food that's out of their reach, they quickly move an object so they can stand on it to reach the food.

   a) What type of learning is described in this example?

   b) Do you think the elephants learned to move objects to reach food purely by chance? Explain your answer.

> **Q6** If a person holds a nut just above a hamster's head, the hamster will stand on its back legs to reach the nut. If the person holds a nut above the hamster's head and says 'stand', the hamster will show the same response. After repeating this many times, the hamster will stand on its back legs any time the person says 'stand'.
>
> a) What type of learning is described in this example?
>
> b) Describe in detail how the hamster has learned to respond to the word 'stand'.

Understanding human behaviour

Tip: See p. 16 if you can't remember about neurotransmitters and their receptors.

An animal's behaviour depends on the structure and function of its brain (e.g. neurotransmitters, synapses, receptors, etc.). Even fairly small differences in the brain can produce big differences in behaviour. Much of our understanding of human behaviour comes from studying people with abnormal behaviour, to see how their brains are different from the brains of people who behave 'normally'. Any differences in the brain give scientists clues to understanding how normal behaviour is controlled.

The dopamine receptor D_4

Tip: The D_4 receptor can also be called DRD4.

Dopamine is a neurotransmitter. Its actions in the body can affect behaviour, e.g. it can affect mood and make people feel more outgoing. There are five different receptors for dopamine (called D_1 to D_5 receptors), and the effects of dopamine vary depending on which receptor it binds to. Each dopamine receptor is coded for by a different gene, e.g. the D_4 receptor protein is coded for by the DRD4 gene.

Having too many D_4 receptors in the brain has been linked to abnormal behaviour, e.g. the abnormal behaviour seen in schizophrenia — a disorder that affects thinking, perception, memory and emotions. The evidence for this link includes:

Tip: Having a higher density of D_4 receptors means it's more likely that dopamine will bind to these receptors and trigger a response.

- If drugs that stimulate dopamine receptors are given to healthy people, it causes the abnormal behaviour seen in schizophrenia.

- Drugs that block D_4 receptors reduce symptoms in people with schizophrenia.

- People with schizophrenia have a higher density of D_4 receptors in their brain.

- One of the drugs that's used to treat schizophrenia binds to D_4 receptors better than it binds to other dopamine receptors.

The link between the D_4 receptor and abnormal behaviour helps us to understand the role that the D_4 receptor plays in normal behaviour, e.g. it's involved in thinking, perception, memory and emotions.

Social behaviour in primates

Many animals live together in large groups. Behaviour that involves members of the group interacting with each other is called social behaviour. The primates (e.g. baboons, apes, humans) have more developed social behaviour than other animals, which has many advantages — see the example on the next page.

Example — baboons

Social behaviour: Baboons live in groups, with about 50 baboons in each group.

Advantage: A large group like this is more efficient at hunting for food — together the baboons can search a large area and communicate back to the group where there's a good source of food.

Social behaviour: Within each group there's a clear-cut hierarchy of adult males.

Advantage: This helps to prevent fighting (which wastes energy) because the males already know their rank order in the group.

Social behaviour: As each group moves through its own territory hunting for food, baboons cooperate with each other — infant baboons stay with their mother in the middle of the group and the adult males stay on the outside of the group.

Advantage: Infants and the females are protected if they're on the inside of the group. The young baboons need to be kept safe and there needs to be enough female baboons for the males to mate with, to make sure that reproduction is successful and the group continues.

Social behaviour: Members of the group groom each other (they pick out small insects and dirt from each other's fur).

Advantage: Grooming is hygienic and helps to reinforce the social bonds within the group.

Exam Tip
For your exam, you need to learn the advantages of the social behaviours displayed by a specific primate. Unless you've learnt about another primate that you prefer, you need to learn the examples here about baboons.

Figure 5: A young baboon showing social behaviour by grooming an adult member of its group.

Practice Question — Application

Q1 Mountain gorillas usually live in troops of about 10 individuals. As with other primates, they display several social behaviours. Suggest an advantage of each social behaviour listed below:

A There is always at least one adult male gorilla in the troop.

B Young gorillas play fight with older members of the troop.

C Infant gorillas never venture more than 5 metres away from their mother until they are 12 months old.

D Gorillas call out and beat their chests if they are threatened.

E Food sources are shared within the troop.

Tip: Think about how each behaviour could help the gorillas to survive and reproduce.

Practice Questions — Fact Recall

Q1 a) Describe what is meant by the term 'innate behaviour'.

b) Give an advantage of innate behaviour.

c) State three types of innate behaviour and give a brief description of each.

Q2 Describe what is meant by the term 'learned behaviour'.

Q3 Describe how an animal's response to an unimportant stimulus is altered with habituation.

Q4 a) In classical conditioning, what term is used to describe a natural stimulus that triggers a natural response?

b) Describe how classical conditioning can result in animals responding to a natural stimulus and a neutral stimulus in the same way.

Q5 When does an animal show it has learned something through latent learning?

Q6 Is it quicker for an animal to solve a problem using operant conditioning or insight learning? Explain your answer.

Q7 a) Explain why imprinting is described as a combination of innate and learned behaviour.

b) What is meant by 'the critical period' in relation to imprinting?

Q8 Name a neurotransmitter and a receptor that scientists have linked to abnormal behaviour.

Q9 a) Name a primate species that displays social behaviour.

b) For the primate species you named in part a), give an example of a social behaviour it displays and give one advantage of this social behaviour.

Section Summary

Make sure you know:

- That plants need to respond to stimuli to avoid predators and abiotic (non-living) stress.
- That a tropism is the response of a plant to a directional stimulus.
- That growth hormones coordinate how a plant responds to changes in its environment, e.g. auxins move to shaded parts of shoots and roots to control growth in response to the direction of light.
- How to evaluate experimental evidence for the role of auxins in the control of apical dominance (the growth of the apical bud being dominant over the side shoots) and for the role of gibberellins in the control of stem elongation.
- That auxins inhibit leaf loss and ethene stimulates leaf loss in deciduous plants.
- How plant hormones are used commercially, e.g. ethene is used to control when fruit ripens, auxins and gibberellins are used to make fruit develop without fertilisation, auxins are used to control when fruit drops from a tree and as selective weedkillers and as rooting hormones.
- That animals respond to changes in their external environment to increase their chances of survival and that they respond to changes in their internal environment to keep conditions optimal for metabolism.
- That mammals coordinate their response to stimuli via the nervous and/or endocrine (hormonal) systems, which communicate information from receptors to effectors.
- That the nervous system is split into the central nervous system (brain and spinal cord) and the peripheral nervous system (the neurones that connect the CNS to the rest of the body).
- That the autonomic nervous system is the part of the peripheral nervous system that controls unconscious activities and is split into the sympathetic nervous system and the parasympathetic nervous system, which have opposite effects on the body.

- That the 'fight or flight' response is coordinated by the sympathetic nervous system and the endocrine system. It prepares the body for action by increasing the heart rate and force of contraction, relaxing the bronchiole muscles, contracting the intercostal and diaphragm muscles, converting glycogen into glucose, and diverting blood from the skin and the gut to the heart, lungs and skeletal muscles.

- The functions of the cerebrum (vision, hearing, learning, thinking), the hypothalamus (controlling body temperature and producing hormones that control the pituitary gland), the medulla oblongata (controlling breathing and heart rate) and the cerebellum (muscle coordination, posture, balance) and the locations of these structures in the brain.

- That the CNS coordinates muscular movement by sending impulses to muscles along motor neurones.

- That coordinated movement requires the action of skeletal muscles about joints and how the biceps and triceps muscles work together to bend and straighten the arm at the elbow joint.

- The sliding filament theory — myosin and actin filaments slide over one another to make the sarcomeres contract (the myofilaments themselves don't contract).

- How actin, myosin, calcium ions and ATP work together to make a myofibril contract.

- That energy from ATP is used for muscle contraction and that ATP generation involves aerobic respiration, anaerobic respiration and the ATP-phosphocreatine (PCr) system.

- The structural and functional differences between voluntary (skeletal) muscle, involuntary (smooth) muscle and cardiac (heart) muscle.

- That a neuromuscular junction is a synapse between a motor neurone and a muscle cell, and the similarities and differences between neuromuscular junctions and other synapses.

- That innate behaviour is genetically-determined, stereotyped behaviour that organisms do instinctively, and that the advantage of innate behaviour is that organisms respond in the right way to a stimulus straight away, because no learning is needed.

- That an escape reflex is a movement that gets an organism away from potential danger (e.g. running away from a threat), a tactic response (taxis) is a directional movement in response to a stimulus (e.g. moving away from light) and a kinetic response (kinesis) is a non-directional movement in response to a stimulus (e.g. moving around in low humidity).

- That a learned behaviour is non-stereotyped behaviour that's influenced by the environment and is modified as a result of experience.

- That habituation is a reduced response to an unimportant stimulus after repeated exposure over time, that classical conditioning is learning to respond naturally to a stimulus that doesn't normally cause that response, that operant conditioning is learning to associate a particular response with a reward or a punishment, that latent learning is hidden learning where an animal doesn't immediately show it's learned something, and that insight is learning to solve a problem by working out a solution using previous experience.

- That imprinting is a combination of learned behaviour and innate behaviour where a new-born animal learns to recognise and follow a moving object that it sees within the critical period (a certain period of time soon after the animal is born).

- The link between the D_4 receptor (DRD4) and abnormal behaviour, the evidence for this link and how this helps us to understand the role that the D_4 receptor plays in normal behaviour.

- One example of a primate species, e.g. baboons, that displays social behaviour and why this behaviour is advantageous to the species.

Exam-style Questions

1 A bodybuilder lifts weights to increase the size of the muscles in his arms.

(a) Describe how the biceps and triceps muscles bend and straighten the arm.

(5 marks)

(b) Explain the role of acetylcholine in causing depolarisation of cells in the biceps muscle following a nervous impulse.

(5 marks)

(c) (i) Fig 1.1 shows part of a **myofibril** in the biceps muscle when it is **contracted**. Complete the table by naming the sections of the myofibril labelled A-C and stating how the sections will appear when the biceps relaxes, compared to how they appear in Fig 1.1.

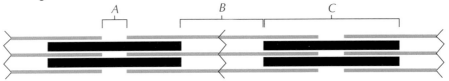

Fig 1.1

	Name	Appearance when the biceps relaxes, compared to Fig 1.1.
A		
B		
C		

(6 marks)

(ii) A myofibril contains myosin filaments. Describe the structure of a myosin filament.

(3 marks)

(iii) Describe the role of the myosin filament and ATP in muscle contraction.

In your answer, you should make it clear how the steps in the process of muscle contraction are sequenced.

(7 marks)

(d) The bodybuilder manages to lift an extremely heavy weight with a short burst of explosive power. He can only sustain the lift for a few seconds.

(i) Describe how ATP is likely to be generated in the bodybuilder's arm muscles when he lifts the heavy weight.

(2 marks)

(ii) Give **three advantages** of ATP being generated in this way.

(3 marks)

(e) A biceps muscle is a voluntary muscle. Give **three structural** differences between a voluntary muscle fibre and an involuntary muscle fibre.

(3 marks)

2   Scientists took three Goosegrass seedlings and planted them in individual pots with soil taken from the same source. They let each seedling grow for 15 days in the conditions shown in Fig 2.1.

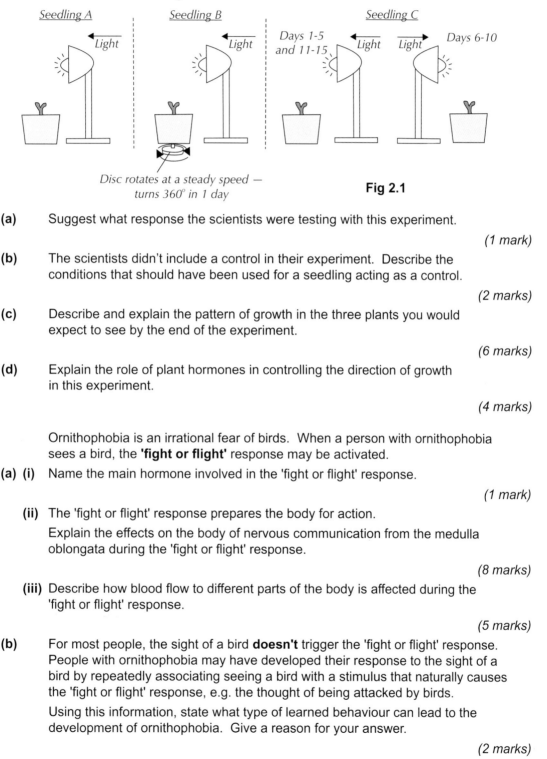

Fig 2.1

(a)   Suggest what response the scientists were testing with this experiment.

(1 mark)

(b)   The scientists didn't include a control in their experiment. Describe the conditions that should have been used for a seedling acting as a control.

(2 marks)

(c)   Describe and explain the pattern of growth in the three plants you would expect to see by the end of the experiment.

(6 marks)

(d)   Explain the role of plant hormones in controlling the direction of growth in this experiment.

(4 marks)

3   Ornithophobia is an irrational fear of birds. When a person with ornithophobia sees a bird, the **'fight or flight'** response may be activated.

(a) (i) Name the main hormone involved in the 'fight or flight' response.

(1 mark)

(ii)   The 'fight or flight' response prepares the body for action.

Explain the effects on the body of nervous communication from the medulla oblongata during the 'fight or flight' response.

(8 marks)

(iii) Describe how blood flow to different parts of the body is affected during the 'fight or flight' response.

(5 marks)

(b)   For most people, the sight of a bird **doesn't** trigger the 'fight or flight' response. People with ornithophobia may have developed their response to the sight of a bird by repeatedly associating seeing a bird with a stimulus that naturally causes the 'fight or flight' response, e.g. the thought of being attacked by birds.

Using this information, state what type of learned behaviour can lead to the development of ornithophobia. Give a reason for your answer.

(2 marks)

Exam Help

1. Exam Structure

You'll take two exams as part of A2 Level Biology. Everything you need to know about them is summarised below.

Unit 4 exam (F214) — Communication, Homeostasis and Energy

- There are 60 marks to be had.
- It's 1 hour 15 minutes long (so that's just over 1 minute per mark).

Unit 5 exam (F215) — Control, Genomes and Environment

- There are 100 marks in total.
- It's 2 hours long (again, that's just over 1 minute per mark).

Both exams will contain some **synoptic questions** — these are questions that test you on both AS and A2 material (as well as your ability to link the two). Synoptic questions in the Unit 5 paper could also test your knowledge of Unit 4.

2. Command Words

Command words are just the bits of a question that tell you what to do. You'll find answering exam questions much easier if you understand exactly what they mean, so here's a brief summary table of the most common ones:

Command word:	What to do:
Give / Name / State	Give a brief one or two word answer, or a short sentence.
Define	Give the meaning of a word.
What is meant by...	Give the meaning of a word or phrase.
Describe	Write about what something's like, e.g. describe the structure of fish gills.
Explain	Give reasons for something.
Suggest	Use your scientific knowledge to work out what the answer might be.
Compare	Give the similarities and differences between two things.
Outline	Write about the main points of a topic.

Some questions will also ask you to answer 'using the information provided' (e.g. a graph, table or passage of text) — if so, you must refer to the information you've been given or you won't get the marks.

3. Quality of Written Communication (QWC)

Tip: There are usually two questions in each exam that test QWC — both have one QWC mark available.

Examiners like to know you can write answers that include correct scientific terms and avoid waffle. There are some questions in the exam where extra marks are available for being able to do this.

How to get QWC marks

In each exam there are two marks you can pick up for having good quality of written communication (QWC). The questions are easy to spot because they have a little pencil symbol underneath them and some advice on what to include in your answer.

Examiners like to know you can use the right scientific terms in your answers and spell them correctly. They also need to be able to read your answer easily to give you the marks, so make sure your writing is clear, your answer is in a logical order and your punctuation and grammar are up to scratch.

Exam Tip
The advice next to the pencil symbol tells you what the examiners are looking for to give you the QWC marks, so make sure you pay attention to it. E.g. if it tells you to use information from a table or make it clear how the steps in a process are sequenced, make sure you include these details in your answer.

4. Answering Data Questions

You'll get lots of questions about data in the exam, so you need to be a dab hand at describing the data, drawing conclusions from it and commenting on its reliability. It's quite a lot to get your head around, but this will help...

Describing the data

You need to be able to describe any data you're given. The level of detail in your answer should be appropriate for the number of marks given. Loads of marks = more detail, few marks = less detail.

Example 1 — Experiment A

An experiment was conducted to investigate the effect of temperature on the rate of photosynthesis. The rate of photosynthesis in Canadian pondweed was measured at four different temperatures by measuring the volume of oxygen produced. All other variables were kept constant. The results are shown in the graph on the right.

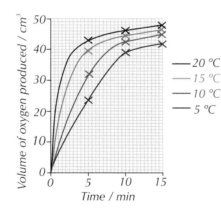

Exam Tip
It's easy to get <u>describe</u> and <u>explain</u> mixed up. If you're asked to describe the data, just state the overall pattern or trend. If you're asked to explain the data, you'll need to <u>give reasons</u> for the trend (see next page).

Describing the data (1 mark):
The data shows that the rate of photosynthesis increases with temperature.

Describing the data (3 marks):
The data shows that the rate of photosynthesis increases with temperature from 5 °C up to 20 °C. The pondweed at 20 °C showed the steepest increase in the rate of photosynthesis. Although the rate at all temperatures increases quickly at first, it eventually slows down with time.

Exam Tip
If you need to describe the data in detail, it's a good idea to include numbers from the graph.

Example 2 — Study B

Study B investigated the link between the number of bees in an area and the temperature of the area. The number of bees was estimated at ten 1-acre sites. The temperature was also recorded at each site. The results are shown in the scattergram on the right.

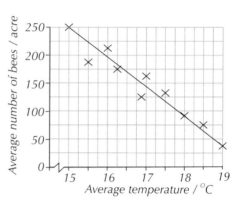

Describing the data (1 mark):

The data shows a negative correlation between the average number of bees and the temperature.

Drawing and checking conclusions

You have to be very careful when drawing conclusions in the exam. For results that show a correlation between the variables, remember that this doesn't prove that a change in one causes a change in the other.

> **Example — Study B**
>
> There's a negative correlation between the average number of bees and temperature. But you can't conclude that the increase in temperature caused the decrease in bees. Other factors may have been involved, e.g. there may have been less food in some areas or more bee predators in others.

The data should always support the conclusion too. This may sound obvious but it's easy to jump to conclusions. Conclusions have to be precise — not make sweeping generalisations.

> **Example — Experiment A**
>
> A science magazine concluded from this data that the optimum temperature for photosynthesis is 20 °C. The data doesn't support this. The rate could be greatest at 22 °C, or 18 °C, but you can't tell from the data because it doesn't go higher than 20 °C and increases of 5 °C at a time were used. The rates of photosynthesis at in-between temperatures weren't measured.

Explaining the evidence

You could also be asked to explain the evidence (the data and results) — basically this just means using your knowledge of the subject to give reasons why those results happened.

> **Example — Experiment A**
>
> Temperature increases the rate of photosynthesis because it increases the activity of enzymes involved in photosynthesis, so reactions are catalysed more quickly.

Commenting on reliability

If the data isn't reliable for whatever reason you can't draw a valid conclusion. Here are some of the things you'll need to think about if you're asked to comment on the reliability of an experiment or study in the exam.

1. Size of the data set

For experiments, the more repeats you do, the more reliable the data. The general rule for studies is the larger the sample size, the more reliable the data is.

> **Example — Study B**
>
> Study B is quite small — they only studied ten 1-acre sites. The trend shown by the data may not appear if you studied 50 or 100 sites, or studied them for a longer period of time.

2. Variables

The more variables you control, the more reliable your data is.

> **Example — Study B**
>
> Ideally, all the sites in Study B would have a similar type of land, similar weather, have the same plants growing, etc. Then you could be more sure that the one factor being investigated (temperature) is having an effect on the thing being measured (number of bees).

3. Data collection

Think about all the problems with the method and see if bias has slipped in. The less bias there is, the more reliable the data.

> **Example — Study B**
>
> It's not clear how the sites in study B were selected. If they weren't picked at random (e.g. by using a random number generator and random letter generator to pick the site co-ordinates on a map), then the results might not be representative of the bee population as a whole.

4. Controls

Without controls, it's very difficult to draw valid conclusions.

> **Example — Experiment A**
>
> In experiment A, the negative control would be all the equipment set up as normal but without the pondweed. If no oxygen was produced at any temperature it would show that the variation in the amount of oxygen produced when there was pondweed was due to the effect of temperature on the pondweed, and not the effect of temperature on anything else in the experiment.

5. Repetition by other scientists

For theories to become accepted as 'fact' other scientists need to repeat the work (see page 2). If multiple studies or experiments come to the same conclusion, then that conclusion is more reliable.

> **Example — Study B**
>
> If a second group of scientists repeated Study B and got the same results, the results would be more reliable.

Exam Tip
If you're asked to evaluate the method used in an experiment, you also need to comment on the same things mentioned here.

Tip: Reliability means the results can be consistently reproduced in independent experiments. See pages 3-5 for more info.

Tip: Bias can also come from the people collecting the data. For example, a company testing its own product might report the data in a way that makes it look better than it is.

Tip: There's more on control experiments and control groups on pages 3 and 4.

Exam Tip
You might be asked to evaluate the reliability of an experiment in the exam — or you might be asked to suggest ways to improve its reliability. Either way, keep these five points in mind.

Analysing the data

Sometimes it's easier to compare data by making a few calculations first, e.g. converting raw data into ratios or percentages.

Tip: Remember, ratios and percentages are used so you can <u>compare</u> different sets of data fairly.

Example

An agricultural scientist investigated the effect of three different pesticides on the number of pests in wheat fields. The number of pests was estimated in each of three fields, using ground traps, before and 1 month after application of one of the pesticides. The number of pests was also estimated in a control field where no pesticide had been applied. The table shows the results.

	Number of pests	
Pesticide	Before application	1 month after application
1	89	98
2	53	11
3	172	94
Control	70	77

You could be asked to calculate the percentage change (increase or decrease) in the number of pests for each of the pesticides and the control.

Pesticide 1: $(98 - 89) \div 89 = 0.10 \times 100 = 10\%$ increase.

Pesticide 2: $(11 - 53) \div 53 = -0.79 \times 100 = 79\%$ decrease.

Pesticide 3: $(94 - 172) \div 172 = -0.45 \times 100 = 45\%$ decrease.

Control: $(77 - 70) \div 70 = 0.10 \times 100 = 10\%$ increase.

Tip: To work out a percentage change you need to calculate:

$$\frac{(new\ value - original\ value)}{original\ value} \times 100$$

You can then use these values to describe what the data shows:

The percentage increase in pests in the field treated with pesticide 1 was the same as for the control (10% increase). Pesticide 3 reduced pest numbers by 45%, but pesticide 2 reduced the pest numbers the most (79% decrease).

Standard deviation

Standard deviation (SD) is a measure of the spread of values about the mean. The smaller the SD the closer all the values are to the mean.

SDs can be shown on a graph using **error bars**. The ends of the bars show one SD above and one SD below the mean. Standard deviation can show how reliable the data is — the lower the standard deviation the more reliable it is. For example, data set 1 on the right has a smaller SD than data set 2, so it's more reliable.

Tip: The mean is the average. To calculate it you add up all the numbers and divide by how many values there are, e.g. for the data set 4, 9, 11 you'd do $(4 + 9 + 11) \div 3 = 8$

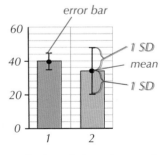

If the error bars overlap (like in the graph above) then the results aren't significantly different. If the error bars don't overlap then it's likely the difference between the results is significant and not due to chance.

5. Graph and Table Skills

If you're worried about graphs or tables in the exam, here are some tips to help.

Reading values off graphs

If there's a key pay close attention to it — you'll be throwing away easy marks if you don't. If the graph has more than one vertical axis make sure you read off the correct one. Also, always put the units on your answer.

Calculating the gradient of a graph

A little trickier is calculating the gradient of the graph:

$$\text{Gradient} = \frac{\text{Change in Y}}{\text{Change in X}} \qquad \text{Units} = \frac{Y}{X}$$

Exam Tip
The x-axis is horizontal, the y-axis is vertical. An easy way to remember this is that 'X' is 'a cross'.

─ **Example** ─────────────

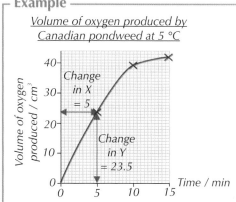

Volume of oxygen produced by Canadian pondweed at 5 °C

If you want to know the rate of this reaction over the first 5 minutes:

Gradient = rate of reaction

$$= \frac{23.5}{5} = 4.7$$

$$\text{Units} = \frac{cm^3}{min} = cm^3min^{-1}$$

So, the answer is 4.7 cm³min⁻¹.

Exam Tip
If the question doesn't say what to use to calculate the gradient (e.g. 'over the first 5 minutes') then use the largest area you can from the straightest part of the graph.

Drawing graphs

Here are a few rules:

- The dependent variable should go on the y-axis (the vertical axis) and the independent on the x-axis (the horizontal axis).
- Always label the axes and include the units.
- If you need to draw a line (or curve) of best fit on a scatter graph, don't just join the points up. Instead, draw the line through or as near to as many points as possible, ignoring any anomalous results.
- To estimate what a result outside the range that you studied might be, just extend the line of best fit then read off the data.

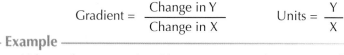

Tip: Units that are given as 'cm³min⁻¹' can also be given in the form, 'cm³/min'.

Tip: Repeating the measurements and calculating a mean allows you to draw a more reliable line of best fit.

Drawing tables

When you draw a table, use a ruler and make sure each column has a heading. The units should be in the column heading, not the table itself.

All the data in a table should be given to the same degree of accuracy, e.g. to one decimal place, rounded up or down correctly.

Average number of bees / acre	Average temperature / °C
30	19.0
75	18.3
90	17.8

heading — column — units — data — row

Tip: You usually have to process raw data in some way to make it useful, e.g. by calculating the mean.

Answers

Unit 4

Section 1 — Communication and Homeostasis

1. Communication Basics
Page 7 — Fact Recall Questions
Q1   Any change in the internal or external environment.
Q2   To increase their chances of survival.
Q3   To detect stimuli.
Q4   Muscle cells, cells found in glands.
Q5   The ways in which cells communicate with each other.

2. The Nervous System
Page 10 — Application Questions
Q1   threshold level
Q2   a) B, because its generator potential reaches -60mV/the
       threshold level.
     b) Approximately -87.5 mV (accept any value between
       -87 mV and -88 mV)
*Make sure you always read the axes carefully — especially on
graphs to do with potential differences across cell membranes,
because they nearly always involve negative numbers.*

Page 10 — Fact Recall Questions
Q1   a) To transmit nerve impulses from receptors to the CNS.
     b) To transmit nerve impulses from the CNS to effectors.
Q2   A — dendrite, B — cell body, C — axon, D — axon
     terminal
Q3   E.g. any two from: the dendrites in a sensory neurone are
     further away from the cell body than they are in a motor
     neurone. / The axon in a sensory neurone is shorter than the
     axon in a motor neurone. / A sensory neurone has one long
     dendron whereas a motor neurone doesn't have a dendron.
     / Dendrites connect directly to the cell body in a motor
     neurone but not in a sensory neurone.
     *The questions asks for two structural differences, so you need
     to concentrate on the structure — not the function — of the
     different types of neurone.*
Q4   Receptor cells detect a stimulus. Sensory neurones transmit
     electrical impulses from the receptors to the CNS. The CNS
     processes the information, decides what to do with it and
     sends impulses along motor neurones to effectors, which
     respond.
Q5   Because they convert the energy of a stimulus into electrical
     energy. / Because they convert one form of energy into
     another.
Q6   When a stimulus is detected, the cell membrane is excited
     and becomes more permeable, allowing more ions to move
     in and out of the cell. This alters the potential difference
     across the cell membrane and therefore produces a
     generator potential.
Q7   A bigger stimulus excites the membrane more, causing a
     bigger movement of ions and a bigger change in potential
     difference, so a bigger generator potential is produced.

3. The Nervous Impulse
Page 15 — Application Questions
Q1   A — The neurone is stimulated.
     B — Depolarisation / Voltage-gated sodium ion channels are
     open and lots of sodium ions are diffusing into the neurone.
Q2   –40 mV
Q3   –60 mV
     *Remember to always include units in your answer when they're
     given on the graph.*
Q4   a) At a potential difference of +40 mV the sodium ion
       channels close and the potassium ion channels open.
       The membrane is more permeable to potassium so
       potassium ions diffuse out of the neurone down the
       potassium ion concentration gradient. This starts to
       get the membrane back to its resting potential. At the
       bottom of the curve the potassium ion channels are slow
       to close so there's a slight 'overshoot' where too many
       potassium ions diffuse out of the neurone. The potential
       difference (–70 mV) is more negative than the resting
       potential (–60 mV). The sodium-potassium pump then
       returns the membrane to its resting potential (–60 mV).
     b) refractory period
Q5   The action potential would have the same potential
     difference values as the graph shown because once the
     threshold is reached, an action potential will always fire
     with the same change in voltage, no matter how big the
     stimulus is. However, there may be another action potential
     shown on the graph because a bigger stimulus will cause
     action potentials to fire more frequently.

Page 15 — Fact Recall Questions
Q1   Sodium-potassium pumps and potassium ion channels.
     *Sodium ion channels are involved when a stimulus excites the
     neurone cells membrane but they're not involved in maintaining
     the resting membrane potential.*
Q2   Sodium ions diffuse into the neurone down the sodium
     ion electrochemical gradient. This makes the inside of
     the neurone less negative and so decreases the potential
     difference across the membrane.
Q3   More sodium ions diffuse into the neurone because sodium
     ion channels open.
Q4   a) The ion channels are recovering and can't be made to
       open.
     b) It makes action potentials discrete/separate impulses.
       It makes action potentials unidirectional.
Q5   During an action potential, some of the sodium ions that
     enter the neurone diffuse sideways. This causes sodium
     ion channels in the next region of the neurone to open and
     sodium ions diffuse into that part. This causes a wave of
     depolarisation.
Q6   A myelinated neurone has a myelin sheath. The myelin
     sheath is made of a type of cell called a Schwann cell which
     is wrapped around the axon (and/or dendron). Between the
     Schwann cells are tiny patches of bare membrane called the
     nodes of Ranvier. Sodium ion channels are concentrated at
     the nodes of Ranvier.
Q7   In a myelinated neurone depolarisation/action potentials
     only happen at the nodes of Ranvier. However in a non-
     myelinated neurone, depolarisation/action potentials occur
     as a wave along the whole length of the axon membrane.
     Conduction along a myelinated neurone is faster than along
     a non-myelinated neurone.

Q8 Axon diameter and temperature.

4. Synapses

Page 18 — Application Questions

Q1 Carbachol mimics the action of ACh so the presence of carbachol will activate even more cholinergic receptors. This will make more action potentials fire in the postsynaptic neurone, so more saliva will be produced.

Q2 a) They will reduce the sensation of pain because no action potentials will be fired and therefore pain signals will not be transmitted.

b) It will reduce the sensation of pain / it will have the same effect as endorphins. This is because it is very similar in structure to an endorphin molecule so it is likely to cause the same effect by binding to the same receptors.

Page 19 — Fact Recall Questions

Q1 neurone, muscle, gland

Q2 A — synaptic knob, B — vesicle, C — Acetylcholine/ACh, D — presynaptic membrane, E — cholinergic/ACh receptor, F — postsynaptic membrane, G — synaptic cleft.

Q3 a) The action potential stimulates voltage-gated calcium ion channels in the presynaptic neurone to open, so calcium ions diffuse into the synaptic knob.

b) The influx of calcium ions into the synaptic knob causes the synaptic vesicles to fuse with the presynaptic membrane. The vesicles release ACh into the synaptic cleft. ACh diffuses across the synaptic cleft and binds to specific cholinergic receptors on the postsynaptic membrane. This causes sodium ion channels in the postsynaptic neurone to open. If the threshold is reached, the influx of sodium ions into the postsynaptic neurone causes an action potential on the postsynaptic membrane.

Q4 a) Information from one neurone can be dispersed to different areas of the body (as one neurone connects to many neurones).

b) Information from many neurones can be amplified (as many neurones connect to one neurone).

Q5 a) Where two or more presynaptic neurones release their neurotransmitters at the same time onto the same postsynaptic neurone, the small amount of neurotransmitter released from each of these neurones can be enough altogether to reach the threshold in the postsynaptic neurone. This makes an action potential more likely.

b) Where two or more nerve impulses arrive in quick succession from the same presynaptic neurone, more neurotransmitter is released into the synaptic cleft. This makes an action potential more likely.

Q6 Neurotransmitters are only released from presynaptic neurones and receptors are only on postsynaptic membranes. This means the neurotransmitter can't activate an action potential back along the presynaptic neurone.

Exam-style Questions — pages 20-21

1 a) It would have no effect *(1 mark)*.
Don't confuse an action potential with a generator potential. A bigger stimulus causes a bigger generator potential, but it has no effect on the size of the action potential.

b) Action potentials have a refractory period *(1 mark)*. During this period the ion channels are recovering and can't be made to open *(1 mark)*. This means that no more sodium ions can diffuse into the neurone to trigger another action potential *(1 mark)*.

c) i) Time 1 shows repolarisation *(1 mark)* because the sodium ion channels are closed and the potassium ion channels are open *(1 mark)*. The membrane is more permeable to potassium so potassium ions diffuse out of the neurone down their concentration gradient *(1 mark)*. Time 2 shows hyperpolarisation/ the refractory period *(1 mark)* because both the sodium and potassium ion channels are closed *(1 mark)*. There is no movement of sodium or potassium through their ion channels (by facilitated diffusion) *(1 mark)*.

If a question tells you to 'use evidence' from a source (like a diagram, graph, table, etc.) this means you need to include figures or descriptions from the source. So in this case, you need to say which ion channels are open and closed in the diagram.

ii) Sodium-potassium pumps use active transport *(1 mark)* to move three sodium ions out of the cell *(1 mark)* for every two potassium ions moved in *(1 mark)*.

iii) The potassium ion channel is slow to close *(1 mark)* so too many potassium ions diffuse out of the neurone *(1 mark)*. The potential difference is more negative than the neurone cell membrane's resting potential, so the pump returns the membrane to its resting potential *(1 mark)*.

d) Sodium ions won't be able to diffuse into the neurone through voltage-gated sodium ion channels *(1 mark)*. This means that the neurone won't be depolarised *(1 mark)* so there will be no action potentials/no nervous impulses *(1 mark)*.

2 a) i) Schwann cell *(1 mark)*

ii)

	Structure	Function
B	axon	Carries nerve impulses from the cell body to effector cells / axon terminal.
C	dendrites	Carry nerve impulses from the central nervous system to the cell body.

(1 mark for each correct answer)

The diagram shows a motor neurone, so dendrites carry information from the CNS.

b) To transmit nerve impulses from receptors to the central nervous system *(1 mark)*.

c) Conduction of nervous impulses in non-myelinated neurones is slower than in myelinated neurones *(1 mark)*. If the myelin is damaged then the nerve impulse may be conducted much more slowly or not at all, resulting in muscle weakness or paralysis *(1 mark)*.

3 a) The action potential arrives in the synaptic knob of the motor neurone and stimulates voltage-gated calcium ion channels to open *(1 mark)*. Calcium ions diffuse into the synaptic knob *(1 mark)* and cause the synaptic vesicles to fuse with the presynaptic membrane *(1 mark)*. The vesicles release acetylcholine (ACh) into the synaptic cleft by exocytosis *(1 mark)*.

b) i) (temporal) summation *(1 mark)*

ii) More neurotransmitter/ACh will be released into the synaptic cleft *(1 mark)*. This means more neurotransmitter/ACh will bind to receptors on the postsynaptic membrane/muscle cell *(1 mark)*. This causes more sodium ion channels to open *(1 mark)* and a greater influx of sodium ions *(1 mark)*, which makes the muscle cell more likely to reach threshold and fire an action potential *(1 mark)*.

c) Tubocurarine prevents ACh from binding to the cholinergic receptors *(1 mark)*. This means sodium ion channels on the muscle cell do not open *(1 mark)* so there's no influx of sodium ions into the muscle cell *(1 mark)*. No action potentials can be fired so the muscles cannot be stimulated to contract/move *(1 mark)*.

5. The Hormonal System and Glands
Pages 24-25 — Application Questions
Q1

Molecule / Structure	Name
Hormone	Oxytocin
Target cells	Myoepithelial cells
Target tissue	Epithelial tissue
Endocrine gland	Posterior pituitary gland
Exocrine gland	Mammary gland

Q2 E.g. because oxytocin has to travel in the blood to the target cells, which may take several minutes.

Page 25 — Fact Recall Questions
Q1 A group of cells that is specialised to secrete hormones.
Q2 A change in concentration of a specific substance/another hormone, electrical impulses.
Q3 Each hormone will only bind to specific receptors for that hormone, found on the membranes of some cells/target cells.
Q4 E.g. endocrine glands secrete hormones whereas exocrine glands secrete chemicals, e.g. enzymes. / Endocrine glands secrete substances directly into the blood and exocrine glands secrete substances into cavities or onto the surface of the body. / Exocrine glands secrete substances through ducts and endocrine glands don't.
Q5 E.g. sweat and enzymes.
Q6 a) cyclic AMP/cAMP
 b) It activates a cascade of enzyme reactions to make more glucose available to the cell.
 c) adrenaline
Q7 a) Endocrine because they secrete hormones (directly into the blood).
 b) The cortex secretes steroid hormones/cortisol and the medulla secretes catecholamine hormones/adrenaline.
Q8 a) islet of Langerhans
 b) i) glucagon
 ii) insulin
 c) They secrete digestive enzymes into the pancreatic duct.

6. Homeostasis Basics
Page 28 — Application Questions
Q1 A is an example of negative feedback because increasing respiration rate will increase the rate at which carbon dioxide is removed from the body. This will increase the pH of the blood back to the normal level. B is an example of positive feedback because more oestrogen being released will increase the levels of LH further and amplify the change.

Q2 a) i) At point A low concentrations of calcium in the blood are detected. This stimulates the secretion of PTH, which travels in the blood to effectors. At point B effectors are responding by increasing the concentration of calcium in the blood.
 ii) At point C high concentrations of calcium in the blood are detected. This stimulates the secretion of calcitonin which travels in the blood to effectors. At point D effectors are responding by decreasing the concentration of calcium in the blood.
 b) The concentration of calcium in the blood may fall very low. This is because less PTH will be released to bring the levels back up to normal.

Page 28 — Fact Recall Questions
Q1 The maintenance of a constant internal environment.
Q2 So that metabolic reactions can occur at an optimum rate. Low temperatures make metabolic reactions slower, but if the temperature gets too high the reaction essentially stops.
Q3 A — receptors detect change, B — communication via hormonal or nervous system, C — effectors respond.
Q4 A positive feedback mechanism amplifies a change from the normal level, whereas a negative feedback mechanism restores the level to normal.

7. Control of Body Temperature
Pages 29-30 — Application Questions
Q1 a) The external temperature was low/it was cold because the snake is an ectotherm and appears dark/is not radiating any heat/is cold.
 b) The mouse because it's warmer than the snake, meaning it has more energy available (from metabolic reactions) for activity.
Q2 a) The internal temperature of the chuckwalla increases as the external temperature increases. This suggests that the chuckwalla is an ectotherm as its internal temperature depends on the external temperature. The internal temperature of the hoatzin stays roughly the same as the external temperature increases. This suggests that the hoatzin is an endotherm as it can control its internal body temperature by homeostasis.
 b) The chuckwalla because it's internal temperature varied the most, meaning its metabolic reactions would have been most disrupted.
 Remember, metabolic reactions are controlled by enzymes and enzyme activity is greatest at an optimum temperature. Any variation from the optimum temperature will reduce enzyme activity and therefore slow down metabolic reactions.

Page 32 — Application Questions
Q1 The hot water in the bath heats up the temperature of the skin. Thermoreceptors in the skin detect body temperature is too high and send impulses to the hypothalamus. The hypothalamus then sends impulses to the arterioles near the surface of the skin causing them to dilate. More blood then flows through the capillaries in the surface layers of the dermis so more heat is lost by radiation and the body temperature is lowered. The increased blood flow in the capillaries might make the skin appear pink.
Q2 A cold external environment. When internal body temperature falls the body's responses include shivering and increased release of adrenaline and thyroxine. These mechanisms increase the rate of metabolism, which means more glucose is used. Blood glucose concentration will fall, so feelings of hunger will occur more quickly than they would do in a hot environment.

Q3 In hot weather the internal body temperature rises. Normally one of the ways the body responds to this is by vasodilation to increase heat loss. However, cocaine causes the opposite effect — vasoconstriction. This will reduce heat loss so the internal temperature will remain high. Also, an increase in muscular activity will increase respiration, so more heat will be produced. This will increase the internal body temperature further and make the person at risk of hyperthermia.

Page 32 — Fact Recall Questions
Q1 a) By changing behaviour.
   b) Internally by homeostasis as well as by changing behaviour.
Q2 Ectotherms have a variable metabolic rate and endotherms have a constantly high metabolic rate.
Q3 When the body's too hot sweat glands secrete more sweat. The water in sweat evaporates from the surface of the skin and takes heat from the body so the skin is cooled. When the body's too cold sweat glands secrete much less sweat, reducing the amount of heat lost.
   In this question you need to write about how sweat glands help the body lose heat and how they help it to conserve heat.
Q4 Muscles in the body contract in spasms when it's cold. This makes the body shiver and more heat is produced from increased respiration. The hormones adrenaline and thyroxine are released, which increases metabolism, so more heat is produced.
Q5 They constrict.
Q6 The hypothalamus.
Q7 Thermoreceptors in the skin/peripheral temperature receptors detect external/skin temperature and send impulses via sensory neurones to the brain/hypothalamus.
Q8 When thermoreceptors detect body temperature is too low, they send impulses to the hypothalamus, which sends impulses to effectors. Effectors respond to decrease heat loss from the body and increase heat production so body temperature returns to normal.

8. Control of Blood Glucose Concentration
Page 34 — Application Questions
Q1 It will increase blood glucose concentration.
   Remember, glycogenolysis is the process of breaking down glycogen into glucose. So when this process is activated, blood glucose concentration increases.
Q2 Carbohydrates are broken down into glucose, so their blood glucose concentration will increase. When the pancreas detects the blood glucose concentration is too high, the β cells will secrete insulin and the α cells will stop secreting glucagon. Insulin will then bind to receptors on liver and muscle cells (the effectors). These cells will respond by taking up more glucose, activating glycogenesis and by respiring more glucose. Blood glucose concentration will then return to normal.
Q3 Glycogenolysis and gluconeogenesis both increase blood glucose concentration. If these processes don't work properly then when blood glucose concentration falls (i.e. if the person doesn't eat regularly) the body will be unable to raise the blood glucose concentration back to normal, so the person will suffer from hypoglycaemia.

Page 37 — Application Questions
Q1 The Type II diabetic doesn't produce as much insulin as the non-diabetic. / The body's cells don't respond properly to the insulin that's produced. Insulin lowers blood glucose concentration when it's too high, so if there's not enough insulin/the body can't respond to insulin properly, this process will be much slower.

Q2 A Type I diabetic wouldn't produce any insulin. This means that blood glucose concentration would remain high for much longer than for this Type II diabetic.
Q3 22.5 minutes. This is because this is the time when the blood glucose concentration is at its upper limit / 110 mg/100 cm³.
   You're told the normal range for blood glucose concentration in the introduction to the question — make sure you always read questions thoroughly in the exam.
Q4 Insulin is a hormone, so it takes time to travel in the blood to receptor cells.
Q5 When blood glucose concentration falls below 82 mg/100 cm³ the pancreas is stimulated to secrete glucagon and stop secreting insulin. Glucagon binds to specific receptors on liver cells. The liver cells respond to increase blood glucose concentration — glycogenolysis is activated, gluconeogenesis is activated and the cells respire less glucose.

Page 37 — Fact Recall Questions
Q1 It increases the permeability of liver and muscle cell membranes to glucose, activates enzymes that convert glucose into glycogen/activates glycogenesis and increases the rate of respiration of glucose in those cells.
Q2 glycogenesis
Q3 Gluconeogenesis — glycerol or amino acids are converted to glucose. Glycogenolysis — glycogen is converted to glucose.
Q4 It is an auto-immune disease, in which the body attacks and destroys the β cells in the islets of Langerhans.
Q5 Any three from: e.g. producing insulin using GM bacteria is cheaper than extracting it from animal pancreases. / Larger quantities of insulin can be produced using GM bacteria. / GM bacteria make human insulin, which is more effective than animal insulin and less likely to trigger an allergic response or be rejected by the immune system. / Some people prefer insulin from GM bacteria for ethical or religious reasons.
Q6 Stem cells could be grown into β cells which would then be implanted into the pancreas of a person with Type I diabetes. This means the person would be able to make insulin as normal.

9. Control of Heart Rate
Page 40 — Application Question
Q1 The chemoreceptors in a person with anaemia will detect low oxygen levels in the blood. The chemoreceptors will send impulses along sensory neurones to the cardiovascular centre, which will send impulses along sympathetic neurones. These neurones will secrete noradrenaline, which will bind to receptors on the sinoatrial node/SAN and cause the heart rate to increase.

Page 40 — Fact Recall Questions
Q1 a) baroreceptor/pressure receptor
   b) aorta, vena cava and carotid arteries
Q2 noradrenaline
Q3 They cause the heart rate to slow down.

Exam-style Questions — pages 42-43
1 a) A mechanism that restores a level back to normal in a system *(1 mark)*.
   b) i) β cell *(1 mark)*

ii) A meal high in carbohydrates has recently been eaten, which increased the person's blood glucose concentration *(1 mark)*. The high blood glucose concentration caused more glucose to enter the β cell by facilitated diffusion *(1 mark)*, which increased the respiration rate *(1 mark)* and caused more ATP to be made *(1 mark)*. The rise in ATP triggered the potassium ion channels to close *(1 mark)*.

iii) The build up of potassium ions inside the cell depolarises the cell membrane *(1 mark)*. This triggers the calcium ion channels in the cell membrane to open *(1 mark)*. Calcium ions diffuse into the cell *(1 mark)*, which causes the vesicles to move to and fuse with the cell membrane *(1 mark)* and release insulin by exocytosis *(1 mark)*.

c) β *(1 mark)*, endocrine *(1 mark)*, insulin *(1 mark)*, glycogenesis *(1 mark)*, increasing *(1 mark)*

2 a) As the temperature increases the activity level of Organism A increases, and as the temperature decreases the activity level of Organism A decreases / there is a positive correlation between the activity level of Organism A and temperature *(1 mark)*. The activity level of Organism B changes randomly as the temperature changes / there is no correlation between the activity level of Organism B and temperature *(1 mark)*.

b) i) Organism A because an ectotherm is more active in warmer external temperatures than it is in colder temperatures *(1 mark)*.

ii) Squirrels are endotherms so they can control their body temperature internally by homeostasis *(1 mark)*. This means their internal temperature is much less affected by external temperature compared to tortoises, so they can survive in a wider range of external temperatures *(1 mark)*.

c) i) Point X was relatively cold, so thermoreceptors/ peripheral temperature receptors in the squirrels's skin will have detected the low temperature *(1 mark)*. The thermoreceptors/peripheral temperature receptors will have sent impulses to the hypothalamus *(1 mark)* which will have sent impulses to erector pili muscles/effectors to make the hairs stand up *(1 mark)* to trap more air and so prevent heat loss *(1 mark)*.

ii) Any two from: e.g. more sweat may be secreted from the squirrel's sweat glands *(1 mark)*. When the sweat evaporates it will take heat from the body so the skin is cooled *(1 mark)*. / The squirrel's erector pili muscles may relax so its hairs lie flat *(1 mark)*. This means less air is trapped, so the skin is less insulated and heat can be lost more easily *(1 mark)*. / Vasodilation may occur near the surface of the squirrel's skin *(1 mark)*. This means more heat is lost from the skin by radiation so the temperature of the skin is lowered *(1 mark)*. *(Maximum of 4 marks available, plus 1 mark for the correct use and spelling of three terms from: evaporates / erector pili muscles / insulated / vasodilation / radiation.)*

3 a) i) The adrenal glands / adrenal medulla *(1 mark)*.

ii) Adrenaline binds to specific receptors in the cell membrane *(1 mark)*, which activates an enzyme/ adenylate cyclase in the cell membrane *(1 mark)*. The activated enzyme/adenylate cyclase catalyses the production of cyclic AMP/cAMP *(1 mark)*, which triggers a cascade.

iii) E.g. it causes the cardiac muscle to contract more frequently *(1 mark)* and with more force *(1 mark)*.

b) Baroreceptors/pressure receptors detect low blood pressure *(1 mark)* and send impulses (along sensory neurones) to the cardiovascular centre in the medulla oblongata *(1 mark)*. This then sends impulses along sympathetic neurones *(1 mark)*, which secrete noradrenaline *(1 mark)*. Noradrenaline binds to receptors on the SAN, which causes the heart rate to increase *(1 mark)*.

Examiners can be pretty picky — make sure you use specific technical terms in your answers, e.g. here you're more likely to pick up a mark if you state 'the cardiovascular centre in the medulla oblongata' rather than just writing 'the medulla'.

Section 2 — Excretion

1. The Liver and Excretion

Page 47 — Application Questions

Q1 a) The level of argininosuccinate in the blood would be low. This is because argininosuccinate would still be used up in the cycle but there would be a lack of AS to convert citrulline to more argininosuccinate.

b) The level of citrulline would be high. This is because citrulline would still be made in the cycle but it would not be converted to argininosuccinate, so it would build up in the blood.

Q2 The proteins that we eat are made up of amino acids, which contain nitrogenous substances. Via deamination, these nitrogenous substances enter the ornithine cycle in the form of ammonia. If a person suffering from AS deficiency eats a low protein diet then fewer excess amino acids will be produced by digestion, so less ammonia will enter the ornithine cycle.

Page 47 — Fact Recall Questions

Q1 The removal of the waste products of metabolism from the body.

Q2 The duodenum and the ileum / the small intestine.

Q3 the hepatic vein

Q4 The capillaries that connect the hepatic artery and the hepatic portal vein to the central vein in the liver.

2. The Kidneys and Excretion

Page 50 — Application Questions

Q1 A — renal capsule
B — loop of Henle
C — distal convoluted tubule/DCT
D — ureter

Q2 a) X — basement membrane
Y — epithelium / podocyte

b) E.g. the structure of the barrier normally prevents larger molecules such as proteins from entering the tubules. If its structure is affected, large molecules such as proteins may be able to pass into the tubules and eventually end up in the urine, producing proteinuria.

Page 50 — Fact Recall Questions

Q1 a) afferent arteriole
b) renal capsule
c) Because vessel A/the afferent arteriole is larger in diameter than vessel B/the efferent arteriole, the blood in the glomerulus is under high pressure. The high pressure forces liquid and small molecules in the blood out of the capillary and into the renal capsule (ultrafiltration).

If you're struggling to remember the difference between the afferent and efferent arterioles, think afferent comes first, because it's first alphabetically.

Q2 Any three from: e.g. glucose / amino acids / vitamins / salts / urea / water.

3. The Kidneys and Water Content

Page 53 — Application Questions

Q1 a) The runner is dehydrated because he has sweated a lot and not replaced any of the fluids he has lost. This has caused his blood water content to drop.

b) The low water content of the runner's blood is detected by osmoreceptors in his hypothalamus.

c) ADH molecules bind to receptors on the plasma membranes of cells of the runner's distal convoluted tubule/DCT and collecting duct. When this happens, protein channels called aquaporins are inserted into the plasma membrane. These channels allow water to pass through via osmosis, so make the walls of the DCT and collecting duct more permeable to water. This allows water to be reabsorbed from these tubules into the medulla and into the blood by osmosis, therefore conserving water in the runner's body.

d) The presence of sodium (Na^+) and chloride (Cl^-) ions in the sports drink increases the concentration of Na^+ and Cl^- in the runner's filtrate. These ions are used to lower the water potential of the medulla in the loop of Henle in order to create a water potential gradient to drive the reabsorption of water back into the blood by osmosis.

Make sure you understand water potential. If you don't, it makes understanding the regulation of water content by the kidneys pretty tricky. Remember, high water potential means a high concentration of water molecules and low water potential means a low concentration of water molecules. Water moves from a region of higher water potential to a region of lower water potential — from where there are more water molecules to where there are fewer.

Q2 a) Normally if a person has consumed too much fluid, the osmoreceptors in the hypothalamus detect that the water content of the blood, and so its water potential, has risen. This causes the posterior pituitary gland to release less ADH into the blood. Less ADH means that the DCT and collecting duct are less permeable, so less water is reabsorbed into the blood by osmosis. This causes a large amount of dilute urine to be produced and so more water is lost.

b) If the body can't suppress ADH production, the DCT and collecting duct will continue to be made permeable, so water is reabsorbed into the blood by osmosis. This means that the excess water is not excreted and therefore accumulates, potentially affecting the balance of fluid in cells.

Page 53 — Fact Recall Questions

Q1 the ascending limb

Q2 A longer ascending limb allows more ions to be actively pumped out into the medulla, which creates a really low water potential in the medulla. This means more water moves out of the nephron and collecting duct into the capillaries, giving very concentrated urine.

4. Kidney Failure

Page 55 — Application Questions

Q1 B

Q2 In order to maintain a steep concentration gradient between the two fluids. This increases the rate of diffusion of waste products and excess water and ions across the membrane out of the blood and into the dialysis fluid.

Q3 E.g. the patient will have to undergo a major operation, which is risky. / The patient's immune system may reject the transplant.

5. Detecting Hormones

Page 57 — Fact Recall Questions

Q1 human chorionic gonadotrophin (hCG)

Q2 white / it won't change colour
Remember, the test strip will only change colour in a positive pregnancy test (when hCG is present).

Q3 Anabolic steroids increase muscle mass.

Q4 a) gas chromatography

b) The urine sample is vaporised and passed through a column containing a liquid. Different substances move through the column at different speeds, so the length of time taken for substances in the urine sample to pass through the column is compared to the time taken for a steroid to pass through the column. If the time taken is the same then the sample contains the steroid.

Exam-style Questions — pages 58-59

1 a) i) Useful substances are reabsorbed back into the blood from the tubules / selective reabsorption takes place *(1 mark)*.

ii) Microvilli *(1 mark)*. The epithelium of the wall of the PCT has microvilli to provide a large surface area *(1 mark)* for the reabsorption of useful materials from the filtrate into the blood *(1 mark)*.

b) i) glomerulus *(1 mark)*

ii) E *(1 mark)*, F *(1 mark)*

iii) Loop of Henle *(1 mark)*. The longer the loop of Henle, the more water that can be reabsorbed from the filtrate *(1 mark)*. When there's a longer ascending limb, more ions are actively pumped out into the medulla *(1 mark)*, which creates a really low water potential in the medulla *(1 mark)*. This means more water moves out of the nephron and collecting duct into the capillaries, giving very concentrated urine *(1 mark)*. This allows the camel to conserve as much water as possible *(1 mark)*.

2 a) i)

Substance	TF/P ratio of 1.0
glucose	✓
serum albumin (protein)	X
sodium ions (Na^+)	✓
urea	✓
red blood cells	X

(1 mark for each correct answer)

Don't let the numbers throw you in this question. All you're really being asked is which substances can cross the filtration barrier and which can't.

ii) Normally proteins like serum albumin can't pass through the filtration barrier into the tubular fluid, so it stays in the blood *(1 mark)*.

iii) E.g. high blood pressure can damage the capillaries in the glomeruli *(1 mark)*. This means larger molecules like proteins may be able to get through the capillary walls and into the tubular fluid *(1 mark)*. This could cause the concentration of proteins like serum albumin to be the same in the plasma as in the tubular fluid, producing a TF/P ratio of 1.0 *(1 mark)*.

b) The reabsorption of Na⁺ from the kidney tubule back into the capillaries lowers the water potential of the medulla *(1 mark)*. This drives the reabsorption of water from the kidney tubule via osmosis *(1 mark)*. If the amount of sodium reabsorbed is decreased then the amount of water reabsorbed will also decrease *(1 mark)*. This means more water will be removed from the body in the urine, lowering the water content of the blood *(1 mark)*. This in turn will reduce blood volume, and therefore blood pressure *(1 mark)*.

c) i) deamination *(1 mark)*, the ornithine cycle *(1 mark)*

   ii) E.g. weight loss / vomiting *(1 mark)*.

   iii) E.g. she could feel increasingly unwell between dialysis sessions because waste products and fluid would start to build up in her blood *(1 mark)*. Dialysis can be inconvenient for the patient *(1 mark)*.

   If a question asks for two things, make sure you give two. You won't get any extra marks for writing more than two, and it'd be a waste of your time in the exam.

3   gonadotrophin *(1 mark)*, pregnant *(1 mark)*, antibodies *(1 mark)*, blue *(1 mark)*

Section 3 — Photosynthesis and Respiration

1. Storing and Releasing Energy
Page 61 — Fact Recall Questions
Q1   Any three from, e.g. photosynthesis / active transport / DNA replication / cell division.

Q2   An autotroph is an organism that can make its own food (e.g. a plant). A heterotroph is an organism that can't make its own food (e.g. an animal).

Q3   ATP is the immediate source of energy in a cell.

Q4   A molecule of ATP is made from adenine, a ribose sugar and three phosphate groups.

If you're asked to describe the structure of ATP in the exam, make sure you're specific and put that it's a 'ribose sugar'. If you just put 'sugar' you won't get the mark.

Q5   a) ADP and P$_i$

   b) hydrolysis

2. Photosynthesis and the Light-dependent Reaction
Page 66 — Application Questions
Q1   a) proton/hydrogen ion/H⁺

   b) Because this forms a proton gradient across the membrane. Protons move down their concentration gradient, into the stroma, via an enzyme called ATP synthase. The energy from this movement combines ADP and inorganic phosphate (P$_i$) to form ATP.

Q2   PSII / photosystem II

Q3   D

Q4   ATP

   Cyclic photophosphorylation doesn't produce any reduced NADP or O$_2$— just ATP.

Page 66 — Fact Recall Questions
Q1   A – outer membrane of envelope
   B – inner membrane of envelope
   C – stroma
   D – thylakoid
   E – thylakoid membrane
   F – lamella

Q2   a) Coloured substances that absorb the light energy needed for photosynthesis.

   b) chlorophyll a

Q3   Any three from: e.g. the chloroplast envelope keeps the reactants for photosynthesis close to the reaction site. / The thylakoids have a large surface area to allow as much light energy to be absorbed as possible. / Lots of ATP synthase molecules are present in the thylakoid membranes to produce ATP in the light-dependent reaction. / The stroma contains all the enzymes, sugars and organic acids for the light-independent reaction to take place.

Q4   hydrogen

Q5   the thylakoid membranes

Q6   ATP and reduced NADP

   In the exam, always read the question very carefully. For example, this question didn't ask for all the products of the light-dependent reaction — it specifically asked for the products that are needed for the light-independent reaction. So if you put oxygen it would be wrong because it's not needed for the light-independent reaction.

Q7   The process of adding phosphate to a molecule using light.

Q8   A chain of proteins through which excited electrons flow.

Q9   a) protons, electrons and oxygen

   b) To replace excited electrons in PSII.

Q10 a) Photosystems: photosystem I/PSI and photosystem II/PSII
   Products: ATP, reduced NADP and oxygen

   b) Photosystem: photosystem I/PSI
   Product: ATP

3. Light-independent Reaction
Page 69 — Application Questions
Q1   X = ribulose bisphosphate (RuBP)
   Y = glycerate 3-phosphate (GP)
   Z = triose phosphate (TP)

Q2   A = ribulose bisphosphate carboxylase (rubisco)
   B = reduced NADP

Q3
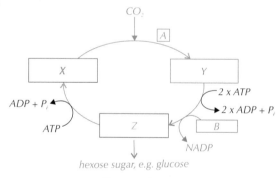
hexose sugar, e.g. glucose

Page 69 — Fact Recall Questions
Q1   It is combined with ribulose bisphosphate to form glycerate 3-phosphate.

Q2   a)
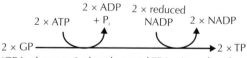
   (GP is glycerate 3-phosphate and TP is triose phosphate)

   b) reduction

   Although the conversion of GP to TP is a reduction reaction, ATP and reduced NADP are both oxidised.

Q3   In the Calvin cycle ATP is needed for the reduction of glycerate 3-phosphate (GP) to triose phosphate (TP). It's also needed for the regeneration of ribulose bisphosphate (RuBP) from triose phosphate.

Q4   five

Q5 a) six
Six turns of the Calvin cycle produces 12 molecules of triose phosphate (TP). Ten of these molecules (5 out of every 6) are used to make ribulose bisphosphate (RuBP) and two are used to make one hexose sugar.
    b) 18
Six turns of cycle × 3 ATP molecules per turn = 18 ATP
    c) 12
Six turns of cycle × 2 reduced NADP molecules per turn = 12 reduced NADP
Q6 a) Two triose phosphate molecules are joined together to produce a hexose sugar. Large carbohydrates are then made by joining the hexose sugars together.
    b) Lipids are made from glycerol and fatty acids. Glycerol is synthesised from triose phosphate, while fatty acids are made from glycerate 3-phosphate.
    c) Some amino acids are made from glycerate 3-phosphate.

4. Limiting Factors in Photosynthesis
Page 74 — Application Questions
Q1 a) Outside plants week 2 height = 60 cm
        (accept 55-65 cm).
        Outside plants week 5 height = 150 cm
        Difference in plant height = 150 – 60 = 90 cm
        % difference in plant height =
        (difference ÷ original) × 100 = (90 ÷ 60) × 100 = **150%**
        Greenhouse plants week 2 height = 140 cm
        (accept 135-145 cm).
        Greenhouse plants week 5 height = 225 cm
        (accept 220-230 cm).
        Difference in plant height = 225 – 140 = 85 cm
        % difference in plant height = (85 ÷ 140) × 100 = **60.7%**
    b) E.g. the farmer may have increased the carbon dioxide concentration in the greenhouse by burning a small amount of propane in a carbon dioxide generator. / The farmer may have used lamps to provide light at night. / The farmer may have made use of heaters and cooling systems in order to keep a constant optimum temperature.
Q2 a) Plant B. This is because plant A has been under a green light, which is reflected by the plant, reducing the rate of photosynthesis. However, plant B has been under blue light, which is absorbed by photosynthetic pigments, increasing the rate of photosynthesis. This means plant B will have made more glucose and so had more energy for growth.
    b) E.g. even though the plant is getting enough light and water, it is exposed to high temperatures of around 40°C. At these temperatures its stomata may close to avoid losing too much water. This means less carbon dioxide can enter the leaf, so photosynthesis will slow right down. In turn, the plant will produce much less glucose, which means it'll have much less energy to carry out all its life processes and may die.

Page 74 — Fact Recall Questions
Q1 A test tube containing the pondweed and water is connected to a capillary tube full of water, which is connected to a syringe. A source of white light is placed at a specific distance from the pondweed. The pondweed is left to photosynthesise for a set amount of time. At the end of the experiment, the syringe is used to draw the gas bubble in the tube up alongside a ruler and the length of the gas bubble (proportional to the volume of O_2) is measured. The experiment is repeated and the average length of gas bubble is calculated. The whole experiment is then repeated with the light source placed at different distances from the pondweed.

Q2 A low light intensity will slow down the light-dependent reaction, so that less ATP and reduced NADP are produced. This means there will be less ATP and reduced NADP entering the Calvin cycle, which means the Calvin cycle will slow down.
Q3 a) The concentration of RuBP will decrease.
The level of RuBP decreases at low light intensities because the light-dependent reaction is slower, so less ATP and reduced NADP are produced and the conversion of GP to TP and RuBP is slower.
    b) The concentration of RuBP will decrease.
The level of RuBP decreases at low temperatures because the enzymes in the Calvin cycle work more slowly.
    c) The concentration of RuBP will increase.
The level of RuBP increases at low CO_2 concentrations because there is less CO_2 and so less RuBP will be combined with CO_2 to produce GP.

Exam-style Questions — pages 75-76
1   a) autotroph *(1 mark)*
    b) i)   A – stroma *(1 mark)*
             B – thylakoid membrane / lamella *(1 mark)*
             C – outer membrane of envelope *(1 mark)*
        ii) Structure B has a large surface area to allow as much light energy to be absorbed as possible. / Structure B has lots of ATP synthase molecules to produce ATP in the light-dependent reaction *(1 mark)*.
             Structure C keeps the reactants for photosynthesis close to their reaction sites *(1 mark)*.
        iii) A/stroma *(1 mark)*
    c) i)   Any five from: carbon dioxide is combined with the ribulose bisphosphate/RuBP to form an unstable six carbon compound *(1 mark)*. This reaction is catalysed by the enzyme ribulose bisphosphate carboxylase/rubisco *(1 mark)*. The compound quickly breaks down to form two molecules of glycerate 3-phosphate/GP *(1 mark)*. Glycerate 3-phosphate/GP is reduced to triose phosphate/TP *(1 mark)* using energy from ATP *(1 mark)* and H⁺ ions/protons/hydrogen ions from reduced NADP *(1 mark)*. *(1 mark for correct use and spelling of three terms from: ribulose bisphosphate / ribulose bisphosphate carboxylase / glycerate 3-phosphate / triose phosphate)*.
        ii) ATP is used *(1 mark)* to convert the five molecules of triose phosphate/TP/the 3-carbon compound back into ribulose bisphosphate/RuBP *(1 mark)*.
    d) respiration *(1 mark)*
2   a) In tube B light energy was absorbed by photosystem I in the chloroplasts *(1 mark)* and electrons were excited to a very high energy level *(1 mark)*. Then these excited electrons were transferred to DNIP to produce reduced DNIP *(1 mark)*.
NADP is a coenzyme that can accept from or give hydrogen (and therefore electrons) to another molecule. The question says DNIP is an artificial hydrogen acceptor. This means it can accept hydrogen (and therefore electrons) from other molecules too — it works in the same way as NADP.
    b) Tube A receives no light energy so the light-dependent reaction of photosynthesis can't take place *(1 mark)*. The chloroplasts in test tube C have been boiled, which will have denatured the enzymes in the chloroplast, therefore preventing photosynthesis from taking place *(1 mark)*.
    c) Glycerate 3-phosphate/GP is reduced to triose phosphate/TP *(1 mark)* using hydrogen ions from reduced NADP *(1 mark)*.

3   a) No. The student hasn't taken into account the amount of oxygen that the plant has used for respiration *(1 mark)*.

    b) i) In experiment 1, the rate of photosynthesis increased with increasing light intensity *(1 mark)*. However, after about 200 µmoles/m²/s the rate of photosynthesis levelled off *(1 mark)* because light intensity was no longer the limiting factor *(1 mark)*.

        ii) The limiting factor in experiment 2 must be temperature because the graph for experiment 3 levels off at a higher point *(1 mark)* but experiment 3 had the same light intensity and CO_2 concentration as experiment 2 *(1 mark)*.

    c) The level of RuBP will have increased because there would have been less CO_2 to combine with RuBP to form GP / because RuBP is still being made but isn't being used up *(1 mark)*. The level of TP will have decreased because it's being used up to make RuBP but isn't being remade *(1 mark)*.

If you get a question like this in the exam, make sure you think of the substances before the reactant in the cycle as well as those that come after it.

5. Aerobic Respiration
Page 78 — Application Questions
Q1 a) ATP
    b) reduced NAD
    c) inorganic phosphate (P_i)
    d) hexose bisphosphate
    e) triose phosphate
    f) H^+ ions/hydrogen ions
Q2 a) phosphorylation
    b) oxidation
Q3   The formation of hexose phosphate in the first part of the reaction and the formation of 4ATP from 4ADP + 4P_i in the second part of the reaction.

Page 80 — Application Questions
Q1 a) oxaloacetate = 4C, citrate = 6C
    b) Decarboxylation and dehydrogenation occur, producing one molecule of reduced FAD and two of reduced NAD. ATP is produced by substrate-level phosphorylation.
Q2   24
Two molecules of carbon dioxide are produced per turn of the Krebs cycle and the Krebs cycle turns twice for each molecule of glucose. So for one molecule of glucose four molecules of carbon dioxide are produced. Therefore if six molecules of glucose were respired, 24 (6 × 4) molecules of carbon dioxide would be produced in the Krebs cycle.
Q3   Acetyl coenzyme A can enter the Krebs cycle, leading to the formation of reduced coenzymes, which are then used in oxidative phosphorylation

Page 81 — Application Questions
Q1   Carrier 1 will be in a reduced state because it has received electrons from reduced NAD but can't pass them on. Carrier 3 will be in an oxidised state because it has passed its electrons onto oxygen, but hasn't received any more from carrier 2.
If a substance gains electrons it is reduced. If a substance loses electrons it is oxidised.

Q2   Antimycin A inhibits carrier 2 and so stops electrons moving down the electron transport chain. This means no more energy will be lost from electrons moving down the chain, so H^+ ions will not be transported across the inner mitochondrial membrane and the electrochemical gradient across the membrane won't be maintained. This means the synthesis of ATP by ATP synthase will stop. If a fish can't produce ATP it will die as energy from ATP is needed to fuel all biological processes.

Page 83 — Fact Recall Questions
Q1   E.g. the inner mitochondrial membrane is folded into cristae, which increases the membrane's surface area to maximise respiration. There are lots of ATP synthase molecules in the inner mitochondrial membrane to produce lots of ATP in the final stage of respiration. The mitochondrial matrix contains all the reactants and enzymes needed for the Krebs cycle to take place.
Q2   In the cytoplasm.
Q3   ATP is used to phosphorylate glucose, making triose phosphate.
Q4   By active transport.
Q5   In the mitochondrial matrix.
Q6 a) Pyruvate is decarboxylated — one carbon atom is removed from pyruvate in the form of carbon dioxide. Then NAD is reduced — it collects hydrogen from pyruvate, changing pyruvate into acetate.
    b) It combines with acetate to form acetyl coenzyme A.
    c) Acetyl coenzyme A enters the Krebs cycle. Reduced NAD is used in oxidative phosphorylation. Carbon dioxide is released as a waste product.
Q7   substrate-level phosphorylation
Q8 a) It is reused in the link reaction.
    b) It is regenerated for use in the next Krebs cycle.
Q9   They lose energy.
Q10 oxygen
Q11 E.g. the conversion of pyruvate to acetate in the link reaction. / The conversion of citrate to the 5-carbon compound in the Krebs cycle. / The conversion of the 5-carbon compound to oxaloacetate in the Krebs cycle.
Every time CO_2 is lost in a reaction, decarboxylation is happening.
Q12

Substance	Glycolysis	Link reaction	Krebs cycle	Oxidative phosphorylation
ATP	X		X	X
reduced NAD	X	X	X	
reduced FAD			X	
CO_2		X	X	

Remember, oxidative phosphorylation also produces (oxidised) NAD and FAD, and water.
Q13 E.g. some of the reduced NAD formed in the first three stages of aerobic respiration is used in other reduction reactions in the cell instead of in oxidative phosphorylation. Some ATP is used up by actively transporting substances into the mitochondria during respiration. The inner mitochondrial membrane is leaky — some protons may leak into the matrix without passing through ATP synthase and without making ATP.

6. Respiration Experiments
Page 86 — Application Question
Q1   The fact that ATP synthesis stops when DCC is added suggests that the movement of protons through the ATP synthase is essential for ATP production. This supports the chemiosmotic theory because it suggests that the proton gradient is being used to synthesise ATP.

Page 86 — Fact Recall Questions

Q1 It absorbs carbon dioxide.

Q2 20 g

You know the answer here is 20 g because the mass of the mouse and the mass of the glass beads in the control tube have to be the same.

Q3 The theory that energy lost from electrons moving down the electron transport chain creates a proton gradient (a concentration gradient of H^+ ions), which is then used to synthesise ATP.

7. Anaerobic Respiration
Page 88 — Application Questions

Q1 a) anaerobically

b) two

c)

Q2 a) i) lactate/lactic acid
ii) pyruvate
iii) ethanol

b) i) A
ii) B
iii) A

c) two

Q3 Blue, because without oxygen the yeast will have respired anaerobically producing ethanol from pyruvate. This reaction uses hydrogen ions, so Janus Green B will be oxidised.

Page 88 — Fact Recall Questions

Q1 In the cytoplasm.

Q2 E.g. both start with glycolysis. / Both produce ATP. / Both require NAD.

Q3 a) E.g. mammals / some bacteria
b) E.g. yeast / plants

Q4 Reduced NAD (from glycolysis) transfers hydrogen to pyruvate to form lactate and NAD.

Q5 Reduced NAD (from glycolysis) transfers hydrogen to ethanal to form ethanol and NAD.

Q6 a) 30 fewer ATP

If aerobic respiration can produce 32 molecules of ATP per molecule of glucose and anaerobic respiration produces 2 molecules of ATP, then 32 − 2 = 30 fewer.

b) Because anaerobic respiration only includes one energy-releasing stage (glycolysis), whereas aerobic respiration includes more energy-releasing stages (Krebs cycle, oxidative phosphorylation).

8. Respiratory Substrates
Page 90 — Application Questions

Q1 RQ = molecules of CO_2 released ÷ molecules of O_2 consumed = 12 ÷ 12 = **1**

Q2 RQ = molecules of CO_2 released ÷ molecules of O_2 consumed = 16 ÷ 23 = **0.70**

Q3 a) RQ = molecules of CO_2 released ÷ molecules of O_2 consumed = 57 ÷ 80 = **0.71**
b) A lipid because lipids have a respiratory quotient of 0.7. *Carbohydrates have an RQ of 1 and proteins have an RQ of 0.9.*

Q4 a) RQ = volume of CO_2 released ÷ volume of O_2 consumed = 180 ÷ 250 = **0.72**
b) E.g. more carbohydrates are being respired. / Fewer fats are being respired.

An increase or decrease in an organism's RQ doesn't mean that it is respiring more or less substrate overall — it just means that the type of substrate being respired has changed.

Page 90 — Fact Recall Questions

Q1 Any biological molecule that can be broken down in respiration to release energy.

Q2 carbohydrates

Q3 They can be used to determine what kind of respiratory substrates an organism is respiring and what type of respiration it's using.

Exam-style Questions — pages 93-94

1 a) i) A – mitochondrial matrix *(1 mark)*
B – crista/inner mitochondrial membrane *(1 mark)*
C – outer mitochondrial membrane *(1 mark)*
ii) There is less folding of the inner membrane/fewer crista *(1 mark)*.

b) i) Because glycolysis takes place in the cytoplasm of the cell *(1 mark)*.

Because glycolysis takes place in the cytoplasm and not the mitochondria, it doesn't matter whether you have functioning mitochondria or not — glycolysis can still happen.

ii) Any three from: Glucose is phosphorylated by adding a phosphate from a molecule of ATP *(1 mark)*. / This creates one molecule of hexose phosphate *(1 mark)*. / Hexose phosphate is phosphorylated by ATP to form hexose bisphosphate *(1 mark)*. / Two molecules of ADP are produced overall *(1 mark)*.
iii) In the oxidation of triose phosphate to pyruvate, NAD collects the hydrogen ions from triose phosphate *(1 mark)*, forming reduced NAD *(1 mark)*.

c) RQ = molecules of CO_2 released ÷ molecules of O_2 consumed = 6 ÷ 7 = **0.86**
(2 marks for correct answer, otherwise 1 mark for correct working).

2 a) Alcoholic fermentation occurs / pyruvate is converted to ethanal *(1 mark)* which releases CO_2 *(1 mark)*.

b) The smell of alcohol *(1 mark)*.

Ethanol is the final product in alcoholic fermentation.

c) i) The production of ethanol (from ethanal) regenerates NAD *(1 mark)*, which is then used in the reactions of glycolysis *(1 mark)*.
ii) Lactate fermentation occurs / pyruvate is converted to lactate *(1 mark)* and NAD is produced *(1 mark)*.

d) The second experiment because more ATP is made in aerobic respiration than anaerobic respiration *(1 mark)*.

3 a) i) The oxidation of triose phosphate to pyruvate produces one molecule of reduced NAD *(1 mark)*. The conversion of pyruvate to acetate produces one molecule of reduced NAD *(1 mark)*. The conversion of citrate to a 5-carbon compound in the Krebs cycle produces one molecule of reduced NAD *(1 mark)*. The conversion of this 5-carbon compound to oxaloacetate produces another two molecules of reduced NAD *(1 mark)* and one molecule of reduced FAD *(1 mark)*.
ii) The electrons move along the electron transport chain *(1 mark)* losing energy at each electron carrier *(1 mark)*. Finally they are passed onto oxygen as it is the final electron acceptor *(1 mark)*.

b) There would be no electrochemical gradient produced across the inner mitochondrial membrane *(1 mark)*. This means there would be no movement of ions across the mitochondrial membrane to drive ATP synthase *(1 mark)* so no ATP would be made *(1 mark)*. The cells would only get ATP from anaerobic respiration *(1 mark)*.

Even though H⁺ ions will still be pumped across the inner mitochondrial membrane into the intermembrane space, the uncoupler will be moving them back into the matrix at the same time — so no gradient would be produced.

Unit 5

Section 1 — Protein Synthesis and Cellular Control

1. DNA, RNA and Protein Synthesis
Page 97 — Application Questions
Q1 a) His-Tyr-Tyr-Arg-Gly-Cys-His-Arg-Gly
    b) Arg-Tyr-Asp-Asp-Cys-His-Gly-Tyr-His
    For questions like this, it's a good idea to split up the DNA base sequence into groups of three letters (CAT/TAC/TAC, etc.). Then you'll be able to see what's going on more easily.
Q2 E.g. GACTACTGCAGAAGAGGCTGCGGCTACCAT GGCGAC
    There are lots of possible combinations you could have given here, because each of the amino acids in the table is coded for by more than one base triplet.

Page 97 — Fact Recall Questions
Q1 a) A sequence of three DNA bases in a gene.
    b) Each DNA triplet codes for an amino acid or tells the cell when to start or stop production of a protein.
Q2 It's the sequence of bases that codes for amino acids.
Q3 a) mRNA/messenger RNA
    b) tRNA/transfer RNA
    If you get a question like this in the exam you need to be <u>specific</u>. Always write down the type of RNA you mean (e.g. mRNA) rather than just 'RNA'.

2. Transcription and Translation
Page 99 — Application Question
Q1 It will inhibit protein synthesis. By inhibiting RNA polymerase, α–amanitin will prevent the transcription of mRNA from DNA, preventing protein synthesis from taking place.

Page 100 — Application Questions
Q1 E.g. it may affect the function of the ribosomes, preventing them from translating mRNA into amino acids. This could prevent/impair protein synthesis.
    You don't need to have learnt about Diamond-Blackfan anaemia to answer this question — so long as you know the process of translation, you can work out the answer.
Q2 It could be shorter and so could be a different protein. Translation of the mRNA sequence only continues until a stop codon is reached. Any codons after the stop codon would not be translated into amino acids.

Page 100 — Fact Recall Questions
Q1 An enzyme. RNA polymerase attaches to the DNA double helix, and it lines up free RNA nucleotides alongside the template strand. It then moves along the DNA strand, assembling a complementary mRNA sequence from free RNA nucleotides.
Q2 It joins together amino acids to make a protein/polypeptide, following the sequence of codons carried by the mRNA.

Q3 a) A tRNA molecule with an anticodon that's complementary to the first codon on the mRNA attaches itself to the mRNA by complementary base pairing. A second tRNA molecule attaches itself to the next codon on the mRNA in the same way, and so on.
    b) translation
    Don't get transcription and translation mixed up in the exam — it's easy to do and it means you'd miss out on a mark.

3. Control of Protein Synthesis and Protein Activation
Page 103 — Application Questions
Q1 Any three from, e.g. temperature / the presence of other nutrients in the medium / the length of time the bacteria were left for / volume of culture / number of bacteria / amount of lactose/glucose added.
Q2 The normal *E. coli* have been included as a control. They show that any differences in the results were down to the mutations and nothing else.
Q3 a) E.g. Mutant 1 always produces mRNA and β-galactosidase, even in the absence of lactose. This may mean that Mutant 1 has a faulty lac repressor. If the repressor is faulty, it may not be able to bind to the operator and block transcription even in the absence of lactose (so mRNA and β-galactosidase are always produced).
    b) E.g. in Mutant 2, mRNA is produced in the presence of lactose, but active β-galactosidase isn't. This suggests that Mutant 2 is producing faulty β-galactosidase (e.g. because a mutation has affected its active site) / Mutant 2 isn't producing any β-galactosidase (e.g. because the mutation has affected a protein involved in translation).
Q4 E.g. by carrying out multiple repeats of the experiment and comparing the results.

Page 103 — Fact Recall Questions
Q1 By starting or stopping transcription.
Q2 a) These code for useful proteins, e.g. enzymes.
    b) These include a promoter (a DNA sequence located before the structural genes that RNA polymerase binds to) and an operator (a DNA sequence that transcription factors bind to).
    c) This codes for a transcription factor.
Q3 Activators — start/activate transcription. Repressors — stop/repress transcription.
Q4 The *lac* operon contains a regulatory gene (lacI), control elements and three structural genes (lacZ, lacY and lacA). When lactose is not present, lacI produces the lac repressor, which binds to the operator and blocks the transcription of lacZ, lacY and lacA. This means no mRNA is produced so no proteins are made. When lactose is present, it binds to the lac repressor, changing the lac repressor's shape so that it can't bind to the operator. RNA polymerase can now bind to the promoter and begin transcription of the structural genes. This produces mRNA, which can be used to make the proteins.
Q5 Molecules like hormones can bind to cell membranes. This triggers the production of cyclic AMP (cAMP) within the cell. cAMP then activates proteins in the cell by changing their 3D structure.

4. Body Plans

Page 105 — Fact Recall Questions

Q1 The general structure of an organism.

Q2 Homeotic genes.

Q3 Because it's controlled by similar homeotic genes in each type of organism.

Q4 Homeotic genes have regions called homeobox sequences that code for a part of the protein called the homeodomain. The homeodomain binds to specific sites on DNA, enabling the protein to work as a transcription factor. The proteins bind to DNA at the start of developmental genes, activating or repressing transcription and so altering the production of proteins involved in the development of the body plan.

Q5 a) Lysosomes inside the cell release enzymes that break down cell components, e.g. proteins and DNA. The cells shrink and break up into fragments. The fragments are engulfed by phagocytes and digested.

    b) Apoptosis refines the body parts created by mitosis and differentiation by removing unwanted structures.

5. Gene Mutations

Page 108 — Application Questions

Q1 a) Mutation A = a substitution mutation
The third base along is now C, not T.
Mutation B = a substitution mutation
The seventh base along is now C, not G.
Mutation C = a deletion mutation
The fourth base, C, has been deleted.
Mutation D = a duplication mutation
The first triplet, CTT, has been repeated.

    b) Mutation A: Leu-His-Asp-Thr
Mutation B: Leu-His-His-Thr
Mutation C: Leu-Met-Ile
Mutation D: Leu-Leu-His-Asp-Thr

Q2 a) Mutation A is likely to have the least serious effect on the protein's structure. CTC still codes for Leu so the amino acid sequence/primary structure of the protein won't change.

    b) Mutation C is likely to have the most serious effect on the protein's structure as it is a frameshift mutation, which means all the amino acids coded for after the mutation will be different.

Page 108 — Fact Recall Questions

Q1 A change in the DNA base (nucleotide) sequence.

Q2 E.g. if the mutation changes a base in a triplet, but the amino acid the triplet codes for doesn't change. If the mutation produces a triplet that codes for a different amino acid, but the amino acid is chemically similar to the original so it functions like the original amino acid. If the mutated triplet codes for an amino acid not involved with the protein's function.

Q3 a) It may alter the function of the protein produced so that it increases the organism's chance of survival.

    b) It may alter the function of the protein produced so that it decreases the organism's chance of survival.

Exam-style Questions — pages 110-111

1 a) AGCGGUUGUUGUGAG *(1 mark)*
5 amino acids *(1 mark)*

    b) i) ribosome *(1 mark)*

      ii) tRNA molecules carry amino acids to the ribosome *(1 mark)*. A tRNA molecule with an anticodon that's complementary to the first codon on the mRNA attaches itself to the mRNA *(1 mark)* by complementary base pairing *(1 mark)*. A second tRNA molecule attaches itself to the next codon on the mRNA in the same way and the two amino acids are joined by a peptide bond *(1 mark)*. The first tRNA molecule moves away, leaving its amino acid behind *(1 mark)*. A third tRNA molecule binds to the next codon on the mRNA, its amino acid binds to the first two and the second tRNA molecule moves away *(1 mark)*. This process continues until there's a stop codon *(1 mark)*.
(1 mark for making clear that the role of tRNA is to carry amino acids to the ribosomes according to the codons in mRNA.)

2 a) By the order of bases in the glucagon gene *(1 mark)*.

    b) E.g. glucagon could bind to cell membranes *(1 mark)* causing the production of cAMP inside the cell *(1 mark)*. cAMP would then activate the protein inside the cells by changing its three-dimensional stucture *(1 mark)*.

    c) i) An operon is a section of DNA *(1 mark)* that contains structural genes, control elements and sometimes a regulatory gene *(1 mark)*.

      ii) Once bound to the promoter, RNA begins the transcription of the structural genes in the *lac* operon *(1 mark)*. The structural genes produce proteins/enzymes that help the bacteria to digest lactose *(1 mark)*. This means the bacteria are able to respire lactose instead of glucose *(1 mark)*.

3 a) i) A single-base deletion will cause a frameshift *(1 mark)* and this could cause a change in the amino acid sequence/primary structure of the protein *(1 mark)*. This could change the tertiary structure of the protein and prevent it from functioning *(1 mark)*.

      ii) A single-base substitution will only affect one amino acid *(1 mark)*, whereas a single-base deletion will probably alter all the amino acids after the mutation *(1 mark)*.

      iii) Mutations that have a neutral effect on a protein's function won't affect an organism overall *(1 mark)*. This may happen because the mutation doesn't change the amino acid coded for by a triplet *(1 mark)* or because it changes the amino acid to one that is chemically similar to the original *(1 mark)*. Alternatively, the mutation may affect an amino acid that isn't involved in the protein's function *(1 mark)*.

    b) i) nucleus *(1 mark)*

      ii) RNA polymerase attaches to the DNA double helix at the beginning of a gene *(1 mark)*. The hydrogen bonds between two DNA strands in the gene break, separating the strands and the DNA molecule uncoils to allow one of the strands to be used as a template *(1 mark)*. The RNA polymerase lines up free RNA nucleotides alongside the template strand *(1 mark)*. Once the RNA nucleotides have paired up with their complementary bases on the DNA strand they're joined together, forming a complementary mRNA molecule *(1 mark)*. The RNA polymerase moves along the DNA, separating the strands and assembling the mRNA strand *(1 mark)* until it reaches a stop codon and stops making the mRNA *(1 mark)*.
(1 mark for making the correct sequence of steps in the process clear.)

4   a) i) Homeotic genes code for proteins that control the development of the body plan *(1 mark)*. The ag-1 mutation alters the body plan (by causing petals to grow in place of stamens), so ag-1 must be a homeotic gene *(1 mark)*.
        ii) A homeobox sequence codes for a part of the protein called the homeodomain *(1 mark)*. The homeodomain binds to specific sites on DNA, enabling the protein to work as a transcription factor *(1 mark)*. The protein binds to DNA at the start of developmental genes, activating or repressing transcription *(1 mark)* and so altering the production of proteins involved in the development of the body plan *(1 mark)*.
    b) Because other organisms (e.g. animals and fungi) have similar homeotic genes to plants *(1 mark)*, so the development of their body plans will be controlled in a similar way *(1 mark)*.
    c) i) The highly controlled breakdown and death of cells *(1 mark)*.
        ii) E.g. it refines plant body parts created by mitosis and differentiation *(1 mark)* by removing unwanted structures *(1 mark)*.

Section 2 — Inheritance

1. Meiosis

Page 115 — Application Questions
Q1 a) metaphase I
    b) anaphase II
    There are half the number of chromosomes in this cell (compared to the previous cell) and they're being pulled apart — that's how you know it must be in anaphase II.
    c) prophase I
    d) metaphase II
Q2

Page 115 — Fact Recall Questions
Q1 a) diploid
    b) haploid
    c) diploid
Q2 a) The chromosomes condense, homologous chromosomes pair up and crossing-over occurs. The centrioles start moving to opposite ends of the cell, forming the spindle, and the nuclear envelope breaks down.
    b) The homologous pairs line up across the centre of the cell and attach to the spindle fibres by their centromeres.
    c) The spindles contract, pulling the homologous pairs apart (one chromosome goes to each end of the cell).
    d) A nuclear envelope forms around each group of chromosomes and the cytoplasm divides so there are now two haploid daughter cells.
Q3 The two daughter cells from meiosis I undergo prophase II, metaphase II, anaphase II and telophase II. Four haploid daughter cells are produced.
Q4 a) Crossing-over of chromatids, the independent segregation of chromosomes and the independent segregation of chromatids.

b) Crossing-over is when chromatids twist around each other and bits of chromatid swap over. The resulting chromosomes contain the same genes but now have a different combination of alleles. This means that when the chromatids separate at meiosis II, each of the four daughter cells will contain chromatids with different alleles. The independent segregation of chromosomes is when different combinations of maternal and paternal chromosomes go into each cell. The independent segregation of chromatids at meiosis II is when different combinations of chromatids go into each daughter cell. These last two processes also mean that each gamete ends up with a different combination of alleles.
Q5 When alleles on the same chromosome end up in the same daughter cell, so are inherited together.

2. Genetic Terms

Page 117 — Application Questions
Q1 A = tufted tail, B = tufted tail, C = non-tufted tail
Q2 a) yellow
    b) YY
    c) yy

3. Genetic Diagrams — Monohybrid Crosses

Page 122 — Application Questions
Q1 The only possible genotype of offspring is heterozygous, e.g. Tt. Worked example:
    T — tall dominant allele
    t — dwarf recessive allele

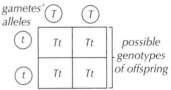

The question asked you to show your working. So even though you know that a monohybrid cross with two homozygous parents always produces all heterozygous offspring, you must draw a genetic diagram of some kind to show how you would work that out.
Q2 a) Worked example:
        H^N— normal allele
        H^S— sickle-cell allele

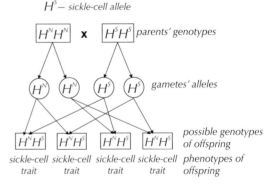

b) There is a 25% chance that any of these children will have sickle-cell anaemia. Worked example:

H^N — normal allele
H^S — sickle-cell allele

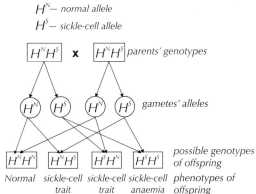

parents' genotypes

gametes' alleles

possible genotypes of offspring

| Normal | sickle-cell trait | sickle-cell trait | sickle-cell anaemia | phenotypes of offspring |

Q3 1:0:1 ratio of blue: yellow: striped organisms / 1:1 ratio of blue : striped organisms. Worked example:

C^Y — yellow allele
C^B — blue allele

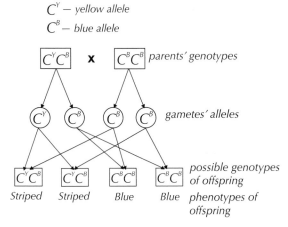

parents' genotypes

gametes' alleles

possible genotypes of offspring

| Striped | Striped | Blue | Blue | phenotypes of offspring |

Q4 $X^F X^F$ (sufferer female), $X^F Y$ (sufferer male), $X^F X^f$ (sufferer female), $X^f Y$ (normal male). Worked example:

$X^F Y$ — male sufferer
$X^F X^f$ — female heterozygous

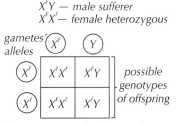

gametes' alleles

possible genotypes of offspring

This question doesn't ask you to show your working, but it's best to always do so. Then if you write an answer down wrong for any reason, you could still pick up marks in your exam for your working.

Q5 ¼ / 0.25 / 25%. Worked example:

$X^N Y$ — normal male
$X^N X^n$ — female carrier

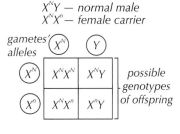

gametes' alleles

possible genotypes of offspring

Q6 Y-linked characteristics can only be passed on down the male (XY) line. So for a son to have a Y-linked disorder, his father must also have the disorder. So if a son has hairy ears but his dad doesn't, the dad might question if he was the father.

This is fairly tricky, but drawing a quick diagram would help you out:

XY^N — normal male
XX — female

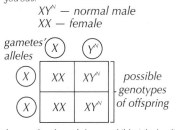

gametes' alleles

possible genotypes of offspring

A normal male can't have a child with the disorder.

Page 122 — Fact Recall Questions
Q1 The ratio of different phenotypes in the offspring.
Q2 a) 3 : 1 ratio of dominant : recessive characteristics
    b) 1 : 2 : 1 ratio of homozygous for one allele : heterozygous : homozygous for the other allele
    The phenotypic ratios are always the same for these types of crosses, so it's well worth learning them.
Q3 Male — XY, Female — XX.
Q4 ½ / 0.5 / 50%
Q5 If a characteristic is sex-linked it means that the allele that codes for it is located on a sex chromosome (X or Y).
Q6 Males are more likely than females to have X-linked disorders because males only have one X chromosome. Because they only have one copy of any alleles on the X chromosome, they express the characteristic of those alleles even if they're recessive, whereas women would need to inherit two copies to express the same characteristics.

4. Dihybrid Crosses and Epistasis

Page 126 — Application Questions
Q1 a) i) EEBB, EeBB, EEBb, EeBb
        For the dog to be black it must be able to express the dark pigment, so it much have at least one dominant E allele. Also, it must have at least one copy of the dominant B allele for the black pigment to be shown in the phenotype.
        ii) Eebb, EEbb
        For the dog to be chocolate it must be able to express the dark pigment, so it much have at least one dominant E allele. Also, it must have two copies of the recessive b allele for the chocolate pigment to be shown in the phenotype.
        iii) eeBB, eeBb, eebb
        For the dog to be yellow it must have two copies of the recessive e allele, so that it can't express the dark pigment. Gene 1 is epistatic over gene 2, so it doesn't matter what B or b alleles the dog has — it will still be yellow.

b) A cross between EEBB and eebb parents will give a
9 : 3 : 4 phenotypic ratio in the F_2 generation of black
: chocolate : yellow. This is because gene 1 has a
recessive epistatic allele (e) and two copies of the
recessive epistatic allele (ee) will mask the expression of
gene 2. Here's the cross to prove it:
B = black pigment, b = chocolate pigment, E = can
express dark pigment, e = can't express dark pigment

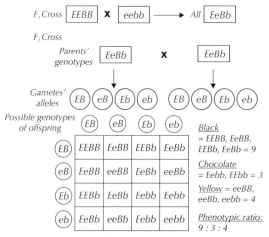

In the exam, you wouldn't need to draw out the genetic
cross unless the question specifically asked you to. We've
just included it here to help you out.

Q2 a) dominant epistasis
b) A cross between WWPP and wwpp produces a
48 : 12 : 4 or 12 : 3 : 1 phenotypic ratio in the F_2
generation of white : purple : red. This is because gene
1 has a dominant epistatic allele (W) and one or more
copies of the dominant epistatic allele (Ww or WW) will
mask the expression of gene 2.
c) W = white pigment, w = red pigment, P = purple
pigment, p = no purple pigment

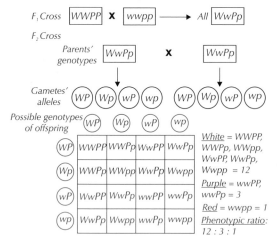

5. The Chi-Squared Test

Pages 130-131 — Application Questions
Q1 a) Yes, the difference would be significant because the
chi-squared value is greater than the critical value
(6.20 > 5.99).
*If the difference is significant it means the difference is not
just due to chance and that the null hypothesis is rejected.*

b) No, the difference would not be significant because the
chi-squared value is smaller than the critical value
(4.85 < 5.99).
*If the difference is not significant it means that the difference
is due to chance and the null hypothesis is accepted.*

Q2

Phenotype	Ratio	Expected result (E)	Observed result (O)	O − E	(O − E)²	$\frac{(O − E)^2}{E}$
Grey body	3	48	45	−3	9	0.19
Ebony body	1	16	19	3	9	0.56
					Total =	0.75

Therefore $\chi^2 = 0.75$

Q3 a)

Phenotype	Ratio	Expected result (E)	Observed result (O)	O − E	(O − E)²	$\frac{(O − E)^2}{E}$
Round, green	9	72	74	2	4	0.06
Round, yellow	3	24	21	−3	9	0.38
Wrinkled, green	3	24	26	2	4	0.17
Wrinkled, yellow	1	8	7	−1	1	0.13
					Total =	0.74

Therefore $\chi^2 = 0.74$

b) There are 4 phenotypes which means there are 4 − 1 = 3
degrees of freedom. From the table, the critical value for
a test with 3 degrees of freedom and a 0.05 probability
level is 7.82. The chi-squared value is smaller than the
critical value (0.74 < 7.82) so the difference between the
observed and expected results is not significant.
This means the null hypothesis can be accepted.

Q4 a) That there is no significant difference between the
observed and expected results.

b)

Phenotype	Ratio	Expected result (E)	Observed result (O)	O − E	(O − E)²	$\frac{(O − E)^2}{E}$
Tall	3	39	43	4	16	0.41
Dwarf	1	13	9	−4	16	1.23
					Total =	1.64

Therefore $\chi^2 = 1.64$.
There are two phenotypes (tall and dwarf) which means
there is 2 − 1 = 1 degree of freedom. From the table, the
critical value for a test with 1 degree of freedom and a
0.05 probability level is 3.84. The chi-squared value
is smaller than the critical value (1.64 < 3.84) so the
difference between the observed and expected results is
not significant. This means that the null hypothesis can
be accepted, so the results from this experiment support
the scientist's theory.

Q5 a)

Phenotype	Ratio	Expected result (E)	Observed result (O)	O − E	(O − E)²	$\frac{(O − E)^2}{E}$
Red	1	40	24	−16	256	6.40
Pink	2	80	92	12	144	1.80
White	1	40	44	4	16	0.40
					Total =	8.60

Therefore $\chi^2 = 8.6$.
There are 3 phenotypes which means there are 3 − 1 = 2
degrees of freedom. From the table, the critical value for
a test with 2 degrees of freedom and a 0.05 probability
level is 5.99. The chi-squared value is greater than the
critical value (8.6 > 5.99) so the difference between the
observed and expected results is significant. This means
that the null hypothesis is rejected, so this is not an
example of codominance.
*Be careful — the order that observed results are written in
the question won't necessarily be the same as the order that
things need to be written in the table.*

b)

Phenotype	Ratio	Expected result (E)	Observed result (O)	O – E	(O – E)²	$\frac{(O - E)^2}{E}$
Red	3	30	24	–6	36	1.20
Pink	9	90	92	2	4	0.04
White	4	40	44	4	16	0.40
					Total =	1.64

Therefore $\chi^2 = 1.64$.
The critical value is 5.99 (the same as for part a). This time the chi-squared value is smaller than the critical value (1.64 < 5.99) so the difference between the observed and expected results is not significant. This means that the null hypothesis can be accepted and that recessive epistasis is involved.

The critical value is the same here as in part a) because the number of degrees have freedom haven't changed (there are still 4 phenotypes involved).

Exam-style Questions — pages 133 – 134

1 a) i) Between hours 10 - 40 *(1 mark)* as the chromosome number doubles during this period *(1 mark)*.
   ii) 15 hours *(1 mark)*
Interphase ends at 40 hours, so this must be when meiosis I begins. Meiosis I ends when the chromosome number has halved again at 55 hours.
   iii) During prophase I, the chromosomes condense *(1 mark)*, homologous chromosomes pair up *(1 mark)*, centrioles move to opposite ends of the cell forming the spindle *(1 mark)* and the nuclear envelope breaks down *(1 mark)*. Metaphase I then takes place, during which homologous pairs line up across the centre of the cell *(1 mark)* and attach to the spindle fibres by their centromeres *(1 mark)*. Next, during anaphase I, the spindles contract, pulling the pairs apart *(1 mark)*. Finally, in telophase I the nuclear envelope forms around each group of chromosomes *(1 mark)* and the cytoplasm divides *(1 mark)*. *(1 mark for making the correct sequence of events in meiosis I clear)*.
   iv) They are undergoing meiosis II *(1 mark)*.
 b) i) Crossing-over occurs in prophase I *(1 mark)* and is when chromatids twist around each other and bits of chromatid swap over *(1 mark)*.
   ii) locus *(1 mark)*

2 a)

Genotype	Growth on substance 1
AaBb	✓
aaBb	✗
AAbb	✗
AABb	✓

(1 mark for each)
 b) They must have the genotype aaBb or aaBB *(1 mark)*. They can't produce enzyme A but can produce enzyme B *(1 mark)*, so if they're given substance 2 they can convert it to substance 3 *(1 mark)*.
 c) Homozygous — an organism that carries two copies of the same allele *(1 mark)*.
Dominant — an allele whose characteristic appears in the phenotype even when there's only one copy *(1 mark)*.
Recessive — an allele whose characteristic only appears in the phenotype when two copies of the allele are present *(1 mark)*.

3 a)

X^hY — *haemophiliac male*
X^HX^h — *female carrier*

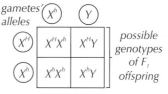

Possible phenotypes of F_1 offspring: carrier female (X^HX^h), normal male (X^HY), haemophiliac female (X^hX^h) and haemophiliac male (X^hY).
(1 mark for correct gametes, 1 mark for correct F_1 genotypes, 1 mark for F_1 phenotypes matched to correct F_1 genotypes).
 b) i)

Phenotype	Ratio	E	O	O – E	(O – E)²	$\frac{(O - E)^2}{E}$
Carrier female	1	68	72	4	16	0.24
Haemophilic female	1	68	70	2	4	0.06
Normal male	1	68	69	1	1	0.02
Haemophilic male	1	68	61	–7	49	0.72
					Total =	1.04

Therefore $\chi^2 = 1.04$.
(3 marks for correct answer, otherwise 1 mark for correct expected results, 1 mark for correct $(O – E)^2 \div E$ calculation.)
   ii) The difference between the observed and expected results is not significant *(1 mark)*.
This is because the critical value for this test is 7.82 and the chi-squared value (1.04) is less than this.

Section 3 — Variation and Evolution

1. Variation

Page 137 — Application Questions
Q1 a) monogenic
   b) Both. MAOA production is controlled by a gene, but it is also influenced by the environment (e.g. taking anti-depressants or smoking tobacco causes it to drop).
Q2 Environmental factors (smoking) affect birth mass. Women who smoked showed a mean reduction in the birth mass of their babies of 377 g. Genetic factors also affect birth mass of babies born to women who smoke. The reduction in birth mass was as much as 1285 g among women who smoked and had certain genotypes.
If you're asked to give evidence from a study, make sure you quote some figures to back up what you're saying.

Page 137 — Fact Recall Questions
Q1 polygenic
Q2 continuous

2. Evolution by Natural Selection and Genetic Drift

Page 141 — Application Questions
Q1 a) The frequency of the three alleles in Population 1 is relatively even. However in Population 2 there is a very high frequency of the white allele and much lower frequencies of the purple and pink alleles.
   b) By chance, the white allele was passed onto offspring more than the other alleles. As a result, the number of individuals with the white allele increased and the number of individuals with purple and pink alleles fell.

c) Population 2, because genetic drift has a much greater effect in smaller populations.

Q2 a) The peak in allele frequency in 2000 was most likely a result of the fire in 1999. The peak may be due to an increase in the number of mammals emigrating to the south from the north as a result of the fire. The northern population had a slightly higher frequency of the allele, so an influx from this population could have caused an increase in the allele frequency in the south.

b) From 1998 to 2002 there was a big increase in the dark fur allele in the northern population. In 1999, a fire destroyed a large area in the north of the forest. This would have left a large area of barren, darkened forest and blackened soil. Mammals with darker fur would have a selective advantage and so be more likely to survive, reproduce and pass on their alleles for darker fur, causing an increase in the frequency of the dark fur allele.

Page 141 — Fact Recall Questions
Q1 a) The complete range of alleles in a population.
b) How often an allele appears in a population.
Q2 Evolution is the change in the frequency of an allele in a population over time.
Q3 Because individuals vary, it means that some organisms are better adapted to selection pressures than others. These individuals are more likely to survive, reproduce and pass on their beneficial alleles to their offspring than others so that, over many generations, these alleles become more common in a population.
Q4 It makes it more likely that individuals with alleles for characteristics towards the middle of the range will survive and reproduce. This reduces the range of possible phenotypes.
Q5 An event that causes a big reduction in the size of a population. Evolution by genetic drift has a greater effect on a population if there's a genetic bottleneck.

3. The Hardy-Weinberg Principle
Page 144 — Application Questions
Q1 a) $p + q = 1$
$q = 1 - p$
$q = 1 - 0.10 = \textbf{0.90}$
You're given one allele frequency in the table and are asked to find the other, so its the simple equation.
b) $p = 0.1$, $q = 0.9$, so $2pq = 2 \times 0.1 \times 0.9 = \textbf{0.18}$
c) No, it does not apply. The frequency of the allele changes between the generations, and the Hardy-Weinberg principle is only true in cases where the allele frequency stays the same.

Q2 $q = 0.16$ and $p + q = 1$, so $p = 1 - q$
$p = 1 - 0.16 = 0.84$
homozygous dominant genotype frequency $= p^2$
$p^2 = 0.84^2 = \textbf{0.71}$
Q3 recessive wrinkled allele $= q^2 = 31\% \div 100 = 0.31$
$q = \sqrt{0.31} = 0.557$
$p + q = 1$, so $p = 1 - q$
$p = 1 - 0.557 = 0.443$
Heterozygous genotype $= 2pq$
$2pq = 2 \times 0.443 \times 0.557 = 0.49$
$0.49 \times 100 = 49$, so **49%** of the population have a heterozygous genotype.

Page 144 — Fact Recall Questions
Q1 The Hardy-Weinberg principle is a mathematical model that predicts that the frequencies of alleles in a population won't change from one generation to the next as long as the population is large, there's no immigration, emigration, mutations or natural selection, and mating is totally random.
Q2 $p + q = 1$ and $p^2 + 2pq + q^2 = 1$, where p = the frequency of the dominant allele, q = the frequency of the recessive allele, p^2 = the frequency of the homozygous dominant genotype, q^2 = the frequency of the homozygous recessive genotype and $2pq$ = the frequency of the heterozygous genotype.

4. Artificial Selection
Page 146 — Fact Recall Questions
Q1 a) E.g. females with large udders and males whose mothers had large udders were selected and bred together. The offspring with the largest udders were then selected and bred together. This process was continued over several generations until a cow with very large udders was produced.
b) E.g. high milk yield / high milk quality / a long lactation period / resistance to mastitis/disease / a calm temperament
Q2 *Triticum aestivum*
Q3 Any two from, e.g. high wheat yield/large ears / a high tolerance to the cold / short stalks / uniform stalk height
Q4 E.g. both change the allele frequencies in the next generation / the alleles that code for beneficial characteristics will become more common in the next generation. Both may make use of random mutations when they occur.

5. Speciation
Page 148 — Application Question
Q1 E.g. the two elephant populations separated and became geographically isolated. The different habitats caused different selective pressures, so in each habitat elephants with different alleles were more likely to survive, reproduce and pass on their advantageous alleles. Over time this caused the frequencies of the advantageous alleles in each habitat to increase. Mutations also took place independently in each population, which also altered the allele frequencies in each habitat. Eventually the differences in allele frequencies resulted the phenotypes of the two populations changing so much that they became reproductive isolated. Speciation had occurred.

Page 149 — Fact Recall Questions
Q1 a) The development of a new species.
b) When populations of the same species can no longer breed together to produce fertile offspring (as a result of changes in allele frequencies).
c) When a physical barrier divides two populations of a species.
Q2 E.g. seasonal, mechanical, behavioural
Q3 the biological species concept, the phylogenetic species concept/cladistic species concept/evolutionary species concept

Exam-style Questions — pages 150-151
1 a) i) That it is influenced by only one gene *(1 mark)*.
ii) Discontinuous variation is where individuals fall into only one of two or more distinct categories *(1 mark)* and there are no intermediates *(1 mark)*.

b) $q^2 = 5 \div 1000 = 0.005$
    $q = \sqrt{0.005} = 0.0707$ *(1 mark)*
    $p = 1 - 0.0707 = 0.9293$ *(1 mark)*
    $2pq = 0.1314$
    $0.1314 \times 100 = $ **13.14%** *(1 mark)*

You want to find the frequency of Ee (the heterozygous genotype), so you need to calculate 2pq.

c) Genetic drift *(1 mark)*. The syndrome does not increase a person's chance of surviving, so the allele must have become more common in the population by chance *(1 mark)*.

2 a) i) As a group of similar organisms that can breed together to produce fertile offspring *(1 mark)*.
    ii) E.g. you can't always see an organism's reproductive behaviour *(1 mark)*.
  b) i) E.g. the geographically isolated populations experienced different conditions *(1 mark)*. These conditions created different selective pressures *(1 mark)*, so in each lake fish with different alleles were more likely to survive, reproduce and pass on their advantageous alleles *(1 mark)*. Over time this caused the frequencies of the advantageous alleles in each habitat to increase *(1 mark)*. Mutations also took place independently in each population, again altering allele frequencies *(1 mark)*. Eventually the differences in allele frequencies resulted in the phenotypes of the two populations changing so much that they became reproductively isolated *(1 mark)*. At this point speciation had occurred *(1 mark)*. *(1 mark for making the link between geographical isolation, changing allele frequencies and speciation clear.)*
    ii) A random mutation could take place in a population *(1 mark)* resulting in a (behavioural/mechanical/seasonal) change that prevents the two populations from breeding successfully together *(1 mark)*.

3 a) i) Continuous variation *(1 mark)*. E.g. there are no distinct categories *(1 mark)* and the average yield per crop plant can take any value within a range *(1 mark)*.
    ii) A combination of genotype and the environment, because the data shows continuous variation *(1 mark)*.
  b) i) When humans select individuals in a population to breed together to get desirable traits *(1 mark)*.
    ii) E.g. wheat plants with a high yield (e.g. large ears) are bred together *(1 mark)*. The offspring with the highest yields are then selected and bred together *(1 mark)*. This is continued over several generations to produce a plant with a very high yield *(1 mark)*.
  c) i) Some goatgrass plants had alleles which gave them a higher cold tolerance than others *(1 mark)*. These plants were better adapted to the selective pressure of a cold environment *(1 mark)*. This made them more likely to survive, reproduce and pass on the alleles for cold tolerance *(1 mark)*. As a result, a greater proportion of the next generation inherited the alleles for cold tolerance *(1 mark)*. These plants are also more likely to survive, reproduce and pass on their alleles, so the frequency of the cold tolerance alleles increases from generation to generation *(1 mark)*.

Regardless of which species you're writing about, when explaining the process of natural selection you need to make sure you get across the idea that the organisms involved are more likely to survive, reproduce and pass on the allele(s) for the beneficial characteristic to their offspring.

ii) E.g. in the natural selection of goatgrass, the organisms that reproduce are selected by the environment but in the artificial selection of *Triticum aestivum* this is carried out by humans *(1 mark)*. The artificial selection of *Triticum aestivum* aims for a predetermined result, but in the natural selection of goatgrass the result was unpredictable *(1 mark)*. The natural selection of goatgrass made the species better adapted to the environment, but the artificial selection of *Triticum aestivum* made the species more useful for humans *(1 mark)*.

Section 4 — Cloning and Biotechnology

1. Animal Cloning
Page 154 — Application Questions
Q1 Reproductive cloning. Non-reproductive cloning only generates embryonic stem cells and the scientist wants whole organisms.
Q2 a) nuclear transfer
   b) (i) The embryo would implanted into a surrogate mother where it would grow into a dog that is genetically identical to the one being cloned.
      (ii) Stem cells that are genetically identical to the dog being cloned would harvested from the embryo and grown in culture.

Page 154 — Fact Recall Questions
Q1 a) Reproductive cloning is cloning that is used to make a complete organism that is genetically identical to another organism.
   b) Non-reproductive cloning is cloning that is used to make embryonic stem cells that are genetically identical to another organism.
Q2 Advantages: e.g. desirable genetic characteristics are always passed onto the clones. Infertile animals can be reproduced. Animals can be cloned at any time. Disadvantages: e.g. undesirable genetic characteristics are always passed on to the clones. Reproductive cloning is very difficult/expensive/time-consuming. Clones may not live as long as natural offspring.
Q3 E.g. they may believe that destroying embryos is destroying a human life and feel it is unethical. They may think a cloned human would have a lower quality of life. They may think that cloning humans would be wrong because it undermines natural sexual reproduction, and traditional family structures.

2. Cloning Plants
Page 157 — Application Questions
Q1 a) Micropropagation. Clone the plant using tissue culture, then take cells from the developing clone. Subculture the cells in fresh medium to make even more clones, then repeat the process.
   b) E.g. the unusual pattern on the petals will always be passed on to the clones. / The plant could be reproduced in any season. / If the plant is sterile it can still be reproduced. / If the plant takes a long time to produce seeds it can be reproduced very quickly.
Q2 a) Any three from: e.g. strawberry plants use runners, whereas elm trees use suckers. / Vegetative propagation occurs from the stem in strawberry plants, whereas in elm trees it occurs from the roots. / Strawberry plants undergo vegetative propagation when they are growing well, whereas elm trees undergo vegetative propagation when they are under stress. / In strawberry plants the runners develop overground, whereas in elm trees they suckers develop underground.

All the information you needed to know about strawberry plants was given to you in the question. In the exam, always make sure you read the whole question carefully, including any background information you're given — it's always there for a reason.

b) E.g. any undesirable characteristics the strawberry plant has will be passed on to all the clones. The cloned strawberry plant population will have no genetic variability and so a single disease could kill them all.

For questions like this you can't just list off all the possible disadvantages of cloning plants. You have to pick out the disadvantages that apply to the particular situation in the question. For example, in this question you couldn't have given high production costs as a disadvantage because the strawberry plants produce the clones naturally.

Page 157 — Fact Recall Questions

Q1 Cells are taken from the original plant that's going to be cloned. The cells are sterilised to kill any microorganisms and are placed on a culture medium containing plant nutrients and hormones. This takes place under aseptic conditions. When the cells have divided and grown into a small plant they're taken out of the medium and planted in soil — they'll develop into plants that are genetically identical to the original plant.

Q2 Any two from: e.g. to reproduce plants that don't readily reproduce naturally. / To reproduce plants that are rare or endangered. / To grow whole plants from genetically engineered plant cells.

Q3 Micropropagation is when tissue culture is used to produce lots of cloned plants very quickly.

Q4 a) Vegetative propagation is the natural production of plant clones from non-reproductive tissues, e.g. roots, leaves and stems.

b) Elm trees have sucker buds scattered around their root system. During times of stress or when a tree is dying, the buds are activated and suckers begin to form. These suckers eventually form completely separate trees — clones of the tree that the suckers grew from.

3. Biotechnology and Enzymes

Page 159 — Application Questions

Q1 By immobilising the enzyme (attaching the enzyme to an insoluble material so it can't become mixed with the products).

Q2 The secreted enzyme would be best to use. Naturally secreted enzymes are cheaper because it can be expensive to extract enzymes from cells.

Page 159 — Fact Recall Questions

Q1 The industrial use of living organisms (or parts of living organisms) to produce food, drugs and other products.

Q2 Any three from: e.g. their ideal growth conditions can be easily created. / They grow rapidly under the right conditions, so products can be made quickly. / They can grow on a range of inexpensive materials. / They can be grown at any time of the year.

Q3 By encapsulating the enzymes in jelly-like alginate beads. By trapping the enzymes in a silica gel matrix. By covalently bonding the enzymes to cellulose or collagen fibres.

Q4 Columns of immobilised enzymes can be washed and reused — this reduces the cost of running a reaction on an industrial scale because you don't have to keep buying new enzymes. The product isn't mixed with the enzymes — no money or time is spent separating them out. Immobilised enzymes are more stable than free enzymes — they're less likely to denature (become inactive) in high temperatures or extremes of pH.

4. Biotechnology — Culturing Microorganisms

Page 163 — Application Questions

Q1 a) Secondary metabolite — it is mainly produced during the stationary phase, so can't be essential for growth.

b) Batch culture — in continuous culture the microorganisms are kept in the exponential phase. This metabolite is mostly produced in the stationary phase, so would not be produced in a continuous culture.

Q2 Batch culture — in continuous culture, if the culture is contaminated the whole culture will have to be discarded and this can be very expensive. As the *E. coli* is prone to contamination, it would be better to use a batch culture. That way if the culture is contaminated only one batch has to be discarded, which is much cheaper than discarding the everything.

It's always a good idea to think about the costs involved when you get a question like this.

Page 163 — Fact Recall Questions

Q1 A population of one type of microorganism that's been grown under controlled conditions.

Q2 When growth of microorganisms takes place in a vessel that's isolated from the external environment.

Q3 a) Lag phase, exponential phase, stationary phase and decline phase.

b) Lag phase — the population size increases very slowly because the microorganisms have to make enzymes and other molecules before they can reproduce. This means the reproduction rate is low.
Exponential phase — the population size increases quickly because the culture conditions are at their most favourable for reproduction. The number of microorganisms doubles at regular intervals.
Stationary phase — the population size stays level because the death rate of the microorganisms equals their reproductive rate. Microorganisms die because there's not enough food and poisonous waste products build up.
Decline phase — the population size falls because the death rate is greater than the reproductive rate. This is because food is very scarce and waste products are at toxic levels.

Q4 Any three from: e.g. pH / temperature / oxygen supply / contamination / nutrient concentration.

Q5 a) Batch culture is where microorganisms are grown in individual batches in a fermentation vessel — when one culture ends it's removed and then a different batch of microorganisms is grown in the vessel.

b) Continuous culture is where microorganisms are continually grown in a fermentation vessel, without stopping.

Q6 Any three from: e.g. batch culture is a closed system, continuous culture is an open system. / In batch culture each culture goes through lag, exponential and stationary growth phases. In continuous culture each culture is kept in the exponential phase. / In batch culture the product is harvested once during the stationary phase. In continuous culture the product is harvested continuously. / Batch culture has relatively low product yield compared to continuous culture. / In batch culture, if contamination occurs only one batch has to be discarded. In continuous culture, if contamination occurs the whole culture has to be discarded. / Batch culture is used when you want secondary metabolites. Continuous culture is used when you want primary metabolites or the microorganisms themselves.

5. Asepsis in Biotechnology
Page 165 — Application Question
Q1 a) E.g. there may have been microorganisms in the milk which competed with the added bacterial culture, giving them a poor yield.
    b) E.g. there may have been enzymes in the milk that catalysed unwanted reactions and changed the flavour of the yoghurt.
    c) Pasteurise the milk before adding the bacterial culture.

Page 165 — Fact Recall Questions
Q1 The practice of preventing contamination of cultures by unwanted microorganisms.
Q2 Any three from: e.g. regularly disinfect work surfaces. / Wear gloves. / Tie back long hair. / Sterilise instruments before and after use. / Flame necks of culture bottles. / Don't put lids down on work surfaces.
Q3 The process of sterilising food by heating it.
Q4 It kills unwanted microorganisms and it denatures enzymes.

Exam-style Questions — pages 166-167
1 a) i) Any three from: e.g. pH probe — monitors the pH and keeps it at an optimum level so enzymes work more efficiently *(1 mark)*. / Water jacket — keeps the temperature at an optimum level so enzymes work more efficiently *(1 mark)*. / Paddles — circulate the medium around the vessel so the bacteria can always access the nutrients needed for growth *(1 mark)*. / Sterile air-in pipe — pumps oxygen into the vessel when needed, so the microorganisms can always respire to provide energy for growth *(1 mark)*.
The question asks you to identify three features of the fermentation vessel in Fig. 1.1., so make sure you only write about features shown on the vessel in the diagram or you won't get the marks.
       ii) It prevents unwanted microorganisms from entering the vessel *(1 mark)* which may compete with the bacteria for nutrients and reduce the yield *(1 mark)*.
    b) i) 35 minutes *(1 mark)*
        ii) E.g. The population size initially increases very slowly because the bacteria have to make enzymes and other molecules before they can reproduce *(1 mark)*. It takes less time for the bacterial population to then double in size again because these enzymes and molecules have already been made *(1 mark)*.
        iii) E.g.

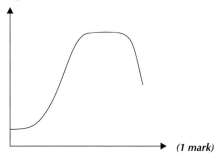

(1 mark)

       iv) In a closed culture, no extra nutrients are added and waste products aren't removed *(1 mark)*. After a time, there's not enough food and waste products start to build up *(1 mark)*. This causes the bacteria to reproduce more slowly and die faster *(1 mark)*. The graph levels off when death rate equals reproduction rate *(1 mark)* and decreases when death rate is higher than reproduction rate *(1 mark)*. In a culture like the one in Fig. 1.2, this doesn't happen because the constant addition of nutrients and removal of waste products keep conditions favourable for growth *(1 mark)*.
The question asks you to explain the differences between the two growth curves, so you don't get marks for just describing them.
    c) i) Non-reproductive cloning — embryonic stem cells are being made rather than a whole organism *(1 mark)*.
        ii) The body cell is taken and the nucleus is extracted *(1 mark)*. This nucleus is then inserted into an egg cell *(1 mark)*, which has been enucleated *(1 mark)*. The egg is then stimulated to divide *(1 mark)*, and an embryo is produced *(1 mark)* from which embryonic stem cells can be harvested *(1 mark)*. *(1 mark if the correct order of steps is clear)*.
2 a) i) These cells are stem cells *(1 mark)*, so they can develop into any of the cell types needed to produce a new plant *(1 mark)*.
        ii) Any two from: e.g. desirable characteristics will always be passed onto the clones *(1 mark)*. / Sterile plants can be reproduced *(1 mark)*. / Plants that take a long time to produce seeds can be reproduced quickly *(1 mark)*.
    b) The clones are all genetically identical *(1 mark)*, so they will all be susceptible to the bacterial infection *(1 mark)*.
    c) i) Their ideal growth conditions can be easily created *(1 mark)*. They grow rapidly, so products can be made very quickly *(1 mark)*. They can grow on a range of inexpensive materials *(1 mark)*. They can be grown at any time of year *(1 mark)*.
        ii)

	Batch	Continuous
The culture is a closed system	✓	
The culture is kept in the exponential phase of growth.		✓
Product is harvested in the stationary phase of growth.	✓	
The product yield is relatively high.		✓
Used if secondary metabolites are required.	✓	

(1 mark for each correct answer. If more than four boxes have been ticked, lose 1 mark for each incorrect answer.)
With questions like these, don't hedge your bets and give more answers than you're asked for — you could end up losing marks.

Section 5: Gene Technologies

1. Common Gene Technologies
Page 172 — Application Questions
Q1 a) top strand = CGTA, bottom strand = GGTA
b) $2 \times 2 \times 2 \times 2 \times 2 \times 2 \times 2 = \mathbf{128}$
Remember, you start with two single stands of DNA.
The amount of DNA then doubles with each PCR cycle.

Q2 There is a *Bam*HI site on the left hand side of the fragment and an *Eco*RI site towards the right hand side. The DNA sample could be incubated with *Bam*HI and *Eco*RI, which would cut the DNA via a hydrolysis reaction at these sites. This is because the shape of each recognition sequence is complementary to each enzyme's active site.
Make sure you use the correct terms in the exam, e.g. the shape of the recognition sequence is <u>complementary</u> to the enzyme's active site, <u>not</u> the same as the enzyme's active site.

Page 172 — Fact Recall Questions
Q1 polymerase chain reaction
Q2 A sequence of DNA that consists of antiparallel base pairs/base pairs that read the same in opposite directions.
Q3 Small tails of unpaired bases at the end of a DNA fragment. They can be used to bind/anneal the DNA fragment to another piece of DNA that has sticky ends with complementary sequences.
Q4 gel electrophoresis
Q5 At the top / near the cathode.
Q6 a) Because it has a specific base sequence that's complementary to the target sequence.
b) They're used to identify DNA fragments that contain specific sequences of bases, e.g. to locate genes on chromosomes/to see if a person's DNA contains a mutated gene.

2. Genetic Engineering and Gene Cloning
Pages 176-177 — Application Questions
Q1 a) Vector DNA was cut with the same restriction enzymes as the DNA fragment, so complementary sticky ends were produced. The DNA fragment and cut vector were mixed with DNA ligase, which joined together the sugar-phosphate backbones of the two pieces to form recombinant DNA. A marker gene/genetic marker must also be present in the recombinant DNA, so may have been inserted at the same time as the DNA fragment or existed in the vector DNA already.
In the exam, put down as much information as you can. Here there are a few details on how the DNA fragment was made and how the marker gene/genetic marker got in there, as they all form part of the recombinant DNA.
b) It's likely he put a marker gene/genetic marker for resistance to penicillin in as part of the recombinant DNA. He grew the plates on agar containing penicillin so he could identify which colonies contained transformed cells (cells with the desired gene in).
Q2 a) The plasmids are vectors — they're used to transfer the desired gene into the host cells/*E.coli*.
b) The ampicillin-resistance gene is a marker gene/genetic marker. It means that only *E. coli* containing the plasmid will grow on the agar (which contains ampicillin).

c) *E.coli* that have taken up plasmids containing the desired gene will be white/colourless because the desired gene has disrupted the LacZα gene in the bacterial plasmids. This means the LacZα gene won't have produced the correct protein, so the *E.coli* won't have been able to produce β-galactosidase and therefore won't have been able to break down X-gal into a blue pigment. *E.coli* containing plasmids without the desired gene will be blue because they will contain both the LacZα and LacZΩ genes — this will enable them to produce functional β-galactosidase and therefore breakdown X-gal into a blue pigment.

Page 177 — Fact Recall Questions
Q1 The manipulation of an organism's DNA.
Q2 DNA formed by joining together DNA from different sources.
Q3 E.g. a plasmid / bacteriophage
Q4 restriction enzymes
Q5 DNA ligase is used to join the sticky ends of the DNA fragment containing the desired gene to the sticky ends of the vector DNA. They join together the sugar-phosphate backbones of the two bits of DNA.
Q6 That it has taken up the vector containing the desired gene.
Q7 Any two from, e.g. the DNA fragment has to be isolated from other cell components. / It's a slower process. / It uses more laboratory space and equipment.

3. More on Genetic Engineering
Page 181 — Fact Recall Questions
Q1 E.g. using restriction enzymes, using reverse transcriptase
Q2 E.g. It's identical to the insulin in our bodies, so it's more effective than animal insulin/there's less risk of an allergic reaction. / It's cheaper and faster to produce than animal insulin, providing a more reliable and larger supply of insulin. / Using genetically engineered insulin overcomes any ethical or religious issues arising from using animal insulin.
Q3 a maize plant, a soil bacterium
Q4 To reduce vitamin A deficiency in areas where there's a shortage of dietary vitamin A (e.g. south Asia, parts of Africa).
Q5 Scientists are trying to genetically engineer animals, so that their organs aren't rejected when transplanted into humans.
Q6 E.g. there is a shortage of donor organs in the UK and some people die whilst waiting for them. Xenotransplantation could be used to match the demand, so fewer people would suffer and possibly die.
Q7 E.g. environmentalists are worried that GM crops may encourage farmers to carry out monoculture, which could decrease biodiversity. / Some people are concerned about the possibility of 'superweeds'. / Some people are concerned that large biotechnology companies may use GM crops to exploit farmers in poor countries.
Q8 E.g. some people worry humans will be genetically engineered (e.g. to be more intelligent), creating a genetic underclass.

4. Gene Therapy
Page 183 — Application Questions
Q1 The virus is acting as a vector — it is being used to carry the normal FIX gene into the body cells of the sufferers of haemophilia.
Q2 $2 + 2 + 3 + 4 + 8 + 12 \div 6 = 5.16 = \mathbf{5.2\%}$
Q3 E.g. Yes. The maximum level after gene therapy was more than 1% for all the patients and so could improve their health.

Q4 E.g. Advantages: this therapy could provide sufferers with a greater quality of life, as they may not have to receive injections for the protein multiple times a week in the future. / This therapy could save health authorities money, as the injections usually required by sufferers are expensive. Disadvantages: the effects of the treatment may be short-lived. / Multiple treatments still may be required. / The patients may have suffered from side effects, e.g. the body could identify vectors as foreign bodies and start an immune response against them. / The allele could be inserted into the wrong place in the DNA, possibly causing more problems, e.g. cancer. / The allele could be over expressed and produce too much of the protein, causing other problems.

Page 183 — Fact Recall Questions
Q1 A possible treatment option for genetic disorders and some cancers that involves altering defective alleles inside cells.
Q2 Somatic gene therapy involves altering the alleles in body cells (particularly those most affected by the disorder being treated). Germ line gene therapy involves altering the alleles in sex cells.

5. Sequencing Genes and Genomes
Pages 187-188 — Application Questions
Q1 ATAAGCCATTCG
Remember — DNA sequencing gels are read from the bottom up. This will give you a DNA sequence that is complementary to the original sequence (TATTCGGTAAGC). To get the original sequence, remember that A always pairs with T and C pairs and G.
Q2 Species 2, because it has the same DNA sequence as the bone.

Exam-style Questions — pages 189-190
1 a) Any two from, e.g. they may have been concerned that the crop would encourage farmers to plant monocultures, reducing biodiversity *(1 mark)*. / They may have been concerned about the possibility of 'superweeds' — weeds that are resistant to herbicides because they've bred with genetically engineered herbicide-resistant crops *(1 mark)*. / They may have been concerned that the agricultural company may use the crop to exploit farmers in developing countries *(1 mark)*.
  b) i) A DNA probe is a short single strand of DNA *(1 mark)* with a base sequence that is complementary to a target sequence *(1 mark)*.
    ii) A sample of DNA containing the resistance gene is digested using restriction enzymes *(1 mark)* and the digested fragments are separated by electrophoresis *(1 mark)*. The separated fragments are then transferred to a nylon membrane *(1 mark)* and incubated with a fluorescently or radioactively-labelled DNA probe *(1 mark)*. The probe will hybridise to any DNA fragment that contains a complementary DNA sequence *(1 mark)*. The membrane is then exposed to UV light / X-ray film, so that the band the probe has attached to can be visualised *(1 mark)*. *(1 mark for making clear the correct sequence of steps involved in locating the gene.)*

c) i) Colonies were added to the plate containing penicillin to identify the transformed cells (those that have taken up the recombinant DNA containing the target gene) *(1 mark)*. A marker gene/genetic marker for penicillin resistance was added to the recombinant DNA so that only transformed cells will grow on plates containing penicillin, allowing them to be identified *(1 mark)*. Colonies of bacteria were also added to a standard agar plate as a control to show that the penicillin stopped colonies without the penicillin-resistance gene growing *(1 mark)*.
  ii) Bacteria A is a negative control *(1 mark)*, to make sure nothing in the host cells on their own makes them resistant to penicillin/ to make sure the penicillin is working *(1 mark)*.
There's more on negative controls in the How Science Works section at the front of the book.
  iii) Any one of 1, 3, 5 or 7. These grew on the penicillin plate, and so must be transformed cells/contain the recombinant DNA with the gene of interest and the marker gene/genetic marker for penicillin-resistance *(1 mark)*.
2 a) E.g. plasmids / BACs/Bacterial artificial chromosomes *(1 mark)*
Bacteriophages are vectors too, but they are a type of virus that infects bacteria, so this doesn't answer the question. Make sure you read the question carefully before and, if you've time, after you answer it.
  b) i) Nine out of the ten patients had a functional immune system after gene therapy *(1 mark)*. However, two out of the ten patients developed leukaemia within 3 years of the treatment *(1 mark)*.
    ii) Any two from: e.g. a larger sample size could be used *(1 mark)*. / The patients could be followed for longer than three years after treatment *(1 mark)*. / Indicators other than developing leukaemia could be used to check the health status of the patients *(1 mark)*.
  c) E.g. the technology could be used in ways other than for medical treatment, e.g. to reverse the cosmetic effects of aging *(1 mark)*. / There's the potential to do more harm than good by using the technology, e.g. by causing the overexpression of genes *(1 mark)*. / Gene therapy is expensive and the resources may be better spent on treatments that have already passed clinical trials *(1 mark)*.
3 a) E.g. they could use restriction enzymes *(1 mark)* to cut the DNA at specific palindromic recognition sequences *(1 mark)*.
  b) They are important in *in vivo* cloning as complementary sticky ends *(1 mark)* are required to anneal (bind) the target DNA fragment and vector DNA together *(1 mark)*.

c) Any six from: the vector DNA is cut using the same restriction enzyme to produce complementary sticky ends *(1 mark)*. The DNA fragment containing the desired gene and vector DNA are mixed together with DNA ligase *(1 mark)*, which joins the sticky ends/ sugar-phosphate backbones of the two strands together creating recombinant DNA *(1 mark)*. Marker genes/ genetic markers are inserted into the vector at the same time as the DNA fragment *(1 mark)*. The vector with the recombinant DNA and the fluorescent marker gene/ genetic marker is then used to transfer the gene into host cells *(1 mark)*. The host cells are grown on agar plates to produce colonies of cloned cells *(1 mark)*. If the agar plate is placed under UV light, only colonies of transformed cells will fluoresce because only these cells will contain the marker gene/genetic marker *(1 mark)*. Identified transformed cells are allowed to grow more producing lots of copies of the cloned gene *(1 mark)*.

d) E.g. *In vivo* cloning can be a cheaper method than *in vitro* cloning *(1 mark)*. / Larger fragments of DNA can be cloned using *in vivo* cloning compared to *in vitro* cloning *(1 mark)*. / *In vivo* cloning can be less technically difficult than *in vitro* cloning *(1 mark)*. / There are usually fewer mutations with *in vivo* cloning compared to *in vitro* cloning *(1 mark)*.

Section 6 — Ecology

1. Ecosystems and Energy Flow
Page 196 — Application Questions
Q1 a) net productivity = gross productivity − respiratory loss
net productivity = 22 861 − 17 000 = **5861 kJm^{-2}yr^{-1}**
  b) % efficiency of energy transfer =
(net productivity of trophic level ÷ net productivity of previous trophic level) × 100
= (627 ÷ 5861) × 100 = **10.7%**
Q2 a) respiratory loss = gross productivity − net productivity
respiratory loss = 8072 − 2073 = **5999 kJm^{-2}yr^{-1}**
  b) gross productivity = net productivity + respiratory loss
gross productivity = 119 + 450 = **569 kJm^{-2}yr^{-1}**
  c) E.g. because some parts of the small fish aren't eaten so the energy isn't taken in. / Because some parts of the small fish are indigestible and will pass through the large fish and come out as waste.
Some questions like this are tricky to work out — you need to think about what the key phrases, like gross productivity and net productivity, actually mean. Here the question is actually asking you 'Why is the energy absorbed by the large fish less than the energy available to them from the small fish?'
  d) % efficiency of energy transfer =
(net productivity of trophic level ÷ net productivity of previous trophic level) × 100
Between plant plankton and animal plankton =
(8105 ÷ 31 023) × 100 = **26.1%**
Between animal plankton and small fish=
(2073 ÷ 8105) × 100 = **25.6%**
Between small fish and large fish =
(119 ÷ 2073) × 100 = **5.7%**
This example of a food chain is a bit different — the efficiency of energy transfer decreases as you go up it. But you don't need to worry about this when you're doing the calculations — just use the equation as normal.

Q1 photosynthesis
Q2 a) An organism that produces organic molecules using sunlight energy.
  b) An organism that eats other organisms.
Q3 gross productivity
Q4 Carnivores, because more of the food they eat is digestible.
Remember, herbivores only eat plants, which contain a lot of indigestible material. This means lots of the available energy is lost as waste, e.g. in faeces.
Q5 E.g. use a calorimeter / measure the dry mass/biomass of the organisms.
Q6 Any two from: e.g. herbicides — these kill weeds that compete with crops for energy. Reducing competition means crops receive more energy, so they grow faster and become larger. / Fungicides — these kill fungal infections, so the crops use more energy for growth and less for fighting infection. / Insecticides — these kill insect pests so less biomass is lost from crops. / Natural predators are introduced to the ecosystem. These eat the pest species so crops lose less energy and biomass. / Fertilisers — these replace minerals in the soil, so more energy from the ecosystem can be used to grow. / Intensive rearing of livestock — this controls the conditions animals live in, so more of their energy is used for growth and less is used for other activities.

2. The Nitrogen Cycle
Page 198 — Fact Recall Questions
Q1 To make proteins/nucleic acids. / For growth.
Q2

Name of process	Bacteria responsible
Nitrogen fixation	*Rhizobium*
Ammonification	Decomposers
Nitrification	*Nitrosomonas* and *Nitrobacter*
Denitrification	Denitrifying bacteria

Q3 Nitrogen compounds from dead organisms and animal waste are turned into ammonium compounds.
Q4 denitrification

3. Succession
Page 201 — Application Questions
Q1 Primary succession, because there is no soil present in 1800.
Remember, the key difference between primary and secondary succession is soil — it's present in secondary succession, but not in primary succession. If you have a good look at the graph you'll see that there's no soil moisture in 1800. That's a pretty good sign that there's no soil, either.
Q2 The dominant plant species would have been adapted to survive without much water/in a soil with low moisture content and fluctuating ground temperatures. They would have had seeds that could remain viable for long periods of time. They would have been species of small plants / they would not have been tree species.
There's a lot going on in the graph with all the different lines — and you could get something like this in the exam. Don't let the graph's complexity put you off though. Take your time and make sure you really understand what the graph is showing, and read the questions carefully so you pick out the right bits from the graph for your answers.

Q3 E.g. the average length of time dominant plant seeds remained viable for was relatively high between 1800 and 1860. This might have been because seeds that remained viable for a long time could lie dormant until conditions were favourable enough to germinate. Between about 1860 and 1880 the average length of time fell sharply, and then continued to fall more slowly until levelling off at around 1960. This may have been because the plants that were dominant between 1800 and 1860 were succeeded by other plant species which were more suited to the changed conditions, e.g. a higher soil moisture content, so they no longer needed to be viable for long periods of time.

Q4 Between 1800 and 1920 because there were no tree species present during this time, so there would have been more light / less shade cast by the trees.

Q5 The soil moisture content is 0 between 1800 and 1820 because there is no soil. The soil moisture content increased gradually from 1820 until 1940 as the soil developed, then it increased more rapidly between 1940 and 2000 because the addition of decomposed organic material helped to increase soil moisture content and the deeper soil was able to retain more water.

Page 202 — Fact Recall Questions
Q1 The process by which an ecosystem changes over time.
Q2 primary succession
Q3 pioneer species
Q4 The largest and most complex community of plants and animals that an ecosystem can support.
Q5 E.g. deforestation / volcanic eruption / fire
Q6 The climax community for a particular climate.
Q7 The climax community that exists when succession is stopped artificially by human activities.

4. Variation in Population Size
Page 206 — Application Questions
Q1 the number of mice
Remember, biotic factors are the living things in an ecosystem.
Q2 As the temperature fell, the size of the mouse population decreased. This could have been because the cold weather caused the temperature of the surroundings to fall below the body temperature of the mice. Mice are mammals, so if that had happened the mice would have used up more energy maintaining their body temperature. This would have meant less energy was available for growth and reproduction, causing their population size to fall.
Q3 As the mouse population size increased, there was more food for the owls and so the owl population grew. As the owl population increased, more mice were eaten and so the mice population began to fall. This meant there was less food for the owls, so their population decreased — and so this cycle continued.

Page 206 — Fact Recall Questions
Q1 All organisms of one species in a habitat.
Q2 a) Interspecific competition is when organisms of different species compete with each other for the same resources.
  b) i) The population size of both of the species competing will be lowered. This is because there are fewer resources available to both populations, so they will both be less likely to reproduce.
    ii) The less well adapted species will be outcompeted and won't be able to exist alongside the better adapted species.

  c) E.g. Grey squirrels and red squirrels in the UK compete for the same food sources and habitats. In areas where they both live, both populations are smaller than they would be if only one species lived there. The red squirrel has also disappeared from large areas as the grey squirrel is better adapted to the surroundings.
Q3 a) Intraspecific competition is when organisms of the same species compete with each other for the same resources.
  b) The population of a species increases when resources are plentiful. As the population increases, there'll be more organisms competing for the same amount of space and food. Eventually, resources such as food and space become limiting, so the population begins to decline. A smaller population then means that there's less competition for space and food, which is better for growth and reproduction, so the population starts to grow again.
Q4 It is the maximum stable population size of a species that an ecosystem can support.
Q5 It will cause the predator population to increase as well because there is more food available for the predators.
Q6 limiting factor

5. Investigating Populations
Pages 209-210 — Application Questions
Q1 a) She could place the quadrat on the ground at random locations across the field and count how much of the quadrat is covered by daisies. A square should be counted if it's more than half-covered.
  b) E.g. the student could divide the field into a grid and use a random number generator to select coordinates. The quadrat could then be placed at these coordinates and the number of daisies in each quadrat counted.
Q2 a) The kite diagram shows that species A is present between 20 and 45 m from the road with a low percentage cover. It's also present between 80-140 m, and is most abundant between 130-140 m. Species B is present between 55-130 m from the road, and is most abundant between 60-85 m. Species C is present between 0-50 m from the road and is most abundant between 0-35 m. The graph shows that soil salinity is high between 0-30 m from the road, falls sharply between 30-40 m, continues to fall until around 50 m and then remains low.
  b) Species C, as it is present between 0-50 m from the road and is the most abundant species between 0-30 m from the road, where soil salinity is highest.
  c) The data shows that at a high soil salinity there is an absence of species B, but this doesn't prove that salt spray from the road is the cause. Species B might be absent for other reasons, e.g. because it is out-competed by species C.

Page 210 — Fact Recall Questions
Q1 a) The number of individuals of one species in a particular area.
  b) Where a particular species is in the area being investigated.
Q2 a) Because it would be too time-consuming to measure the abundance of the entire species in the area being investigated.
  b) To avoid biased results.
Q3 It would be put on the ground at random points within the field. Pins would be dropped through the holes in the frame and every plant that each pin touched would be recorded.
In the exam, if you're asked to describe a method you could use to investigate a population, don't forget to say that you would use random samples of the area you are investigating.

For a line transect, a tape measure is placed along the transect and the species that touch the tape measure are recorded. For a belt transect, data is collected along the transect using frame quadrats placed next to each other.

6. Conservation of Ecosystems

Page 213 — Fact Recall Questions

Q1 That conservation methods need to be adapted to the constant changes that occur within ecosystems.

Q2 Restoring ecosystems that have been damaged or destroyed so they can be used again.

Q3 Ecosystems provide resources for lots of things that humans need and these are traded on a local and global scale. If the ecosystems aren't conserved, the resources that we use now will be lost, so there will be less trade in the future.

Q4 E.g. because people use them for activities such as walking.

Q5 Preservation keeps ecosystems exactly as they are, so nothing is removed. Conservation, on the other hand, does allow the removal of resources from ecosystems.

Q6 Any two from: E.g. Explorers and sailors many years ago ate some of the animals which directly affected their populations. / Non-native animals have been introduced to the islands by humans. The non-native animals eat some native species, causing a decrease in the populations of native species. / Non-native plants have been introduced to the islands by humans. The non-native species compete with native plant species, causing a decrease in their populations. / Fishing has caused a decrease in the populations of some of the sea life. / An increase in tourism has caused damage to the ecosystems as more land is cleared and pollution is increased.

Exam-style Questions — pages 215-216

1 a) i) The population sizes of species A and B rise and fall cyclically over the 20 year period **(1 mark)**. The population sizes increase when resources are plentiful but decrease when resources become limited **(1 mark)**. This is because of intraspecific competition / organisms of species A are competing with each other for the same resources, and organisms of species B are competing with each other for the same resources **(1 mark)**.

   ii) (biotic) limiting factor **(1 mark)**

   b) Regular grazing would prevent the normal climax community from developing **(1 mark)**, so succession would be deflected from its natural course **(1 mark)**.

2 a) i) E.g. they could set up a belt transect / place quadrats next to each other along a transect **(1 mark)** leading from the edge of the field that's next to the stream into the middle of the field **(1 mark)**.

   ii) They could count how many squares of each quadrat are covered by marsh marigolds by counting a square if it's more than half-covered **(1 mark)**. Measuring percentage cover is a quick way to investigate the abundance of marsh marigolds **(1 mark)** and they wouldn't have to count all the individual marsh marigolds **(1 mark)**.

   b) The non-living features of an ecosystem **(1 mark)**.

3 a) Light / the Sun **(1 mark)**

   b) net productivity = gross productivity – respiratory loss
   net productivity = 2143 – 1571 = **572 kJm⁻²yr⁻¹**
   (1 mark for correct working only, 2 marks for correct answer)

   c) E.g. because some parts of food, e.g. roots or bones, aren't eaten by organisms so the energy isn't taken in **(1 mark)**. Also, some parts of food are indigestible so pass through organisms and come out as waste, e.g. faeces **(1 mark)**.

   d) percentage efficiency of energy transfer =
   (net productivity of trophic level ÷ net productivity of previous trophic level) × 100
   Between the producer and primary consumer 1 =
   (2619 ÷ 38750) × 100 = 6.76%
   Between the producer and primary consumer 2 =
   (1265 ÷ 38750) × 100 = 3.26%
   6.76 – 3.26 = **3.5%**
   (1 mark for each correct percentage efficiency of energy transfer or 3 marks for correct answer)

   e) Nitrogen compounds from dead organisms/animal waste are turned into ammonium compounds **(1 mark)** by decomposers (e.g. bacteria or fungi) **(1 mark)**. Nitrosomonas **(1 mark)** change ammonium compounds into nitrites **(1 mark)**. Nitrobacter **(1 mark)** change nitrites into nitrates **(1 mark)**. Nitrates are converted into nitrogen gas **(1 mark)** by denitrifying bacteria **(1 mark)**.
   (1 mark for correctly describing the roles of at least two named microorganisms).

4 a) E.g. it's the right thing to do, especially if the ecosystem is at risk because of human activity. / There is a moral responsibility to conserve ecosystems for future generations, so they can enjoy and use them. **(1 mark)**

   If the question tells you to 'outline' a reason for something (like this one), you need to give a bit more than a one word answer — make sure you include a little bit of detail.

   b) It means taking enough resources from the woodland to meet the needs of people today **(1 mark)**, but without reducing the ability of people in the future to meet their own needs **(1 mark)**.

   c) Any three from: e.g.:

Method	Explanation
Trees cleared in strips or patches.	Woodland grows back more quickly in smaller areas between bits of existing woodland than it does in larger, open areas.
Cleared strips or patches of woodland aren't too large or exposed.	Lots of soil erosion can occur on large areas of bare ground. If the soil is eroded, newly planted trees won't be able to grow.
Timber is harvested by coppicing/cut down in a way that lets them grow back.	New trees don't need to be planted.
Only native species are planted.	Native species grow most successfully because they're adapted to the climate.
Planted trees are attached to posts / grown in plastic tubes.	This makes it more likely the trees will survive to become mature adults as they're supported/protected.
Trees aren't planted too close together.	The trees aren't competing with each other for space or resources, so they're more likely to survive.

Maximum of 6 marks available (1 mark for each correct method up to a maximum of 3 marks. 1 mark for each correctly matched explanation of how the method works).

Section 7 — Responding to the Environment

1. Plant Responses

Page 220 — Application Questions

Q1 The auxin will have diffused straight down from the sponge into the left-hand side of the shoot. This will have stimulated the cells on this side to elongate, so the shoot grew towards the right.

Q2 Equal amounts of auxin will have diffused down both sides, making all the cells elongate at the same rate.

Q3 The shoots in experiment B were exposed to a light source. This will have caused the auxin to diffuse into the shoot and accumulate on the shaded side (left-hand side) regardless of where the sponge was placed. All the shoots grew towards the right because most auxin accumulated on the left, stimulating cell elongation there.

Q4 Sponge D was a control (a sponge soaked in water rather than auxin), included to show that it was the auxin having an effect and nothing else.

Q5 The sponges were soaked in glucose so that the shoots would have energy to grow in the dark, as no photosynthesis can take place.
Sponges from experiment B were also soaked in glucose, even though they were in the light, so were able to photosynthesise. This is done in order to keep the set up of both experiments as similar as possible.

Pages 222-223 — Application Questions

Q1 To minimise the differences between plants at the start of the experiment. The more variables the student controls, the more reliable her results will be. Choosing plants of a similar age, height, mass, etc., makes it less likely that any differences observed between the three experimental conditions will result from differences between the plants.

Q2 The plants watered with a 100 µg/ml gibberellin solution. Gibberellins are growth hormones that stimulate the stems of plants to grow by stem elongation, so the higher the concentration of gibberellin, the taller the plant will grow.
This is only true up to a point though — as the concentration of gibberellin gets higher, the effect it has on the plant changes and it doesn't stimulate the plant to grow any further.

Q3 a) Total growth = 26 cm – 8 cm = 18 cm
6 weeks = 6 × 7 days = 42 days
Average growth rate = 18 ÷ 42 = **0.43 cm/day**
b) Total growth = 18 cm
Percentage increase = (18 ÷ 8) × 100 = 2.25 × 100
= **225%**
To calculate percentage increase, divide the total growth by the initial plant height and then multiply your answer by 100.

Q4 auxins

Page 223 — Fact Recall Questions

Q1 Anything harmful that's non-living.
Q2 Growth away from a (directional) stimulus.
Q3 phototropism
Q4 The growing regions of the plant / shoots and leaves.
Q5 a) by active transport and diffusion
b) via the phloem
Q6 a) Auxins move to the more shaded parts of the shoot. This means the cells on the shaded part of the shoot grow faster than the cells most exposed to light. This pattern of growth causes the shoot to bend towards the light.
b) Auxins move to the underside of roots. This means the cells on the underside of the root don't grow as quickly as the cells on the upper-side. This pattern of growth causes the root to grow downwards in the same direction as gravity.

Q7 It saves the plants' energy and prevents side shoots from the same plant competing with the shoot tip for light. This allows a plant in an area where there are loads of other plants to grow tall very fast, past smaller plants, to reach the sunlight (instead of wasting energy growing side shoots).

Q8 If you remove the apical bud then the plant won't produce auxins. The side shoots will no longer be inhibited, so they will start growing by cell division and cell elongation.

Q9 a) Yes — the fact that the hormones are synergistic means that they work together to have a really big effect.
b) E.g. auxins and gibberellins

Q10 a) Losing their leaves helps plants to conserve water, which is lost from the leaves.
Remember, in winter it might be difficult for plants to absorb water from the soil because the soil water may be frozen.
b) Auxins inhibit leaf loss.
c) Ethene stimulates the cells in the abscission layer to expand, breaking the cells walls and causing the leaf to fall off.

2. Animal Responses

Page 226 — Application Questions

Q1 a) cerebrum / (left) cerebral hemisphere
b) cerebellum
c)

Name	Function
Structure A	vision / hearing / learning / thinking
Medulla oblongata	controls breathing rate / controls heart rate
Hypothalamus	controls body temperature

Q2 a) The 'fight or flight' response. This response prepares the body for action in reaction to a threat.
b) The sympathetic nervous system. Noradrenaline is released from the neurones.
c)

Response	Increased or decreased?
strength of contraction of heart muscle	increased
depth of breathing	increased
blood supply to the gut	decreased
blood supply to the skeletal muscles	increased
blood glucose level	increased
blood supply to the skin	decreased

Q3 The cerebellum plays an important role in muscle coordination and coordination of balance. If the cerebellum is abnormally developed it could lead to problems with balance and coordination. This could make tasks such as throwing and catching difficult and make people more likely to fall over.

Page 226 — Fact Recall Questions

Q1 They respond to changes in their external environment to increase their chances of survival. They respond to changes in their internal environment to make sure that the conditions are always optimal for their metabolism.
Q2 The brain and the spinal cord.
Q3 a) To control unconscious activities of the body.
b) The sympathetic nervous system and the parasympathetic nervous system.
Q4 pituitary gland
Q5 At the base of the brain / top of the spinal cord.

3. Muscle Contraction

Page 229 — Application Questions
Q1 a) B
    b) C
    c) A and C
    d) B

Q2 Option 1. The A-band has stayed the same length, the I-band is shorter and the H-zone is shorter.
Remember, the A-band is the length of the myosin filament and this doesn't get shorter during contraction. During contraction more of the actin filament slides over the myosin filament so the sections with only actin (the I-bands) get shorter and the sections with only myosin (the H-zones) get shorter too.

Page 232 — Application Questions
Q1 a) i) X. The Ca²⁺ concentration is low, suggesting that the muscle is at rest. Muscle fibres are longest when they are relaxed.
      ii) Y. There is an influx of Ca²⁺ ions into the sarcoplasm following an action potential, and the Ca²⁺ ions bind to troponin.
      iii) Y. The Ca²⁺ ion concentration is high and Ca²⁺ ions activate ATPase.
    b) The Ca²⁺ ions are moved by active transport from the sarcoplasm back into sarcoplasmic reticulum, where they're stored.
    c) An action potential from a motor neurone stimulates a muscle cell and depolarises the sarcolemma. Depolarisation spreads down the T-tubules to the sarcoplasmic reticulum, causing the sarcoplasmic reticulum to release stored Ca²⁺ ions into the sarcoplasm.

Q2 The influx of calcium ions triggers muscle contraction, so more calcium ions in the sarcoplasm would increase the strength of contraction of cardiac/heart muscle, which would help to pump more blood around the body of patients with heart failure.

Page 234 — Application Questions
Q1 They might have weaker muscle responses than normal. If receptors are destroyed at neuromuscular junctions then there will be fewer receptors for acetylcholine/ACh to bind to, so there will be less chance of depolarisation being triggered in the postsynaptic cell. This means fewer muscle cells will be stimulated.

Q2 Galantamine would stop acetylcholinesterase/AChE breaking down acetylcholine/ACh, so there would be more ACh in the synaptic cleft and it would be there for longer. This means more nicotinic cholinergic receptors would be stimulated.

Page 235 — Fact Recall Questions
Q1 It receives sensory information and decides what kind of response is needed. If the response is movement, it then sends nervous impulses along motor neurones to make skeletal muscles contract.

Q2 a) biceps and triceps
    b) The biceps muscle contracts and the triceps muscle relaxes. The muscles are attached to the bone in your lower arm with tendons, so as the biceps contracts it pulls the bone up.

Q3 An A-band contains myosin filaments and some overlapping actin filaments. Under an electron microscope it appears as a dark band.

Q4 Myosin and actin filaments slide over one another to make the sarcomeres contract (the myofilaments themselves don't contract).

Q5 Troponin and tropomyosin.

Q6 Calcium ions in the sarcoplasm bind to troponin in the myofibrils, causing troponin to change shape. This pulls the attached tropomyosin out of the actin-myosin binding site on the actin filament. This exposes the binding site, which allows the myosin head to bind and form an actin-myosin cross bridge.

Q7 ATP is broken down by ATPase to provide the energy needed to move the myosin head from side to side, which pulls the actin filament along in a rowing action. ATP also provides the energy needed to break the myosin-actin cross bridge, so the myosin head detaches from the actin filament after it's moved.

Q8 a) Advantage: e.g. the ATP-PCr system generates ATP very quickly / it can be used during short bursts of vigorous exercise / it's anaerobic/doesn't need oxygen / it's alactic/ doesn't form any lactate.
      Disadvantage: e.g. PCr runs out after only a few seconds.
    b) Aerobic respiration and anaerobic respiration.

Q9

	Voluntary	Involuntary	Cardiac
Number of nuclei	many	one	one
Length	e.g. can be many centimetres	~ 0.2 mm	~ 0.2 mm
Shape of muscle fibres	e.g. long, straight shape	spindle-shaped (with pointed ends)	cylinder shaped / branched
Are cross-straitions visible under a light microscope?	yes	no	yes (a few)

Q10 To pump blood around the body.

Q11 A synapse between a motor neurone and a muscle cell.

Q12 Any three from: E.g. a neuromuscular junction always uses acetylcholine but another synapse may use a different neurotransmitter. / A neuromuscular junction has nicotinic cholinergic receptors but another synapse may have different receptors. / A neuromuscular junction has more receptors on the postsynaptic cell than other synapses. / The postsynaptic cell at a neuromuscular junction is a muscle cell, whereas the postsynaptic cell at other synapses is a neurone. / The postsynaptic cell at a neuromuscular junction has clefts (containing AChE), whereas the postsynaptic cell at other synapses is smooth. / When neurotransmitters binds to postsynaptic receptors at a neuromuscular junction the effect is always muscle contraction, whereas at a synapse an action potential may or may not fire in the next neurone. / The neurotransmitter at a neuromuscular junction is removed from the synapse by being broken down by AChE, whereas it may be removed in a different way at another synapse.

4. Behaviour

Page 236 — Application Question
Q1 A — kinetic response, B — escape reflex, C — tactic response.

Pages 239-240 — Application Questions
Q1 a) habituation
    b) It means the cockroach doesn't waste time and energy responding to an unimportant stimulus.

Q2 a) operant conditioning
   b) It would be less likely to sit down when its owner said 'sit' because it associates the response with a punishment (a tap on the nose).

Q3 Latent learning. The rabbit learns the layout of the warren by repeatedly going through it, and only shows it has learnt the layout when it's being punished (chased by a predator).

Q4 a) imprinting
   b) i) Imprinting only happens within the critical period/ during a certain period of time soon after the animal is born. If the bird doesn't imprint on the hang glider during this time, it is unlikely to follow it later in life.
      ii) The cranes may not be able to identify mates from the same species.

Q5 a) insight learning
   b) No, the problem of how to reach the food was probably solved by working out a solution, which is quicker than by chance or by trial and error.

Q6 a) classical conditioning
   b) Before conditioning, the unconditioned stimulus of the nut/food being held above its head resulted in the unconditioned response of the hamster standing on its back legs to reach the nut. During conditioning, the unconditioned stimulus coincided with the word 'stand' (a neutral stimulus) which resulted in the same unconditioned response (the hamster standing on its back legs). Eventually, the hamster learned to respond to the conditioned stimulus (only the word 'stand') to produce the conditioned response (standing on its back legs).

   If you're asked to describe classical conditioning in detail, make sure you include the appropriate terms like 'unconditioned stimulus', etc.

Page 241 — Application Question

Q1 A — E.g. mating is possible within the troop. / The adult male can protect the rest of the troop from predators/other troops.
B — E.g. the young gorillas learn how to fight so they can protect themselves (and other members of their troop) when they're adults.
C — E.g. the infant is protected by its mother from predators / from aggressive behaviour from other members of the troop/ gorillas from other troops.
D — E.g. other members of the troop are warned of the threat. / Other members of the troop can help the gorilla that feels threatened.
E — E.g. all members of the troop are fed to help them survive.

Pages 241-242 — Fact Recall Questions

Q1 a) Behaviour that is instinctive, genetically-determined/ inherited and stereotyped.
   b) It means that an organism will respond the right way to a stimulus straight away.
   c) Escape reflex — this is where an organism moves away from potential danger. Tactic response/taxis — this is where an organism moves in a particular direction in response to a stimulus. Kinetic response/kinesis — this is where an organism moves in a non-directional/random way in response to a stimulus.

Q2 Behaviour that is influenced by the environment, modified as a result of experience and isn't stereotyped.

Q3 An animal reduces or stops its response to the stimulus after repeated exposure.

Q4 a) An unconditioned stimulus.
   b) If a natural/unconditioned stimulus coincides with a neutral stimulus enough times, eventually the neutral/ conditioned stimulus will trigger the same response as the natural/unconditioned stimulus.

Q5 Only when it's given a reward or a punishment.

Q6 Insight learning because problems are solved using previous experience, which is quicker than using trial and error (which is what happens in operant learning).

Q7 a) Innate behaviour is involved in imprinting as new-born animals instinctively follow the first moving object they see. Learned behaviour is also involved as animals have to learn what their parent (or the object they instinctively follow) looks like.
   b) It is the period of time soon after an animal is born when imprinting is possible.

Q8 E.g. dopamine, D_4/DRD4

Q9 a) E.g. baboons
   b) E.g. baboons live in large groups, which are more efficient at hunting for food. / In a group of baboons there's a clear-cut hierarchy of adult males, which helps to prevent fighting within the group. / When groups of baboons are hunting, young baboons and their mothers stay in the middle of the group and adult males stay on the outside. This helps to protect the young baboons so they can grow into adults and it protects the female baboons so they can reproduce again. / Baboons in a group groom each other, which is hygienic and it helps to restore social bonds in the group.

Exam-style Questions — Pages 244-245

1 a) The biceps and triceps work antagonistically/are an antagonistic pair of muscles *(1 mark)*. When the biceps contracts, the triceps relaxes *(1 mark)*. This pulls the bone so the arm bends at the elbow *(1 mark)*. When the triceps contracts, the biceps relaxes *(1 mark)*. This pulls the bone so the arm straightens at the elbow *(1 mark)*.
   b) Acetylcholine is released from (the presynaptic membrane of) a motor neurone *(1 mark)* at a neuromuscular junction *(1 mark)*. It then diffuses across the synaptic cleft *(1 mark)* and binds to nicotinic cholinergic receptors *(1 mark)* on the motor end plate/ postsynaptic membrane, causing the postsynaptic/muscle cell to depolarise *(1 mark)*.
   c) i)

	Name	Appearance when the biceps relaxes, compared to Fig 1.1.
A	H-zone	longer
B	I-band	longer
C	A-band	same length

(1 mark for each correct answer)

   ii) Myosin filaments have globular heads that are hinged *(1 mark)*. Each myosin head has a binding site for actin *(1 mark)* and a binding site for ATP *(1 mark)*.
   iii) The myosin head binds to the actin filament and forms an actin-myosin cross bridge *(1 mark)*. Energy released from ATP moves the myosin head to the side, which pulls the actin filament along in a rowing action/power stroke *(1 mark)*. ATP also provides the energy to break the actin-myosin cross bridge *(1 mark)* so the myosin head detaches from the actin filament after it's moved *(1 mark)*. The myosin head then returns to it's starting position and reattaches to a different binding site further along the actin filament *(1 mark)*. As the cycle is repeated, the myosin head pulls the actin filament along, causing the muscle to contract *(1 mark)*. *(1 mark for making the correct sequence of steps clear — formation of an actin-myosin cross bridge, followed by the actin filament being pulled along, followed by the breaking of the actin-myosin cross bridge and the myosin head returning to its starting position.)*

d) i) ATP is made by phosphorylating ADP *(1 mark)* with a phosphate group taken from phosphocreatine/PCr *(1 mark)*.

Remember, the ATP-phosphocreatine (PCr) system is used during short bursts of vigorous exercise.

ii) ATP is generated very quickly *(1 mark)*. No oxygen is needed / the process is anaerobic *(1 mark)*. The process is alactic / no lactate is formed *(1 mark)*.

e) Any three from: e.g. a voluntary muscle fibre is multinucleate whereas an involuntary muscle fibre is uninucleate. / A voluntary muscle fibre is much longer than an involuntary muscle fibre. / A voluntary muscle fibre has a long, straight shape whereas an involuntary muscle fibre is spindle-shaped with pointed ends. / A voluntary muscle fibre has cross-striations visible under a microscope whereas involuntary muscle doesn't.
(3 marks available)

Always read exam questions carefully — this one asks for three structural differences, so you won't get marks for comparing the functions.

2 a) phototropism *(1 mark)*

b) The seedling should have been a Goosegrass plant and potted in soil from the same source *(1 mark)*. There should have been no lamp/light from any direction present *(1 mark)*.

c) Seeding A will be bent to the right *(1 mark)* because it will have grown towards the light *(1 mark)*. Seedling B will have grown straight up *(1 mark)* because the rotation of the seedling means that the light is not continuously coming from one direction *(1 mark)*. Seedling C will be bent towards the left but will have a kink in, so that it is not a smooth bend *(1 mark)* because it will have grown to the right for five days, then to the left for five days and to the right again for the last five days, as the light has been coming from a different direction *(1 mark)*.

d) Auxins *(1 mark)* move to the most shaded parts of the plant *(1 mark)*. This means the shaded parts of the shoot grow faster/elongate more than the parts exposed to light *(1 mark)*. This uneven growth leads to the shoot bending towards the light *(1 mark)*.

3 a) i) adrenaline *(1 mark)*

ii) The medulla oblongata controls breathing rate *(1 mark)*. During the 'fight or flight' response, nervous impulses from the medulla oblongata cause the muscles around the bronchioles to relax *(1 mark)* so that breathing is deeper *(1 mark)*. Nervous impulses from the medulla oblongata also cause the intercostal muscles and diaphragm to contact faster *(1 mark)*, which increases the rate and depth of breathing *(1 mark)*. The medulla oblongata also controls heart rate *(1 mark)*. Nervous impulses from the medulla oblongata cause the heart to contract faster and with more force *(1 mark)*, so that more blood is pumped around the body *(1 mark)*.

iii) Blood is diverted from the skin *(1 mark)* and from the gut *(1 mark)* to the heart *(1 mark)*, lungs *(1 mark)* and skeletal muscle *(1 mark)*.

Make sure you pay attention to the command word in the question — you are only asked to 'describe' here so don't waste time explaining why these things happen.

b) Classical conditioning *(1 mark)*, because a person with ornithophobia learns to respond (with the 'fight or flight' response) to a stimulus that wouldn't usually cause that response (the sight of a bird) *(1 mark)*.

Glossary

A

Abiotic factor
A non-living feature of an ecosystem.

Abscission layer
A layer of cells at the bottom of a leaf stalk, which expand when stimulated by ethene, breaking the cell walls and causing the leaf to fall off.

Abundance
The number of individuals of one species in a particular area.

Accurate result
A result that is really close to the true answer.

Acetylcholine (ACh)
A type of neurotransmitter that binds to cholinergic receptors.

Actin
The thin myofilament protein in muscle fibres.

Actin-myosin cross bridge
The bond formed when a myosin head binds to an actin filament.

Activator
A transcription factor that starts transcription.

Active transport
Movement of molecules and ions across plasma membranes, against a concentration gradient. Requires energy.

ADP (adenosine diphosphate)
A molecule made up of adenine, a ribose sugar and two phosphate groups. ATP is synthesised from ADP and a phosphate group.

Adrenaline
A hormone secreted from the adrenal glands that has many effects, including increasing the blood glucose concentration.

Aerobic respiration
Process where energy is released from glucose using oxygen.

Alcoholic fermentation
A type of anaerobic respiration that occurs in yeast (and plants). Ethanol is the final product.

Allele
One or more alternative versions of the same gene.

Allele frequency
How often an allele occurs in a population.

Ammonification
The process in which nitrogen compounds from dead organisms or waste material are turned into ammonium compounds by decomposers.

Anaerobic respiration
Process where energy is released from glucose without oxygen.

Anomalous data
Measurements that fall outside the range of values you'd expect or any pattern you already have.

Antagonistic pair of muscles
A pair of muscles that oppose each other's actions to move a bone — one contracts while the other relaxes.

Antidiuretic hormone (ADH)
A hormone which regulates the water content of the blood by controlling the permeability of the cells of the distal convoluted tubule and the collecting duct in the kidney.

Apical dominance
When the apical bud (tip of a plant shoot) grows more than the side shoots.

Artificial selection
When humans select individuals in a population to breed together to get desirable traits.

Asepsis
The practice of preventing contamination of cultures by unwanted microorganisms.

ATP (adenosine triphosphate)
A molecule made up of adenine, a ribose sugar and three phosphate groups. It is the immediate source of energy in a cell.

ATP-phosphocreatine (PCr) system
A system that generates ATP very quickly by phosphorylating ADP using a phosphate group from phosphocreatine.

ATP synthase
An enzyme which catalyses the synthesis of ATP from ADP and a phosphate group.

ATPase
An enzyme which catalyses the hydrolysis of ATP into ADP and a phosphate group.

Autonomic nervous system
A division of the peripheral nervous system that controls unconscious activities, e.g. heart rate.

Autotroph
An organism which can generate its own food (e.g. plants).

Auxin
A type of plant growth hormone produced in the tips of shoots, which stimulates cell elongation.

B

BAC (Bacterial artificial chromosome)
A man-made plasmid used in gene technology.

Batch culture
Where microorganisms are grown in individual batches in a fermentation vessel — when one culture ends it's removed and a different batch of microorganisms is grown.

Bias
When someone intentionally, or unintentionally, favours a particular result.

Biotechnology
The industrial use of living organisms (or parts of living organisms) to produce food, drugs and other products.

Biotic factor
A living feature of an ecosystem.

Body plan
The general structure of an organism.

C

Calvin cycle
Another name for the light-independent reaction of photosynthesis (see that entry).

Carrier
A person carrying an allele which is not expressed in the phenotype but that can be passed on to offspring.

Carrying capacity
The maximum stable population size of a species that an ecosystem can support.

Causal relationship
Where a change in one variable causes a change in the other.

Central nervous system (CNS)
Part of the nervous system made up of the brain and spinal cord.

Cerebellum
Part of the brain, which plays an important role in muscle coordination, posture and coordination of balance.

Cerebrum
The largest part of the brain, which plays an important role in vision, hearing, learning and thinking.

Chain termination method
A technique used to sequence DNA.

Chemiosmosis
The movement of protons (H^+ ions) across a membrane which generates ATP.

Chi-squared test
A statistical test that that's used to see if the results of an experiment support a theory.

Chlorophyll
A photosynthetic pigment found in chloroplasts. There are different types of this pigment, e.g. chlorophyll a.

Chloroplast
A small, flattened organelle found in plant cells. It is the site of photosynthesis.

Cholinergic synapse
A synapse that uses the neurotransmitter acetylcholine.

Chromatid
One 'arm' of a double stranded chromosome.

Chromosome
A thread like structure made up of one long DNA molecule.

Climax community
The largest and most complex community of plants and animals an ecosystem can support.

Cloning
The process of producing genetically identical cells or organisms from the cells of an existing organism.

Closed culture
A culture which has been grown in a vessel that's isolated from the external environment.

Codominant allele
An allele whose characteristic appears together with another allele in the phenotype because neither allele is recessive.

Coenzyme
A molecule that aids the function of an enzyme. They work by transferring a chemical group from one molecule to another.

Coenzyme A (CoA)
A type of coenzyme involved in respiration. It transfers acetate from one molecule to another.

Conservation (of ecosystems)
A dynamic process that involves the protection, management and sometimes the reclamation of ecosystems.

Consumer
An organism that eats other organisms.

Continuous culture
Where microorganisms are continually grown in a fermentation vessel without stopping.

Continuous variation
When the individuals in a population vary within a range — there are no distinct categories.

Control experiment
An extra experiment set up to eliminate the effect of some variables that can't be controlled.

Control group
A group in a study that is treated in exactly the same way as the experimental group, apart from the factor you're investigating.

Control variable
A variable you keep constant throughout an experiment.

Convergence (at a synapse)
When many neurones connect to one neurone.

Correlation
A relationship between two variables.

Countercurrent multiplier mechanism (kidneys)
A mechanism set up by the loop of Henle which allows water to be reabsorbed by the kidney.

Crossing-over
When chromatids twist around each other and bits of them swap over during meiosis.

Culture (microorganisms)
A population of one type of microorganism that's been grown under controlled conditions.

Cyclic AMP (cAMP)
A molecule that activates proteins inside cells by altering their 3D structures.

D

Deamination
The process by which nitrogen-containing amino groups are removed from amino acids, forming ammonia and organic acids.

Decarboxylation
The removal of carbon dioxide from a molecule.

Deciduous plant
A plant that loses its leaves in winter.

Decomposer
An organism that breaks down dead or undigested organic material.

Dehydrogenation
The removal of hydrogen from a molecule.

Denitrification
The process in which nitrates in the soil are converted into nitrogen gas by denitrifying bacteria.

Dependent variable
The variable you measure in an experiment.

Depolarisation
A decrease in the potential difference across a cell's membrane, making it less negative (i.e. more positive) than the resting potential.

Detoxification
The process by which harmful substances are broken down by the liver into less harmful compounds, which can then be excreted from the body.

Diabetes mellitus (Type I)
A condition in which blood glucose concentration can't be controlled properly because the body doesn't produce any insulin.

Diabetes mellitus (Type II)
A condition in which blood glucose concentration can't be controlled properly because the body doesn't produce enough insulin or the body's cells don't respond properly to insulin.

Diffusion (simple)
Net movement of particles from an area of higher concentration to an area of lower concentration.

Dihybrid inheritance
The inheritance of two characteristics which are controlled by different genes.

Diploid
When a cell contains two copies of each chromosome.

Directional selection
Where individuals with alleles for characteristics of an extreme type are more likely to survive, reproduce and pass on their alleles.

Discontinuous variation
When an individual falls into only one of two or more distinct categories — there are no intermediates.

Distribution
Where a particular species is within an area being investigated.

Divergence (at a synapse)
When one neurone connects to many neurones.

DNA ligase
An enzyme that joins together the sticky ends of DNA fragments by joining up their sugar-phosphate backbones.

DNA polymerase
An enzyme that joins together the nucleotides on a new strand of DNA during DNA replication.

DNA probe
A short single strand of DNA that has a complementary base sequence to part of a target sequence.

DNA sequencing
A technique used to determine the order of bases in a section of DNA.

Dominant allele
An allele whose characteristic appears in the phenotype even when there's only one copy.

Double-blind trial
A study involving a control group and an experimental group where neither the scientists involved nor the participants know which group the participants are in.

 E

Ecosystem
All the organisms living in a particular area and all the non-living (abiotic) conditions found there.

Ectotherm
An animal that can't control its body temperature internally.

Effector
A cell that brings about a response to a stimulus, to produce an effect.

Electrochemical gradient
A concentration gradient of ions.

Electron carrier
A protein that transfers electrons from one molecule to another.

Electron transport chain
A chain of proteins through which excited electrons flow.

Embryonic stem cell
A stem cell harvested from an embryo, which can differentiate into any of the cell types in the body.

Endocrine gland
A group of cells specialised to secrete hormones directly into the blood.

Endotherm
An animal that can control its body temperature internally by homeostasis.

Enucleated cell
A cell which has had the nucleus removed.

Enzyme
A protein that speeds up the rate of chemical reactions.

Epistasis
When an allele of one gene masks (blocks) the expression of the alleles of other genes.

Ethene (in plants)
A plant hormone produced by ageing leaves, which stimulates leaf loss.

Evolution
The change in allele frequency in a population over time.

Excretion
The removal of the waste products of metabolism from the body.

Exocrine gland
A group of cells specialised to secrete chemicals through ducts into cavities or onto the surface of the body.

 F

Facilitated diffusion
The diffusion of particles through carrier proteins or channel proteins in the plasma membrane.

FAD
A type of coenzyme involved in respiration. It transfers hydrogen from one molecule to another.

Fair test
A test in which only the independent variable has been allowed to affect the dependent variable.

Fermentation vessel
A large container in which microorganisms can be grown on an industrial scale.

Fertilisation
When a haploid sperm fuses with a haploid egg to generate a diploid zygote.

'Fight or flight' response
A response involving the sympathetic nervous system and adrenaline, which prepares the body for action in reaction to a threat.

Filtrate
The liquid and small molecules present in the kidney tubules following ultrafiltration of the blood. Also called the tubular fluid.

Final electron acceptor
A molecule which accepts an electron at the end of an electron transport chain. E.g. oxygen in respiration.

First messenger
A chemical involved in cell signalling (e.g. a hormone) that binds to a receptor in a cell membrane and triggers activity inside the cell.

Frame quadrat
A square frame, divided into a grid of 100 smaller squares, which can be used to investigate the abundance and distribution of organisms in an area.

 G

Gamete
A sex cell — e.g. the sperm cell in males or the egg cell in females.

Gel electrophoresis
A technique that allows DNA fragments to be separated on a gel according to size (length).

Gene
A section of DNA that codes for a protein (polypeptide) which results in a characteristic.

Gene pool
The complete range of alleles present in a population.

Gene technology
Techniques that allow the study and alteration of genes and their functions.

Gene therapy
Possible treatment option for genetic disorders and some cancers that involves altering defective alleles inside cells.

Generator potential
The change in potential difference across a cell membrane due to the presence of a stimulus.

Genetic bottleneck
An event that causes a big reduction in the size of a population.

Genetic code
The sequence of base triplets (codons) in mRNA which codes for specific amino acids.

Genetic disorder
An inherited disorder caused by an abnormal gene or chromosome.

Genetic drift
The process whereby an allele becomes more common in a population due to chance.

Genetic engineering
The manipulation of an organism's DNA.

Genome
All the genetic material in an organism.

Genotype
The alleles an organism has.

Geographical isolation
When a physical barrier, e.g. a flood, divides a population of a species, causing some individuals to become separated from the main population.

Germ line gene therapy
A possible cure for genetic disorders and some cancers that involves altering defective genes inside sex cells.

Gibberellin
A type of plant growth hormone that is produced in young leaves and in seeds. It stimulates seed germination, stem elongation, side shoot formation and flowering.

Glucagon
A hormone secreted by the pancreas that has an important role in raising blood glucose concentration.

Gluconeogenesis
The conversion of glycerol or amino acids to glucose, activated by glucagon.

Glycogenesis
The conversion of glucose to glycogen, activated by insulin.

Glycogenolysis
The conversion of glycogen to glucose, activated by glucagon.

Glycolysis
The first stage of aerobic respiration — here glucose is converted into pyruvate.

Gross productivity
The energy available to organisms that is absorbed by them.

Habitat
The place where an organism lives.

Haploid
When a cell contains one copy of each chromosome.

Hardy-Weinberg principle
A mathematical model that predicts that the frequency of alleles in a population won't change from one generation to the next provided that certain conditions are met.

Heterotroph
An organism which can't generate its own food (e.g. animals).

Heterozygous
When an organism carries two different alleles for the same characteristic.

Histology
The study of the microscopic structure of tissues.

Homeobox sequence
A sequence in a homeotic gene that codes for the homeodomain (part of the protein that binds to DNA, allowing the protein to act as a transcription factor).

Homeostasis
The maintenance of a constant internal environment.

Homeotic gene
A gene that controls the development of a body plan.

Homologous pair
A pair of matching chromosomes — each chromosome contains the same genes but could have different alleles.

Homozygous
When an organism carries two copies of the same allele.

Host cell
A cell that is used to carry recombinant DNA.

Human chorionic gonadotrophin (hCG)
A hormone that is only found in the urine of pregnant women, which allows it to be used in pregnancy testing.

Hydrolysis
The splitting (lysis) of a molecule using water (hydro).

Hyperpolarisation
An increase in the potential difference across a cell's membrane, making it more negative than the resting potential.

Hypothalamus
A part of the brain that controls body temperature and monitors water content of the blood.

Hypothesis
A specific testable statement, based on a theory, about what will happen in a test situation.

I

Immobilised enzyme
An enzyme that is attached to an insoluble material so it can't become mixed with the products of a reaction.

Independent assortment of chromatids
Where different combinations of chromatids go into each daughter cell during meiosis II.

Independent assortment of chromosomes
Where different combinations of maternal and paternal chromosomes go into each daughter cell during meiosis I.

Independent variable
The variable you change in an experiment.

Innate behaviour
An inherited, stereotyped behaviour that an organism does instinctively.

Insulin
A hormone secreted by the pancreas that has an important role in lowering blood glucose concentration.

Interspecific competition
Competition between organisms of different species for the same resources.

Interspecific variation
Variation between different species.

Intracellular enzyme
An enzyme contained within the cells of organisms.

Intraspecific competition
Competition between organisms of the same species for the same resources.

Intraspecific variation
Variation between members of the same species.

***In vitro* cloning**
When gene copies are made outside of a living organism using PCR.

***In vivo* cloning**
When gene copies are made within a living organism as it grows and divides.

Islet of Langerhans
An area of endocrine tissue in the pancreas, containing α and β cells.

Isolated enzyme
An enzyme not contained within the cells of organisms.

Kinesis (kinetic response)
Non-directional (random) movement in response to a stimulus.

Krebs cycle
The third stage of aerobic respiration. It is a series of oxidation-reduction reactions that produces reduced coenzymes and ATP.

***Lac* operon**
An operon containing the genes responsible for producing the enzymes needed to respire lactose in *E. coli*.

Lactate fermentation
A type of anaerobic respiration that occurs in mammals (and some bacteria). Lactate is the final product.

Learned behaviour
A non-stereotyped behaviour that's influenced by the environment and modified as a result of experience.

Light-dependent reaction
The first stage of photosynthesis. Light energy is absorbed by photosynthetic pigments and converted to ATP and reduced NADP.

Light-independent reaction
The second stage of photosynthesis. Here ATP and reduced NADP (from the light-dependent reaction) are used to make glucose from carbon dioxide.

Limiting factor
A variable that can slow down the rate of a reaction.

Link reaction
The second stage of aerobic respiration where pyruvate is converted into acetyl coenzyme A.

Linkage
When alleles on the same chromosome end up in the same daughter cell and so are inherited together.

Locus
The position on a chromosome where a particular allele is found.

Loop of Henle
Part of the kidney nephron responsible for establishing the water potential gradient, which allows water to be reabsorbed by the kidney.

M

Marker gene
A gene that can be used to identify transformed cells. E.g. a gene for antibiotic resistance or fluorescence.

Mean
The average of the values collected in a sample.

Medulla oblongata
Part of the brain which automatically controls breathing rate and heart rate.

Metabolic pathway
A series of small reactions controlled by enzymes.

Micropropagation
A technique where tissue culture is used to produce lots of cloned plants very quickly.

Mitochondrion
An oval shaped organelle found in plant and animal cells. It is the site of respiration.

Model (scientific)
A simplified picture of what's physically going on.

Monogenic characteristic
A characteristic influenced by one gene.

Monohybrid inheritance
The inheritance of a single characteristic (gene) controlled by different alleles.

mRNA (messenger RNA)
A type of RNA that is the template for protein synthesis. It carries the genetic code from the DNA in the nucleus into the cytoplasm.

Mutation
Any change in the DNA base (nucleotide) sequence.

Myelin sheath
A layer of Schwann cells around a neurone that acts as an electrical insulator and speeds up conduction of nervous impulses.

Myofibril
A long, cylindrical organelle within a muscle fibre that's highly specialised for contraction.

Myosin
The protein that makes up the thick myofilaments in myofibrils.

N

NAD
A type of coenzyme involved in respiration. It transfers hydrogen from one molecule to another.

NADP
A coenzyme involved in photosynthesis. It transfers hydrogen from one molecule to another.

Natural selection
The process whereby an allele becomes more common in a population because it codes for an adaptation that makes an organism more likely to survive, reproduce and pass on its alleles to the next generation.

Negative feedback mechanism
A mechanism that restores a level back to normal in a system.

Nephron
One of the filtering units of the kidney, responsible for removing waste substances such as urea from the blood.

Net productivity
The amount of energy that's available to the next trophic level in a food chain.

Neuromuscular junction
A specialised cholinergic synapse between a motor neurone and a muscle cell.

Neurotransmitter
A chemical that transmits a nerve impulse across a synapse.

Nitrification
The process in which ammonium compounds in the soil are changed into nitrogen compounds by nitrifying bacteria called *Nitrosomonas* and *Nitrobacter*.

Nitrogen cycle
The conversion of nitrogen into a usable form and its movement through living organisms and the non-living environment.

Nitrogen fixation
The process in which nitrogen gas in the atmosphere is turned into ammonia. It can be carried out by bacteria called *Rhizobium*.

Non-reproductive cloning
A type of cloning used to make embryonic stem cells that are genetically identical to another organism.

Nuclear transfer
A technique for cloning animals which involves taking a nucleus from an adult body cell and inserting it into an enucleated egg cell.

O

Operator
A DNA sequence that transcription factors bind to.

Operon
A section of DNA that contains structural genes, control elements and sometimes a regulatory gene.

Ornithine cycle
A cycle of biochemical reactions in which ammonia is combined with carbon dioxide to create urea and water.

Osmosis
Diffusion of water molecules across a partially permeable membrane, from an area of higher water potential to an area of lower water potential.

Oxidation
A chemical reaction where a molecule loses electrons, and may have lost hydrogen or gained oxygen.

Oxidative phosphorylation
The final stage in aerobic respiration. Energy carried by electrons, from reduced coenzymes, is used to make ATP.

P

Palindromic sequence
A sequence of DNA bases that consists of antiparallel base pairs (base pairs that read the same in opposite directions).

Parasympathetic nervous system
A division of the autonomic nervous system which calms the body down. It's the 'rest and digest' system.

Pasteurisation
The process of sterilising food stuffs by heating them for a fixed length of time.

PCR (polymerase chain reaction)
A technique used to make millions of identical copies of a DNA fragment in a few hours.

Peer review
Where a scientific report is sent out to peers (other scientists) who examine the data and results, and if they think that the conclusion is reasonable it's published.

Peripheral nervous system
Part of the nervous system that connects the CNS to the rest of the body. It consists of the somatic and autonomic nervous systems.

Phenotype
The characteristics an organism's alleles produce.

Phenotypic ratio
The ratio of different phenotypes in the offspring.

Phosphorylation
The process of adding phosphate to a molecule.

Photolysis
The splitting (lysis) of a molecule using light (photo) energy.

Photophosphorylation
The process of adding phosphate to a molecule using light energy.

Photosynthesis
The process where energy from light is used to make glucose from carbon dioxide and water.

Photosynthetic pigment
A coloured substance (e.g. chlorophyll a) that absorbs the light energy needed for photosynthesis.

Photosystem
A protein and photosynthetic pigment structure found in the thylakoid membranes of chloroplasts in plants and algae.

Phototropism
The growth of a plant in response to light.

Pioneer species
The first species to colonise an area during succession.

Placebo
A dummy pill or injection that looks exactly like the real drug, but doesn't contain the drug.

Plagioclimax
The climax community produced when succession is artificially stopped by human activities.

Plant growth hormone
A chemical that speeds up or slows down plant growth.

Point quadrat
A horizontal bar on two legs with a series of holes set at intervals along its length, through which pins are dropped. Can be used to investigate the abundance and distribution of organisms in an area.

Polygenic characteristic
A characteristic influenced by many genes.

Population
All the organisms of one species in a habitat.

Positive feedback mechanism
A mechanism that amplifies a change away from the normal level in a system.

Potential difference
The voltage across a cell membrane.

Predation
Where an organism (the predator) kills and eats another organism (the prey).

Prediction
See hypothesis.

Preservation (of ecosystems)
The protection of ecosystems so they're kept exactly as they are.

Primary metabolite
A small molecule produced during a metabolic reaction, which is essential for growth.

Primary succession
Succession which happens on newly formed or exposed land with no soil.

Primer
A short piece of single stranded DNA that is complementary to the bases at the start of the DNA fragment you want.

Probability
How likely something is to happen.

Producer
An organism that produces organic molecules using sunlight energy.

Programmed cell death
The highly controlled breakdown and death of cells. Also known as apoptosis.

Promoter
A DNA sequence (located before the structural genes in an operon) that RNA polymerase binds to.

Phylogenetics
The study of the evolutionary history of organisms.

R

Reaction centre
A site where electrons are excited during the light-dependent reaction of photosynthesis.

Receptor
A cell, or protein on a cell surface membrane, that detects a stimulus.

Recessive allele
An allele whose characteristic only appears in the phenotype if there are two copies present.

Recognition sequence
A specific palindromic sequence in DNA recognised by a restriction enzyme.

Recombinant DNA
The name for DNA formed by joining together DNA from different sources.

Redox reaction
A chemical reaction that involves oxidation and reduction.

Reduction
A chemical reaction where a molecule gains electrons, and may have gained hydrogen or lost oxygen.

Regulatory gene
A gene that codes for a transcription factor.

Reliable evidence
Evidence that can be consistently reproduced in independent experiments.

Repolarisation
The return of a cell membrane to its resting potential.

Repressor
A transcription factor that stops transcription.

Reproductive cloning
A type of cloning used to make a complete organism that's genetically identical to another organism.

Reproductive isolation
When two populations of the same species are unable to breed together to produce fertile offspring.

Respiratory loss
The amount of energy lost to the environment when organisms use energy produced from respiration for movement or body heat.

Respiratory quotient
The volume of carbon dioxide produced when a substrate is respired, divided by the volume of oxygen consumed, in a set period of time.

Respiratory substrate
Any biological molecule that can be broken down in respiration to release energy.

Respirometer
A device that can be used to measure the rate of oxygen being taken up by an organism.

Resting potential
The potential difference across a cell membrane when the cell is at rest.

Restriction enzymes
Enzymes that recognise specific recognition sequences and cut DNA at these places.

Reverse transcriptase
An enzyme that makes a DNA copy of RNA.

Ribosome
An organelle found in the cell cytoplasm that assembles proteins.

Ribulose bisphosphate carboxylase (rubisco)
An enzyme which catalyses the formation of glycerate 3-phosphate from carbon dioxide and ribulose bisphosphate (RuBP) in the light-independent reaction of photosynthesis.

RNA (ribonucleic acid)
A type of nucleic acid, similar to DNA but containing ribose instead of deoxyribose sugar and uracil instead of thymine.

RNA polymerase
An enzyme that synthesises RNA from DNA.

Saltatory conduction
The process in myelinated neurones by which a nervous impulse travels between nodes of Ranvier.

Sample size
The number of samples in the investigation, e.g. the number of people in a drug trial.

Sarcomere
A short contractile unit that's part of a myofibril, made up of overlapping myosin and actin filaments.

Saturation point (in photosynthesis)
The point at which a particular factor no longer limits the rate of reaction. Here another factor has begun to limit the rate of reaction.

Schwann cell
The type of cell that makes up the myelin sheath around neurones.

Second messenger
A chemical that's produced inside a cell in response to a signal outside the cell. The chemical relays the signal to the inside of the cell.

Secondary metabolite
A molecule produced during a metabolic reaction, which is not essential for growth but is useful in other ways.

Secondary succession
Succession which happens on land cleared of all plants but where the soil remains, e.g. after a forest fire.

Selection pressure
Anything that affects an organism's chance of survival and reproduction.

Selective reabsorption (kidneys)
The reabsorption of useful substances along the kidney nephron back into the blood.

Sex-linked characteristic
When the allele that codes for the characteristic is located on a sex chromosome (X or Y).

Sister chromatids
Two identical copies of a chromosome joined together in the middle.

Sliding filament theory
The theory that myosin and actin filaments slide over one another to make sarcomeres contract.

Somatic gene therapy
A possible treatment option for genetic disorders and some cancers that involves altering defective genes inside body cells.

Speciation
The development of a new species.

Species
A group of similar organisms that can reproduce to give fertile offspring.

Stabilising selection
Where individuals with alleles for characteristics towards the middle of the range are more likely to survive, reproduce and pass on their alleles.

Standard growth curve (for microorganisms)
A curve with four phases that represents the growth of a population of microorganisms grown in a closed culture.

Sticky end
A small tail of unpaired DNA bases at each end of a DNA fragment.

Stimulus
A change in an organism's internal or external environment.

Structural gene
A gene that codes for a useful protein, e.g. an enzyme.

Substrate-level phosphorylation
When a phosphate group is directly transferred from one molecule to another.

Succession
The process by which an ecosystem changes over time.

Summation
The process in which the effect of a neurotransmitter released from many neurones (or one neurone that's stimulated a lot in a short period of time) is added together.

Sympathetic nervous system
A division of the autonomic nervous system which gets the body ready for action. It's the 'fight or flight' system.

Synapse
A junction between a neurone and another neurone, or between a neurone and an effector cell.

Target cell (or target tissue)
A cell (or tissue) that has specific receptors for a particular type of chemical, such as a hormone or a neurotransmitter.

Taxis (tactic response)
Directional movement in response to a stimulus.

Theory
A possible explanation for something

Tissue culture (of plants)
A technique for cloning plants which involves taking stem cells from the stem or root tips of a plant and growing them in culture.

Transcription
The first stage of protein synthesis in which an mRNA copy of a gene is made from DNA in the nucleus.

Transcription factor
A protein that controls the transcription of genes.

Transducer
Something that converts one form of energy into another.

Transect
A line used to help measure how plants are distributed across an area, e.g. how species change from a hedge towards the middle of a field.

Transformed cell
A host cell that has taken up recombinant DNA.

Transformed organism
A organism that has had its genes altered by genetic engineering.

Transgenic organism
An organism that has been genetically engineered to include a gene from a different species.

Translation
The second stage of protein synthesis in which amino acids are joined together by ribosomes to make a polypeptide chain (protein).

tRNA (transfer RNA)
A type of RNA involved in translation. It carries the amino acids used to make proteins to the ribosomes.

Trophic level
A stage in a food chain that's occupied by a particular group of organisms.

Tropism
The response of a plant to a directional stimulus.

Tropomyosin
A protein found between actin filaments attached to troponin. Together the two proteins help myofilaments move past each other.

Tumour
A mass of abnormal cells.

Ultrafiltration (kidneys)
The filtering of the blood that takes place under high pressure, as blood passes from the glomerulus into the renal capsule.

Valid conclusion
A conclusion that answers the original question and uses reliable data.

Variable
A quantity that has the potential to change, e.g. weight, temperature, concentration.

Variation
The differences that exist between individuals.

Vasoconstriction
Constriction (narrowing) of a blood vessel.

Vasodilation
Dilation (widening) of a blood vessel.

Vector (in gene technology)
Something used to transfer DNA into a cell, e.g. a plasmid or a bacteriophage.

Vegetative propagation
The natural production of plant clones from non-reproductive tissues, e.g. roots, leaves and stems.

Water potential
The likelihood of water molecules to diffuse into or out of solution.

X

Xenotransplantation
The transfer of cells, tissues or organs from one species to another.

Acknowledgements

OCR Specification reference points are reproduced with the permission of OCR.

Data acknowledgements

Data used to produce the table on page 183 from A.C. Nathwani et al., Adenovirus-Associated Virus Vector–Mediated Gene Transfer in Hemophilia B: N Engl J Med 2011; 365:2357-2365

Data used to construct the graphs on page 190 from S. Hacein-Bey-Abina et al. SCIENCE 302: 415-419 (2003)

Photograph acknowledgements

Cover photo **Power and Syred**/Science Photo Library, p 1 **National Library of Medicine**/Science Photo Library, p 3 **Monty Rakusen**/Science Photo Library, p 4 **Cordelia Molloy**/Science Photo Library, p 8 **Steve Gschmeissner**/Science Photo Library, p 14 **Dr David Furness, Keele University**/Science Photo Library, p 16 **Don Fawcett**/Science Photo Library, p 22 **Ramon Andrade 3DCiencia**/Science Photo Library, p 24 (middle) **Conge, ISM**/Science Photo Library, p 24 (bottom) **CNRI**/Science Photo Library, p 25 **Steve Gschmeissner**/Science Photo Library, p 27 **CNRI**/Science Photo Library, p 29 (side) **Adam Jones**/Science Photo Library, p 29 (bottom) **Edward Kinsman**/Science Photo Library, p 45 (middle) **Prof. P. Motta/Dept. of Anatomy/University "La Sapienza", Rome**/Science Photo Library, p 45 (bottom) **Thomas Deerinck, NCMIR**/Science Photo Library, p 47 **Science Photo Library**, p 48 **Dr Keith Wheeler**/Science Photo Library, p 49 **Steve Gschmeissner**/Science Photo Library, p 50 **Science Photo Library**, p 52 (Fig. 2 top) **Anthony Mercieca**/Science Photo Library, p 52 (Fig. 2 middle) **Tom McHugh**/Science Photo Library, p 52 (Fig. 2 bottom) **Chris Hellier**/Science Photo Library, p 54 **Life in View**/Science Photo Library, p 55 **Life in View**/Science Photo Library, p 56 **Life in View**/Science Photo Library, p 57 **Tek Image**/Science Photo Library, p 58 **Steve Gschmeissner**/Science Photo Library, p 63 **Dr Kari Lounatmaa**/Science Photo Library, p 69 **Biophoto Associates**/Science Photo Library, p 72 **Andrew Lambert Photography**/Science Photo Library, p 73 **GAPS**/iStockphoto, p 75 **Dr. Jeremy Burgess**/Science Photo Library, p 77 **Dr David Furness, Keele University**/Science Photo Library, p 84 **Martin Shields**/Science Photo Library, p 87 **Power and Syred**/Science Photo Library, p 90 **Philippe Psaila**/Science Photo Library, p 99 **Ramon Andrade 3DCiencia**/Science Photo Library, p 102 **Mitchell Lewis, University of Pennsylvania Medical Center**/Science Photo Library, p 104 **Eye of Science**/Science Photo Library, p 105 (top) **Dr Gopal Murti**/Science Photo Library, p 105 (middle) **Dr Keith Wheeler**/Science Photo Library, p 105 (bottom) **Claude Nuridsany & Marie Perennou**/Science Photo Library, p 113 **Science Pictures Ltd**/Science Photo Library, p 114 (top) **Pr. G Gimenez-Martin**/Science Photo Library, p 114 (bottom) **Adrian T Sumner**/Science Photo Library, p 117 **Tony Craddock**/Science Photo Library, p 118 (Fig. 1a) **Wim van Egmond, Visuals Unlimited**/Science Photo Library, p 118 (Fig. 1b) **J.C. Revy, ISM**/Science Photo Library, p 120 **Eye of Science**/Science Photo Library, p 125 **Ed Young/AGStockUSA**/Science Photo Library, p 127 **Science Photo Library**, p 136 **Herve Conge, ISM**/Science Photo Library, p 145 (middle) **Andrew Sacks/AGStockUSA**/Science Photo Library, p 145 (bottom) **Dr. John Brackenbury**/Science Photo Library, p 147 **Paul D Stewart**/Science Photo Library, p 148 (Fig. 3 top) **Tony Camacho**/Science Photo Library, p 148 (Fig. 3 bottom) **Art Wolfe**/Science Photo Library, p 152 **Reinhard Dirscherl, Visuals Unlimited**/Science Photo Library, p 153 **James King-Holmes**/Science Photo Library, p 154 **Ph. Plailly/Eurelios**/Science Photo Library, p 155 (middle) **Tony Craddock**/Science Photo Library, p 155 (bottom) **Rosenfeld Images Ltd**/Science Photo Library, p 156 **Andrew Brown**/Science Photo Library, p 157 **Jerome Wexler**/Science Photo Library, p 158 **Rosenfeld Images Ltd**/Science Photo Library, p 161 (top) **Andrew McClenaghan**/Science Photo Library, p 161 (bottom) **Ed Young**/Science Photo Library, p 162 **James Holmes/Celltech Ltd**/Science Photo Library, p 163 **James King-Holmes/Celltech R & D Ltd**/Science Photo Library, p 164 (middle) **Martyn F. Chillmaid**/Science Photo Library, p 164 (bottom) **Maximilian Stock Ltd**/Science Photo Library, p 169 **Robert Longuehaye, NIBSC**/Science Photo Library, p 170 **TEK Image**/Science Photo Library, p 171 (top) **Philippe Plailly**/Science Photo Library, p 171 (middle) **Peter Menzel**/Science Photo Library, p 174 (top) **J.C. Revy, ISM**/Science Photo Library, p 174 (bottom) **Biozentrum, University of Basel**/Science Photo Library, p 175 **Martin Shields**/Science Photo Library, p 178 **NYPL/Science Source**/Science Photo Library, p 179 **International Rice Research Institute**, p 181 **Peggy Greb/US Department of Agriculture**/

Science Photo Library, p 185 **Larry Mulvehill**/Science Photo Library, p 186 **James King-Holmes**/Science Photo Library, p 187 **Martin Krzywinski**/Science Photo Library, p 197 **Dr. Jeremy Burgess**/Science Photo Library, p 198 (top) **Pasieka**/Science Photo Library, p 198 (middle) **Steve Gschmeissner**/Science Photo Library, p 199 **Annie Haycock**/Science Photo Library, p 200 **Simon Fraser**/Science Photo Library, p 201 (top) **Andrea Balogh**/Science Photo Library, p 201 (middle and bottom) **Simon Fraser**/Science Photo Library, p 202 **Colin Varndell**/Science Photo Library, p 205 **Jeff Lepore**/Science Photo Library, p 208 **Martyn F. Chillmaid**/Science Photo Library, p 212 (top) **goinyk**/iStockphoto, p 212 (middle) **Planetobserver**/Science Photo Library, p 212 (bottom) **David Fleetham/Visuals Unlimited, Inc.**/Science Photo Library, p 213 **Geoff Kidd**/Science Photo Library, p 217 **Martin Shields**/Science Photo Library, p 218 **David R. Frazier Photolibrary, Inc.**/Science Photo Library, p 220 **Scott Sinklier/AGStockUSA**/Science Photo Library, p 221 **Dr Keith Wheeler**/Science Photo Library, p 222 (Fig. 10 top) **lepas2004**/iStockphoto, p 222 (Fig. 10 bottom) **alphacell**/iStockphoto, p 222 (bottom) **Andrew Lambert Photography**/Science Photo Library, p 225 **Pasieka**/Science Photo Library, p 228 (top) **Steve Gschmeissner**/Science Photo Library, p 228 (bottom) **Thomas Deerinck, NCMIR**/Science Photo Library, p 233 (top) **Eric Grave**/Science Photo Library, p 233 (middle) **Science Photo Library**, p 233 (bottom) **CNRI**/Science Photo Library, p 234 **Ed Reschke, Peter Arnold Inc.**/Science Photo Library, p 237 **Science Source**/Science Photo Library, p 238 (top) **Dolphin Inst.**/Science Photo Library, p 238 (middle) **Will & Deni McIntyre**/Science Photo Library, p 239 **Science Photo Library**, p 241 **Peter Chadwick**/Science Photo Library.

Every effort has been made to locate copyright holders and obtain permission to reproduce sources. For those sources where it has been difficult to trace the originator of the work, we would be grateful for information. If any copyright holder would like us to make an amendment to the acknowledgements, please notify us and we will gladly update the book at the next reprint. Thank you.

Index

A

abiotic factors 191
abiotic stress 217
abundance 207
accuracy 3
acetylcholine (ACh) 16, 17
acetylcholinesterase (AChE) 17
acetyl coenzyme A 79, 80
acinar cells 24
actin 228, 230
action potentials 10, 12, 13
activators 101
ADP (adenosine diphosphate) 61
adrenal glands 23
adrenaline 23, 224, 225
aerobic respiration 60, 77-83
alcoholic fermentation 87
allele frequencies 138
alleles 116
all-or-nothing principle (of action potentials) 13
alpha (α) cells 33
ammonification 197
anabolic steroids 56
anaerobic respiration 60, 87
analysing data 250
anomalous data 5
answering data questions 247-250
anticodons 97, 99
antidiuretic hormone (ADH) 52, 53
apical dominance 218, 219
apoptosis 105
aquaporins 52
artificial selection 145, 146
asepsis 164
ATP (adenosine triphosphate) 60, 61, 82, 83
ATP synthase 61, 65, 81
ATPase 61
autonomic nervous system 38, 224
autotrophs 60
auxins 218, 219, 222

B

BACs (bacterial artificial chromosomes) 185
bacteriophages 173
batch cultures 162, 163
behaviour 236-241
belt transects 209
beta (β) cells 33, 35
bias 4
biological species concept 148
biotechnology 158-165
biotic factors 191
blood glucose concentration 33-35
body plans 104, 105
body temperature 29-32
brain 225
bread wheat 145

C

calorimeters 194
Calvin cycle 63, 67-69, 73, 74
cAMP (cyclic AMP) 23, 102
cardiac muscle 233
carriers 117
causal relationships 5
cell signalling 7
central nervous system (CNS) 38, 224
cerebellum 225
cerebrum 225
chain termination method 184
chemiosmosis 65, 81
  evidence for 85, 86
chi-squared test 127-129
chloroplasts 62
cholinergic synapses 16, 17
classical conditioning 237
classifying species 148
climatic climax communities 201
climax communities 200
cloning 152-157
  animals 152-154
  humans 154
  plants 155-157
closed cultures 160

codominant alleles 117
  inheritance of 120
codons 96
coenzyme A 77, 79
coenzymes
  in photosynthesis 63
  in respiration 77
command words 246
comparing genomes 186, 187
complementary base pairing 95
conclusions 5, 248
confounding variables 3
conservation 211
consumers 191
continuous cultures 162, 163
continuous variation 135
control elements 101
control groups 4
controls 3, 4, 249
control variables 3
correlations 5
countercurrent multiplier mechanism 51, 52
critical values 129
crossing-over 114
culturing microorganisms 160-163
cyclic AMP (cAMP) 23
cyclic photophosphorylation 65

D

dairy cattle 145
data collection 249
deamination 46
decarboxylation 79
deciduous plants 221
decision making 6
decomposers 192
deflecting succession 202
dehydrogenation 80
denitrification 198
dependent variables 3
depolarisation 12, 13
describing data 247, 248
detoxification 47
diabetes 36
dialysis 54, 55
dihybrid inheritance 123

respiration 60, 77-90
respiration of glucose 33
respiratory loss 192
respiratory quotients (RQs) 89, 90
respiratory substrates 89, 90
respirometers 84
resting membrane potential of neurones 11
resting membrane potential of sensory receptors 9
restriction enzymes 169, 170, 173, 178, 179, 185
reverse transcriptase 178
Rhizobium 197
ribosomes 99, 100
ribulose bisphosphate (RuBP) 67, 68, 73, 74
ribulose bisphosphate carboxylase (rubisco) 67
RNA 96, 97
RNA polymerase 98

S

saltatory conduction 14
sample sizes 4, 249
sarcomeres 228
Schwann cells 14
scientific journals 2
secondary metabolites 160, 161
second messengers 23
selective reabsorption (in the kidneys) 48, 49
sensory neurones 8
sensory receptors 9
sex-linkage 120, 121
skeletal muscle 227, 233
sliding filament theory 229
smooth muscle 233
social behaviour in primates 240, 241
sodium-potassium pumps 11
somatic gene therapy 182
speciation 147
species 147
stabilising selection 138, 139
standard deviation 250
standard growth curves 160
start codons 96
stem cells 36, 37
steroids 56
  testing for 57
sticky ends 170, 173

stimuli 7, 224
stop codons 96
structural genes 101
substrate-level phosphorylation 80
succession 199-202
  primary 199, 200
  secondary 201
sustainability 213
sympathetic nervous system 224, 225
synapses 16-19
  summation at 18, 19
synaptic convergence 18
synaptic divergence 18

T

tables 251
tactic responses (taxes) 236
target cells 22
target tissues 22
temperate woodlands 213
theories 1
thermoreceptors 31
threshold level (for action potentials) 10
tissue culture 155
transcription 96, 98, 99
transcription factors 101, 104
transects 209
transformed organisms 173
transforming cells 174
transgenic organisms 173
translation 96, 99, 100
triose phosphate (TP) 67-69, 73, 74, 78
triplets (DNA) 96
Triticum aestivum 145
tRNA 97, 99, 100
trophic levels 191
tropisms 217
tropomyosin 230
troponin 230
Type I diabetes 36
Type II diabetes 36

U

ultrafiltration 48
urea 46
urine 50-53
  testing samples of 56, 57

V

variables 3, 249
variation 135-137
vasoconstriction 31
vasodilation 30
vectors 173
vegetative propagation 156
voluntary muscle 233

X

xenotransplantation 180

BRTB61